修 編 序

　　30 多年前，編者開始教升大學英文的時候，碰到所有英文方面的文法難題，都徹底研究，並編在「文法寶典」中。現在修編「文法寶典第二冊」，感觸良多，精彩極了！

　　從前辛苦的研究過程，歷歷在目。例如，She married *young*. 句中 young 這個形容詞到底做什麼用？你不能隨便說 young 是形容詞，做主詞補語，那 married 又是什麼樣的動詞呢？文法就是歸納，要讓讀者能夠舉一反三才行。在「文法寶典」p.191 中，就有說明「形容詞做主詞補語的省略用法」：

> She married *young*.
> = When she got married, she was *young*.

> Tom came home very *tired*.
> = Tom was very *tired* when he came home.

　　全世界的人為了學英文，費了很大的功夫，把語言歸納成規則給別人學，無數的文法規則，有誰學得通？我們在閱讀英文的時候，碰到了與自己想法不同的句子，不知道對或錯，就要查閱「文法寶典」，這本書不需要從頭到尾詳細閱讀，它是一本工具書，就像字典一樣。

　　有人問我，Even a worm will turn. 在句中，Even 到底是什麼詞？在「文法寶典」p.228 就會告訴你，有些副詞，如 also, even, not, only, exactly 等，都可以修飾名詞或代名詞。

Even a worm will turn. (狗急跳牆。)
【副詞 Even 當形容詞用，修飾名詞 worm】

在 p.228 也告訴你，有些副詞甚至可以代替名詞，像：

Now is the time to leave.
【因為 Now 沒有同義的名詞，所以它代替名詞當主詞】

如果你看到這種句子，不查閱「文法寶典」，徹底了解，心裡有疙瘩，英文怎麼學得好？

文法不管怎麼學，對你的英文幫助有限。**學英文最簡單的方法，就**是背「一口氣英語」和「一口氣英語演講」，以三句為一組，九句為一段，背到變成直覺，就終生不忘。只要背 20 篇「一口氣英語演講」，融會貫通，你說的英文、寫的句子，都不會錯。但是碰到了你覺得奇怪的句子，還是要查「文法寶典」，才會豁然開朗。

　　有人問我 yes 和 no 是什麼詞？在「文法寶典」p.238 中，就明確告訴你，它們是表「肯定」或「否定」的副詞：

$$\begin{cases} \text{"Do you know Mr. Smith?"} \\ \text{"\underline{\textit{Yes}}, I know him."} \\ \text{副詞} \end{cases}$$

$$\begin{cases} \text{"Is John here?"} \\ \text{"\underline{\textit{No}}, he isn't here."} \\ \text{副詞} \end{cases}$$

如果你死背 no 是形容詞，not 是副詞，你就完了；查了「文法寶典」，你便知道，no 還可以當副詞用，而且不只一個用法。

　　編者一生從事英語教學，苦心研究學英文的方法，「文法寶典」出版了幾十年，深受讀者的歡迎。早年用鉛字打，現在轉換成電腦排版，版面設計花了很大的功夫，感覺上好像沒有以前手打那麼有感情，但是現在加上彩色印刷，有現代的感覺，加上外國編輯 Laura E. Stewart 和 Christian A. Brieske 的協助，使內容更與時俱進，合乎時代的潮流。

　　編者現在不覺得老，因為不停地在學習和進步。我們最近發明了「一口氣英單字」，成為排行榜的暢銷書，現在正在研發「一口氣英成語」和「一口氣英作文」。有了這些書，任何人只要努力，就可以把英文學好。如果方法不對，沒有好的教材，光有毅力，是沒有用的。呂佳羚小妹妹，才國小五年級，背了「一口氣英語」和「一口氣英語演講」，只花兩年的時間，英文已經超越高中的程度。

　　本書雖經審慎編校，恐仍有疏漏之處，歡迎讀者給我們指正。

劉　毅

CONTENTS

第四篇　形容詞（Adjectives）

第一章　形容詞的種類

第二章　分論

第三篇　代名詞（**Pronouns**）

代名詞是爲了避免重複而用來代替名詞的字，所以其功用與名詞相同，做主詞、受詞或補語。見下面二例：括弧前的代名詞代替括弧內的名詞。

1. The man invited the little Swedish girl because ***he*** (= *the man*) liked ***her*** (= *the little Swedish girl*) .

   （這人邀請了那瑞典小女孩，因爲他喜歡她。）

2. There was once a king of Persia ***who*** (= *this king*) took delight in doing common things in very uncommon ways. Once ***he*** (= *the king*) was in need of a man ***that*** (= *this man*) would do just what ***he*** (= *the man*) was told to do; and ***he*** (= *the king*) used a very strange way to find ***him*** (= *the man*) .

   （從前有位波斯國王，他喜歡用不尋常的方法做平常的事。有一次他需要一個人，這個人只能做人家告訴他要做的事情；這國王用了很奇怪的方法來尋找這樣的人。）

I. 概論：

代名詞
- 1. 功用
  - (1) 做主詞　I am a boy.　　Who came?
  - (2) 做受詞　He loves me.　　Whom do you love?
  - (3) 做補語　It is he.　　Who are you?
- 2. 種類
  - (1) 人稱代名詞 —— 表示人稱的區別
    - 如：I, you, he, it, they,…
  - (2) 指示代名詞 —— 表示指定的人或事物
    - 如：this, that, such, so,…
  - (3) 不定代名詞 —— 表示不確定的人或事物
    - 如：many, some, any, each,…
  - (4) 疑問代名詞 —— 表示疑問
    - 如：who, what, which,…
  - (5) 關係代名詞 —— 等於代名詞 + 連接詞
    - 如：who, which, that, what,…
- 3. 形式變化
  - (1) 格
    - ① 主　格 —— I, you, he, it, who
    - ② 受　格 —— me, you, him, it, whom
    - ③ 所有格
      - a. 形容詞 —— my, your, his, its, whose
      - b. 代名詞 —— mine, yours, his, whose
  - (2) 數
    - ① 單　數 —— I, he, this, that
    - ② 複　數 —— we, they, these, those

II. 代名詞分爲五種

代 名 詞
Pronouns

1. 人稱代名詞（Personal Pronouns）

除了用以表示人稱的區別外，還具有特殊形式 -self 的**複合人稱代名詞**，以及表示所有的**所有代名詞**。（詳見 p.107）

We must not tell lies.（我們不可以說謊。）

You can see her from here.（從這裡你能看見她。）

2. 指示代名詞（Demonstrative Pronouns）

表示指定的人或事物時使用的代名詞稱爲指示代名詞。有 **this, these, that, those, such, same, so** 七個。（詳見 p.122）

This is my hat.（這是我的帽子。）

That is your cane.（那是你的手杖。）

3. 不定代名詞（Indefinite Pronouns）

指數量或對象不確定的人或事物時使用的代名詞稱爲不定代名詞。

You have *many*, but I have *few*.（你有很多，而我卻很少。）

不定代名詞有很多，如 **some, any, either, neither, each, every, all, none, one, other, many, much, more, few, little, several,**…等等皆是。

（詳見 p.130）

4. 疑問代名詞（Interrogative Pronouns）

表示疑問時使用的代名詞稱爲疑問代名詞，有 **who, which, what**（詳見 p.144）通常置於疑問句的句首。

Who are you?（你是誰？）

What is this?（這是什麼？）

Which do you like better?（你喜歡哪一個？）

5. 關係代名詞（Relative Pronouns）

兼具代名詞與連接詞功用的代名詞稱爲關係代名詞，有 **who, which, that, what, whoever, whichever, whatever, as, but, than,**…等。

This is the man *who* came yesterday.

（這是昨天來過的那個人。）

This is the watch *which* I have bought.

（這是我買的錶。）

第一章 人稱代名詞（Personal Pronouns）

Ⅰ. 人稱代名詞的分類：

人　性　數　格　稱			主　格	受　格	所　有　格		複合人稱代名詞
					形 容 詞	代 名 詞	
第一人稱（説話者）	通性	單數	I	me	my	mine	myself
		複數	we	us	our	ours	ourselves
第二人稱（聽話者）	通性	單數	you	you	your	yours	yourself
		複數					yourselves
第三人稱（被談論者）	陽	單	he	him	his	his	himself
	陰	單	she	her	her	hers	herself
	無	單	it	it	its	×	itself
	通	複	they	them	their	theirs	themselves

第二人稱古寫：	單	thou	thee	thy	thine
	複	ye	you	your	yours

【注意】　1. **人稱代名詞的性**僅第三人稱單數時才有陽性、陰性與無性的變化；其餘均為通性，沒有變化。

　　　　　2. **人稱代名詞的所有格**如 my, your, his…都是帶有形容詞的性質，其後必須接名詞，所以稱之為**所有形容詞**（**Possessive Adjectives**）。

　　　　　3. **mine, yours, hers…都有代名詞的性質**，其後不能再接名詞，所以才稱它為**所有代名詞**。傳統文法稱其為**獨立所有格**。

Ⅱ. 人稱代名詞的格的用法：

1. 主格

　(1) **做主詞**：**She** divided her property between two people.（她把她的財產分給兩人。）

　(2) **做主詞補語**：I was thought to be **he**.（我被以為是他。）

　(3) **做同位語**：Ernest Hemingway, **he** was a great novelist.
　　　　　　　　（俄迺斯特・海明威，他是一位偉大的小說家。）

　(4) **做呼喚語**：Hey, **you**, come here!（嘿，你，過來！）

　(5) **做分詞的意義上的主詞**：**He** being here, there is no danger.
　　　　　　　　　　　　（= *Since he is here, there is no danger.*）
　　　　　　　　　　　　（他既然在此地，不會有危險的。）

2. 受格

　(1) **做及物動詞的受詞**：Tell **us** what you want.（告訴我們你要些什麼。）

　(2) **做介系詞的受詞**：Father wants you to go with **him**.（父親要你和他一起去。）

　(3) **做受詞補語**：We do not believe the murderer to be **him**.（我們不相信兇手是他。）

3. 所有格

⑴ 形容詞用法：其後接名詞

His mother is **my** aunt. (他母親是我的阿姨。)

We ought to love **our** country. (我們應該愛我們的國家。)

⑵ 代名詞用法：其後不需接名詞

① 用它代替所有形容詞 + 名詞，以避免名詞的重複：

This watch is $\begin{cases} \text{my watch.【重複】} \\ \textbf{mine}.\text{【較好】} \end{cases}$ (這只錶是 $\begin{cases} \text{我的錶。)【重複】} \\ \text{我的。)【較好】} \end{cases}$

I have found my pen, but not **yours** (= your pen) .

〔 我已經找到我的鋼筆，但不是你的（ 鋼筆）。〕

Mine is a small family. = **My family** is a small one. (我家是個小家庭。)

Give my best regards to **yours** (= your family) . (代我向你家人致意。)

I have just received **yours** (= your letter) of the 7th. (我剛收到你本月七號的來信。)

It is **ours** (= our duty) to help him. (幫助他是我們的責任。)

② 做雙重所有格：

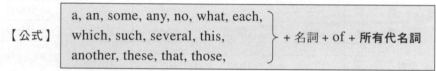

【公式】 a, an, some, any, no, what, each, which, such, several, this, another, these, that, those, 〕 + 名詞 + of + **所有代名詞**

A friend of **mine** has gone to Japan. (我的一個朋友去了日本。)

This hat of **hers** is old. (她的這頂帽子很舊。)

It's no business of **yours**. = None of your business. (那不關你的事。)

Ⅲ. 有關格應注意的要點：

1. 在比較的副詞子句裡，**than** 或 **as** 之後的代名詞有時用主格，有時用受格：

⑴ **than** 或 **as** 前面的子句（ 亦即主要子句 ）其動詞為不及物動詞時，其後的代名詞則用主格。

I am taller than **he** (is). (我比他高。)

He is not so tall as **I** (am). (他沒有我高。)

You are as tall as **I** (am). (你和我一樣高。)

I run faster than **he** (does = runs fast). (我跑得比他快。)

He can not run so fast as **I** (can = can run fast). (他跑得沒我快。)

You run as fast as **I** (do = run fast). (你跑得和我一樣快。)

⑵ **than** 或 **as** 之前的主要子句裡的動詞為及物動詞時，其後的代名詞做主詞時用主格，做受詞時用受格。

He likes Mary better than **I**. (他比我更喜歡瑪麗。)

= He likes Mary better than **I** like Mary.

He likes Mary better than **me**. = He likes Mary better than he likes **me**.

(他喜歡瑪麗甚於喜歡我。 = 他雖喜歡我，但更喜歡瑪麗。)

2. 做補語時，與動詞 "to be" 前面的代名詞或名詞同一格。

定律：當 **A** 是 **B** 時，**A** 和 **B** 同格。

   A　　　是　　　**B**

 I was taken to be **she**. (我被誤認為是她。)

主格 ⟵ 同格 ⟶ 主格

A　是　B

They took **me** to be **her**. （他們誤以為我是她。）

受格←同格→受格

A　是　B

I thought **it** to be **her**. （我認為那就是她。）

受格←同格→受格

A　是　B

I thought **it** was **she**. （我認為那就是她。）

主格←同格→主格

上句 it was she 是個名詞子句，前面省掉了個連接詞 that，做 thought 的受詞；it 是該子句的
主詞，所以屬主格，後面的補語也須用主格（she）。

A　是　B

It was thought to be **she**. （那被以為是她。）

主格 ←—— 同格 ——→ 主格

A 是　B

Can **it** be **John and she** that are ringing the door bell? （正在按門鈴的人可能是約翰和她嗎？）

主格← 同格 →主格

<u>比較下列其他例句</u>：【改成被動後，受詞變成主詞，受詞補語變成主詞補語】

  { I believed **it** to be **him**. （我相信那是他。）

  { **It** was believed to be **he**. （那被認為是他。）

  { He knew **it** to have been **them**. （他知道那是他們。）

  { **It** seemed to be **they**. （那似乎是他們。）

    ※ 如今在口語中用 **It's me.** 代替 **It's I.** （參照 p.116）

3. **its 為 it 的所有格，而 it's 為 it is（was, has）的縮寫，不可混淆。**

   Please go and get my ballpoint pen; it's on the table. （請把我的原子筆拿來，就在桌上。）

   The dog wagged its tail. （那狗搖牠的尾巴。）

4. **下面有幾個特別的名詞，其前雖加同一所有形容詞但可能有不同的意義，要看上下文**
   來決定，我們不能不小心。

  { He asked for **our** assistance. （他求<u>我們的幫助</u>。）

  { He came to **our** assistance. （他來<u>幫助我們</u>。）

  { **His** praise encouraged me. （<u>他的稱讚</u>鼓勵了我。）

  { **His** praise was heard everywhere. （到處可以聽到<u>他被稱讚</u>。）

  { No one came to **his** rescue. （沒人去<u>救他</u>。）

  { Without **his** rescue, I should have been drowned. （若沒<u>他的救援</u>，我可能已溺斃了。）

IV. **we, you, they 的特殊用法：**

1. **we, you 常被用來指一般人**

   We (You) should be kind to old people. （人人都應該對老人和善。）

   We (You) ought to obey the law. （人人應該遵守法律。）

   We (You) should never place our (your) happiness on impossible things; nor our (your)
     unhappiness on inevitable things.

   （人人不應該把幸福寄望於不可能的事；也不要因為一些無法避免的事而難過。）

2. **新聞記者自稱用 "we"**，因爲他們的發言似有代表輿論的意思，譯成中文爲「吾人」或「我們」，這種用法稱爲 "Editorial we"。

We always make it our object to guide the public opinion. (吾人始終把引導輿論做我們的目的。)

【註】 這時 we 的複合代名詞仍用 "ourselves"。

3. **皇帝自稱用 "we" 代替 "I"** 譯成中文爲「朕」之意。這種用法稱爲 "Plural of Majesty"。

The King said, "**We** are pleased with your faithful service." (皇帝說：「朕嘉許卿之功績。」)

【註】 此時 we 的複合代名詞則用 ourself 來代替 ourselves 這是特別的形態。

4. **they 通常用以避免使用被動語態**

$\begin{cases}\text{\textbf{They grow much wheat} in this part of the country. (該國的這一地區種植很多小麥。)}\\ \text{= Much wheat is grown in this part of the country.}\end{cases}$

$\begin{cases}\text{\textbf{Do they teach French} in your school? (你們學校教不教法文？)}\\ \text{= Is French taught in your school?}\end{cases}$

$\begin{cases}\text{\textbf{Do they sell cigarettes} at the store? (那商店賣香煙嗎？)}\\ \text{= Are cigarettes sold at the store?}\end{cases}$

$\begin{cases}\text{\textbf{Do they speak English} in Australia? (澳洲人講英語嗎？)}\\ \text{= Is English spoken in Australia?}\end{cases}$

5. **"they say"**，**"they tell me" 常用來代替 "people say" 或 "it is said"**，意思是「人家說」，「據說」。

They say that he is a genius in nuclear physics. (據說他是核子物理天才。)

= **People say** that he is a genius in nuclear physics.

= **It is said** that he is a genius in nuclear physics.

【註1】 **he 和 we, you 一樣亦可指一般人**，通常用在 **he who** (*or* **that**) 的情形。

He who lives in a glass house should not throw stones.

(住在玻璃房子的人，不該扔石頭。—— 喻自己有缺點，就不該說別人。)

He that steals an egg will steal an ox. (敢偷蛋者，必敢偷牛。)

He who hesitates is lost. (猶豫者必失良機。)

He who touches pitch shall be defiled therewith. (近朱者赤，近墨者黑。)

The plums looked sweet, but **he** could not eat the fruit that **he** had stolen.

(李子看起來很甜，但是偷來的李子不能吃。)

【註2】 **人稱代名詞的排列法：**

① **單數時：**通常按 2, 3, 1 或 3, 2, 1 人稱排列

You, he and I are of the same age. (你，他和我都是同一年齡。)

② **複數時：**按 1, 2, 3 排列

We, you and they are all good citizens. (我們，你們和他們都是好公民。)

③ 第三人稱男女兩性並用時，**男先女後**

Nobody does not agree to this plan except **him and her**.

(除了他和她之外，沒有人不同意這個計劃。)

④ 若一群人中，有男女時，則**先稱呼女性**

Ladies and gentlemen (諸位女士先生)

⑤ **表示不吉祥之事，或有壞的意思時：**

ㄗ. **單數時：**通常按 1, 3, 2 的人稱排列

I, he and you will be punished for being late. (我，他和你都要因遲到受罰。)

> *2* **複數時**：通常按 3, 2, 1 的人稱排列
> **They**, **you and we** should leave there at once.
> （他們，你們和我們，都應馬上離開那裡。）

V. it 的用法：

1. 非人稱的 **it**，指天氣、時間、季節、距離等做主詞

⑴ **天氣**：

A: How is the weather?（天氣如何？）

B: It is fine.

It is sultry.（= It is muggy.）（天氣悶熱。）

It is chilly.（寒意逼人。）

It is cold.

It is cloudy.

It is stormy (*or* rough, wild).（暴風雨；壞天氣；惡劣的天氣。）

It is blowing hard.

It is very hot, isn't it?

It is getting warmer day by day.（天氣一天一天地溫和起來了。）

It rains a lot in June.（在六月雨水多。）

⑵ **時間（或日期）**：

A: What time is **it**?（現在幾點了？）

B: It is half past ten.（十點半。）

It is fourteen hundred hours.（下午兩點。）【軍用語 14:00】

It is still early.（時間尚早。）

It is time to go to bed.（是就寢的時間了。）

It is getting dark.（天黑了。）

It is ten years since the war was over.（自從戰爭結束到現在已經十年了。）

It was Sunday, and there was no school.（那是星期日，不上學。）

It will not be long before he gets well.（不久他當可痊癒。）

A: What day is **it** today?（今天是星期幾？）

B: It is Sunday today.（= Today is Sunday.）（今天是星期日。）

⑶ **季節**：

It is spring (*or* summer, autumn, winter) now.〔現在是春天（或夏天或秋天或冬天）。〕

⑷ **距離**：

A: How far is **it** from here to the station?（從這裡到車站有多遠？）

B: It is ten minutes' walk.（步行十分鐘的路程。）

【注意】 下面的例句是以**時間表距離**的，所以**用 how long**，而不用 *how far*，且此種用法的 it 是形式主詞，代替後面的不定詞片語。

A: How long does it take to go downtown from here?
（從這裡到市中心要多久的時間？）

B: It takes about half an hour to go downtown.（到市中心大約需要半小時。）

2. **爲了避免重複，所以用 it 代替前面已經說過的名詞**

My brother bought a watch, and gave **it** (= the watch which he had bought) to me.
（我哥哥買了一只錶，他把它給了我。）

【註】 **one 和 that 爲了避免重複也可以代替前面提過的名詞，但和 it 不同。**

⑴ **it = the** (**this, that, my,**…) **+ 名詞**

it 所指的事物和前面提到的事物是同一件（個）事物，所以 it 代表的名詞屬於**特定的**。

I bought a knife and lent **it** to him. （我買把小刀並將它借給他。）
it = the knife which I bought 【it 所指的小刀就是前面所提到我買的那把小刀】

I drank some iced tea, but **it** made me more thirsty.
〔我喝了些冰茶，但它（那些冰茶）使我更渴。〕
it = the iced tea I drank 【it 所指的冰茶就是前面所提到我喝的那些冰茶】

⑵ **one = a + 名詞**（參照 p.139）

one 所代表的名詞和前面所提到的名詞只是同一類，並非指同一個，而且指同類中的任一個，不是指其中某一個，所以 one 所指的名詞屬於**不定的**。

This watch is too expensive; show me a cheaper **one** (= watch), please.
（這只錶太貴了；請拿一只便宜一點的給我看。）
【one 只是代表一只錶，並非指前面所提的那一只】

I want a watch, but have no money to buy **one** (= a watch) with.
（我需要一只錶，但卻沒有錢買一只。）
【one 代表一只錶，任何一只錶，並非指前面所提到的那一只】

⑶ **that = the + 名詞**（參照 p.122）

that 所代表的名詞，和前面所提到的名詞只屬同一類，但不是指同一個。
The voice of a woman is sweeter than **that** (= the voice) of a man.
（女人的聲音比男人的聲音悅耳。）
The tail of a rabbit is not so long as **that** (= the tail) of a rat.
（兔子的尾巴沒有老鼠的尾巴長。）

【注意】 **it 與 that** 的比較
１. **相同之點：** 兩者所代表的名詞均爲特定的。
２. **不同之點：** it 所指的名詞與前面所提到的名詞爲**同一個事物**。
that 所指的名詞與前面所提到的名詞爲**同一類的事物**，但並非同一個。
The climate of my native town is mild; I like **it** (= the climate of my native town) very much. （故鄉的氣候溫和，我很喜歡它。）
The climate of my native town is not so warm as **that** (= the climate) of Taiwan. （故鄉的氣候不像台灣的氣候那樣溫暖。）

3. **爲了避免重複，it 也可代替前面已經說過的片語或子句**

I tried <u>to move the stone away from the middle of the road</u>, but found **it** impossible.
（我想把路中間的石頭搬走，但是不可能。）

<u>He is an honest man</u>; I know **it** well. （他是個誠實的人，我知道得很清楚。）

上兩句的 it 是代表下加線的片語和子句，做動詞 found 和 know 的受詞。

4. **虛字用法的 it**

⑴ 做形式主詞，代替後面所要說的不定詞、動名詞或名詞子句

① 不定詞：通常以下面的句型出現。

　　句型結構：**It + be** 動詞 **+ ⋯ + to +** 原形動詞⋯

　　It is not easy <u>to master a foreign language</u>. （要精通一種外國語言是不容易的。）
　　形式主詞　　　　　　　　眞正主詞

　　It 指不定詞 to master a foreign language，做 is 的主詞。這種 it 稱爲形式主詞（Formal Subject），這裡的不定詞 to master a foreign language 稱爲眞正主詞（Real Subject）。

　　上例也可寫成：

　　<u>To master a foreign language</u> is not easy.
　　　　　　主　　　　　詞

　　It is wrong <u>to tell a lie</u>. （說謊是不對的。）
　　形式主詞　　　　眞正主詞

　　= <u>To tell a lie</u> is wrong.

　　It is glorious <u>to die for one's country</u>. （爲國而死是光榮的。）
　　形式主詞　　　　　　眞正主詞

　　= <u>To die for one's country</u> is glorious.

② 動名詞：通常以下面的句型出現。

　　句型結構：**It + be** 動詞 **+ ⋯ + ～ing**⋯

　　It is no use <u>trying to excuse yourself</u>. （辯解是沒有用的。）
　　形式主詞　　　　　　眞正主詞

　　= <u>Trying to excuse yourself</u> is no use.
　　　　　　　主　　　　　　詞

　　It is no use <u>crying over spilt milk</u>. （爲灑了的牛奶哭泣是沒有用的。）（＝後悔無益。）
　　形式主詞　　　　眞正主詞

　　= <u>Crying over spilt milk</u> is no use.

③ 名詞子句：通常以下面的句型出現。

　　句型結構：**It + be** 動詞 **+ ⋯ +** 名詞子句

　　It is true <u>that he has failed</u>. （他失敗是眞的。）
　　形式主詞　　　眞正主詞

　　= <u>That he has failed</u> is true.
　　　　　主　　詞

　　It is uncertain <u>whether he has passed the examination</u>. （他是否已通過那考試尙未確知。）
　　形式主詞　　　　　　眞正主詞

　　= <u>Whether he has passed the examination</u> is uncertain.
　　　　　　　主　　　　　　詞

It is surprising <u>how little he knows</u>. (眞奇怪，他是那麼不懂事。)
形式主詞　　　　　　　眞正主詞

= <u>How little he knows</u> is surprising.
　　主　　詞

(2) **it 做形式受詞，代替後面所要説的不定詞、動名詞或名詞子句，通常用在有形容詞做受詞補語時。**

① **不定詞：**

句型結構：
$$
\begin{cases}
\text{believe} & \text{make} \\
\text{consider} & \text{regard} \\
\text{count} & \text{suppose} \\
\text{deem} & \text{take} \\
\text{feel} & \text{think} \\
\text{find} & \vdots \\
\text{imagine}
\end{cases}
$$
+ **it** + 受詞補語 + **to** + 原形動詞

受詞補語

We consider **it** wrong <u>to cheat in an examination</u>. (我們認爲在考試中做弊是錯的。)
　　　　　形式受詞　　　　　眞 正 受 詞

it 代表不定詞 to cheat in an examination 做 consider 的受詞。這種結構叫作形式受詞 (Formal Object) 或文法受詞 (Grammatical Object)；該不定詞便稱之爲眞正受詞 (Real Object)，形容詞 wrong 爲受詞補語。

受詞補語

I make **it** a rule <u>to take a walk after dinner</u>. (我經常在晚飯後散步。)
　　　形式受詞　　　　　眞 正 受 詞

② **動名詞：**

句型結構：
$$
\begin{cases}
\text{believe} & \text{make} \\
\text{consider} & \text{regard} \\
\text{count} & \text{suppose} \\
\text{deem} & \text{take} \\
\text{feel} & \text{think} \\
\text{find} & \vdots \\
\text{imagine}
\end{cases}
$$
+ **it** + 受詞補語 + **~ing**

受詞補語

The Americans found **it** impossible <u>trying to beat the Chinese team in the Little League</u>
　　　　　　　　　形式受詞　　　　　　　　　　　　　　眞 正 受 詞

<u>World Series</u>. (美國人發現想在世界少棒賽中擊敗中華隊是不可能的。)

受詞補語

Don't you think **it** wrong <u>wasting your time</u>? (你不以爲浪費時間是錯誤的嗎？)
　　　　　　形式受詞　　　　眞 正 受 詞

③ **名詞子句：**

句型結構：
$$
\begin{cases}
\text{believe} & \text{make} \\
\text{consider} & \text{regard} \\
\text{count} & \text{suppose} \\
\text{deem} & \text{take} \\
\text{feel} & \text{think} \\
\text{find} & \vdots \\
\text{imagine}
\end{cases}
$$
+ **it** + 受詞補語 + **that** + 主詞 + 動詞

受詞補語

I want to make **it** clear <u>whether you still love me or not</u>.

形式受詞　　　　　　真　正　受　詞

（我要弄清楚你是不是還愛我。）

受詞補語

I consider **it** true <u>that he is a hypocrite</u>.（我認為他是個偽君子是不會錯的。）

形式受詞　　　　真　正　受　詞

5. 加強語氣用法的 **it**

句型結構：　| **It is (was) + 所要加強的部分 + that + 其餘部分** |

例 1.：　I met your sister in the park last night.

如果我們強調是「誰」昨夜在公園遇到你妹妹，就應寫成下面的樣子：

It was *I* that met your sister in the park last night.

同樣的，如強調遇到了「誰」，就：

It was *your sister* that I met in the park last night.【若將 your sister 改為代名詞要用 her】

如強調「在什麼時候」遇到了你妹妹，就：

It was *last night* that I met your sister in the park.

如果強調「在什麼地方」遇到了你妹妹，就：

It was *in the park* that I met your sister last night.

例 2.：　You are wrong.（你錯了。）

如果我們要強調錯的是「你」就應寫成：It is *you* that (*or* who) are wrong.

It is	主　　格	子　　　　　句	
It is	*I* *you* *he* *we* *they*	that　　am that　　are that　　is that　　are that　　are (who)	wrong.

【註 1】　上述例 1. 中，第一、第二及第四，三個句子的 "It was…" 亦有人用現在時態而成 "It is…" 的，但第三個句子的時態，卻非用過去式不可。

【註 2】　"that" 的前面所指為人時，可用 "**who**"；為物時，可用 "**which**"；為時間時，可用 "**when**"；為地方時，可用 "**where**" 來代 "that"。

It was I **who**…

It was your sister **whom**…

It was last night **when**…

It was in the park **where**…

【註 3】　此種結構中的 that 之後的動詞的人稱與數要與它前面的名詞或代名詞一致，與主詞 it 無關。

It is **I** that **am** wrong.（是我不對。）

It is not **you** that **are** to blame.（不是你的過失。）

It was my two **sons** that **were** hurt.（受傷的是我兩個兒子。）

【註4】 It is (was) 與 that 之間的加強部分有時是一個介詞片語或子句。

It was **on the 10th of October in 1911** that the Republic of China was born.

（在 1911 年 10 月 10 日中華民國誕生了。）

It is **when something unusual happens** that he shows great courage.

（當不平常的事發生時，他表現了很大的勇氣。）

【註5】 下面慣用語的 It 是指後面的 that 子句，與加強語氣用法的 it 不同。（詳見 p.377）

即：**It is + p.p. + that…的形式**

It is agreed that… （同意…）

It is believed that… （大家相信…）

It is (well) known that… （家喻戶曉…）

It is reported that… （據報導…）

It is rumored that… （謠傳…）

It is said that… （據說…）

It is supposed that… （大家推測…）

It is thought that… （大家認爲…）

It is rumored that there will be a holiday tomorrow. （謠傳明天放假。）

6. **it** 可用作不定的形式主詞

Who is **it**? （是誰呀？）

It is I (*or* me, you, he, she, we, you, they, the postman…).

〔是我（你，他，她，我們，你們，他們，郵差…）。〕

I thought **it** was Miss Chang, but **it** was not she. （我以爲是張小姐，但不是她。）

7. **it** 的慣用法：

How is it with your children? （你的孩子們好嗎？）

= *How are your children?*

It is well with them. （他們很好。）

That's it. （這就對啦！）

= ⎰ *That's what I mean.*
⎱ *That's what I want to know.*

It went hard with him. （他遭遇不幸。）

It is all over (*or* up) with me. （我無望了。完了！完了！）

It fared well with me. （我很順遂。）

= *I fared well.*

It is always so (*or* the case) with him. （他總是那個樣子。）

You will catch it. （你會被責罵。）

We must fight it out. （我們必須戰鬥到底。）

I can't help it. （我沒有辦法。）

I am determined to brave it out. （我打定主意硬幹下去。）

He lords it over his friends. （他對他的朋友逞威風。）【lord it over… 向…逞威風】

VI. 複合人稱代名詞（Compound Personal Pronouns）：

1. 複合人稱代名詞的形式：

人　稱	數	性　　　格	主　　　　　格	所　有　格
1	單　數	通　性	myself	my own
	複　數	通　性	ourselves	our own
2	單　數	通　性	yourself	your own
	複　數	通　性	yourselves	your own
3	單　數	陽　性	himself	his own
		陰　性	herself	her own
		無　性	itself	its own
	複　數	通　性	themselves	their own
	（代表形）		oneself *or* one's self	one's own

【註1】　複合人稱代名詞的第一人稱和第二人稱是由**所有格** + self (selves) 而成。第三人稱則由**受格** + self (selves) 而成。

【註2】　oneself 及 one's own 為全部複合人稱代名詞的代表形，就像 be 為全部 be 動詞（am, are, is…）的代表形一樣。

2. 複合人稱代名詞的用法：

⑴ **反身用法**：當及物動詞或介詞之**受詞**與主詞指同一人或物時，要用**複合人稱代名詞**；而此用法中的複合人稱代名詞就被稱為**反身代名詞**（**Reflexive Pronouns**）。

　定律：主詞和受詞為同一人或物時，該用反身代名詞。

　　The doctor told me to take care of *my body*.【誤，非正式】
　　The doctor told me to take care of *myself*.【正】
　　（醫生告訴我要當心我的身體。）

比較 ⎰ He killed himself.（他自殺了。）
　　　　　　└─ 同一人 ─┘
　　　⎱ He killed him.（他把他殺了。）
　　　　　　└─ 二個人 ─┘

主　　詞	動　　詞	反身代名詞（受詞）
I	know	**myself.**
You	love	**yourself.**
He	killed	**himself.**
She	spoke to	**herself.**
It ⎱ History ⎰	repeats（重演）	**itself.**
We	enjoyed	**ourselves.**
You	help	**yourselves.**
They	praise（稱讚）	**themselves.**
One	must know	**oneself.**

其他例句：

> My father shaves *himself* every morning.（我父親每天早上刮鬍子。）
>
> She hanged *herself* in her own room last night.（她昨晚在自己房間上吊死亡。）
>
> (You) Respect *yourself*, or no one else will respect you.
>
> （尊重你自己，不然別人不會尊重你。）
>
> God helps those who help *themselves*.
>
> （上帝幫助那些自己幫助自己的人 —— 天助自助者。）
>
> The vase didn't break *itself*; somebody must have broken it.
>
> （花瓶不會自己打破；一定是有人把它打破了。）
>
> One should have confidence in *oneself*.（一個人對他自己要有信心。）

【註1】 **及物動詞 + oneself** 相當不及物動詞的意味
　　　　seat oneself = sit (down)（坐下）
　　　　raise oneself = rise（起身）
　　　　lay oneself = lie (down)（躺下）
　　　　absent oneself = be absent（缺席）

【註2】 **及物動詞 + oneself = be + 過去分詞**
　　　　seat oneself = be seated（就座）
　　　　amuse oneself = be amused（消遣）
　　　　devote oneself to = be devoted to（專心於；致力於）

(2) **加強語氣的用法（Emphatic Use）**：此用法是強調主詞、受詞或補語的語氣；若將表示強勢的複合代名詞從句中省去，對句意仍無影響。

The chairman **himself** replied to my question.（主席親自回答我的問題。）

Jane told me that **herself**.〔珍親自告訴我那個（消息）。〕

I **myself** wrote this report.（我自己寫這份報告。）

【註1】 在口頭英語裡，尤其在短句中，**強勢複合代名詞常放在句末**。
　　　　I did it **myself**. = I **myself** did it.（我自己做的。）

【註2】 **複合人稱代名詞的人稱、數或性須與其先行詞一致。**

> She looked at *himself* in the mirror.【誤】【性別不一致】
> 陰性　　　　　　　　陽性
>
> **She** looked at **herself** in the mirror.【正】
> （她照鏡子。）

> You should all look after *yourself* during the trip.【誤】【數不一致】
> 複數　　　　　　　　　　　　單數
>
> **You** should all look after **yourselves** during the trip.【正】
> （旅途中你們大家應該照顧你們自己。）

> My little brother cut *myself* with a knife the other day.【誤】【人稱不一致】
> 第三人稱　　　　　第一人稱
>
> My little **brother** cut **himself** with a knife the other day.【正】
> （我小弟弟幾天前用小刀把他自己割傷。）

【註 3】 強勢代名詞是用來加強主詞抑或受詞要辨別清楚，不然會產生誤解。

請比較下面的例子：

I want to see our boss. 【普通】
（我想見我們的老闆。）
I **myself** want to see our boss. 【加強主詞】
（我想親自見我們的老闆。）
I want to see our boss **himself**. 【加強受詞】
（我想見我們的老闆他本人。）

I heard Father say that he would buy me a bicycle. 【普通】
（我聽父親說他要給我買部腳踏車。）
I **myself** heard Father say that he would buy me a bicycle. 【加強主詞】
（我親自聽父親說他要給我買部腳踏車。）
I heard Father **himself** say that he would buy me a bicycle. 【加強受詞】
（我聽父親親口說他要給我買部腳踏車。）

(3) **one's own 的用法：**

① **形容詞用法：是用來加強所有形容詞（my, your…）的語氣。**
This is my book.（這是我的書。）【普通】
This is **my own** book.（這是我自己的書。）【強勢】
I want to be **my own** master.（我要做我自己的主人。）
My own attitude is very foolish.（我自己的態度是非常愚蠢的。）

② **獨立用法：即省掉複合人稱代名詞的所有格後面重複的名詞。**
This hat is mine.【普通】
This hat is my own hat.【重複】
This hat is **my own**.【強勢】
Has he a house of **his own**?（他有自己的房子嗎？）

【註 1】 **one's own 與 a(n), some, any, no, this…同時修飾名詞時要用雙重所有格形式。**

公　式 | a(n), this, that, these, those some, any, several, no, what each, such, another, which | + | 名詞 | + | of + **one's own**

The moon has *no* light *of its own*.（月亮本身無光。）
She has *some* property *of her own*.（她自己略有財產。）
Have you *any* money *of your own*?（你自己有錢嗎？）

【註 2】 **複合人稱代名詞的所有格**（my own, her own,…）**和代名詞所有格**（mine, hers,…）都可形成雙重所有格，只是前者語氣較強而已。

(4) **複合人稱代名詞的慣用語：**

① **動詞 + oneself 形成的慣用語**
　a. **abandon oneself to**（= indulge oneself in）（沉迷於；放縱於）
　　He abandons himself to wine.（他沉迷於喝酒。）
　b. **absent oneself (from)**〔= be absent (from)〕（缺席）
　　He absented himself from school.（他沒去上學。）

c. **accustom oneself to**（= be accustomed to）（使習慣於）
He accustomed himself to the new city.（他使自己習慣於那新城市之中。）

d. **amuse oneself**（= be amused）（消遣）
I amused myself by reading detective stories.（我看偵探小說自娛。）

e. **avail oneself of**（利用；趁）
I will avail myself of your kind invitation and come this evening.
（承你好意相約，今晚一定赴約。）

f. **come to oneself**（甦醒）
When I came to myself, I found myself lying in a hospital.
（當我甦醒過來時，我發現自己躺在醫院裡。）

g. **devote oneself to**（專心於；致力於）
He devoted (applied) himself to his studies.（他專心於學業。）

h. **distinguish oneself for**（以…出名）
She distinguishes herself for dressing all in white.（她以一身白衣出名。）

i. **dress oneself in**（穿著；打扮）
She dresses herself in white.（她穿著白衣。）

j. **enjoy oneself**（玩得愉快）
I enjoyed myself all day. = *I had a good time all day.*（我整天玩得很開心。）

k. **help oneself to**（自行取用）
Help yourself to the cake, please.（請隨意吃蛋糕。）

l. **lose oneself**（迷失）
They lost themselves in the woods.（他們在森林中迷了路。）

m. **make oneself at home**（不要客氣）
Make yourself at home, and help yourself to anything you like.
（不必拘束，喜歡什麼就吃什麼。）

n. **overeat oneself**（吃得過多）
Don't overeat yourself.（不要吃得過多。）

o. **oversleep oneself**（睡得過多）
Don't oversleep yourself.（不要睡得過多。）

p. **overwork oneself**（工作過度；過勞）
Don't overwork yourself.（不要工作過度。）

q. **pride oneself on**（= be proud of）（自誇）
He prided himself on his success.（他誇耀他的成功。）
= *He took pride in his success.*
= *He was proud of his success.*

② 介詞 + **oneself** 形成的慣用語

   a. **among** (**between**) **themselves**（在窩裡；自家人地）

     The three (two) brothers often quarrel among (between) themselves.

     〔三（兩）兄弟時常爭吵。〕

   b. **beside oneself**（= mad）（發狂）

     She was beside herself with joy.（她欣喜若狂。）

   c. **between ourselves**（= between you and me）（不足爲外人道）

     Between ourselves, I am going to get married next Sunday.

     （不要對外人講，我將要在下週日結婚。）

   d. **by oneself**（= alone）（獨自地）

     No one can live by himself.（沒人能獨自生活。）

   e. **for oneself**（= without others' help）（獨力地）

     Do everything for yourself.（一切事都要自己做。）

   f. **in spite of oneself**（不自禁地）

     I laughed in spite of myself.（我不禁發笑。）

   g. **in itself**（在本質上；本身）

     Ambition is not a vice in itself.（野心在本質上不是壞事。）

   h. **of oneself**（= without any external cause）（自行）

     The door opened of itself.（門自行開了。）

   i. **for itself**（= for its own sake）（對其物本質）

     We should love virtue for itself.（我們必須因愛美德而愛美德。）

③ 抽象名詞 + **itself** = **all** + 抽象名詞 = 抽象名詞 + **personified** = **very** + 形容詞（參照 p.70）

> She is beauty itself.（她很漂亮。）
> = She is all beauty.
> = She is beauty personified.
> = She is very beautiful.
>
> He is cruelty itself.（他很殘忍。）
> = He is all cruelty.
> = He is cruelty personified.
> = He is very cruel.

第二章 指示代名詞（Demonstrative Pronouns）

常用的指示代名詞：1. this（單數），these（複數） 2. that（單數），those（複數）
其他做指示代名詞的有：1. such 2. same 3. so

I. this, these, that, those 的用法：

1. **this, these** 指較近的人或物。**that, those** 指較遠的人或物。

   This is my desk; **that** is yours.（這是我的書桌；那是你的。）

   These are fresh oranges; **those** are rotten ones.（這些是新鮮的柳橙；那些是壞的。）

   【註】 如果 **this, that, these, those** 後面接有名詞時，它們便成了**指示形容詞**。

   　　　 This desk is mine.（這張書桌是我的。）

   　　　 That desk is his.（那張書桌是他的。）

2. **this, that** 可以代替前面所提過的片語、子句或句子，以避免重複。these, those 不可做這種用法。

   He promised to pay his debt. **This** he did on the following day.

   （他答應還債，而且第二天就還了。）

   I tried to learn the poem by heart, but **this** was no easy task.

   （我試著想背誦那詩，但這不是容易的事情。）

   It was raining hard, and **this** kept us indoors.（雨下得很大，使我們留在家裡。）

   He has good intentions, but **that** is not enough.（他用心善良，但那是不夠的。）

   I will pay you tomorrow. **That** will satisfy you.（我明天將付錢給你，那樣會使你滿意。）

   【註】 **and that** + 副詞或副詞片語，中譯為「而且」，其中的 **that** 代替前面提過的子句，以避免重複，而且還有**加強語氣**的作用。此句型中可將 that 改成 at that 放在句尾，且較 and that 常用。（this 不可用在此一句型中）

   　　　 I must see him, **and that** immediately.【that = I must see him】

   　　　 = I must see him, **and** immediately **at that**.（我一定要見他，而且要立即見他。）

   　　　 He is now eleven, and yet can do nothing but read, **and that** very poorly.

   　　　 = He is now eleven, and yet can do nothing but read, **and** very poorly **at that**.

   　　　 （他現年十一歲了，還只能讀書，而且讀書也讀得很差。）

3. **that, those** 為了避免重複，可以代替前面已說過的名詞。this, these 不可做這種用法。

   The climate of Korea is not so mild as **that**（= the climate）of Taiwan.
   （韓國的氣候沒有台灣的氣候溫和。）

   The ears of a rabbit are longer than **those**（= the ears）of a fox.
   （兔子的耳朵比狐狸的耳朵長。）

   The population of China is a quarter of **that**（= the population）of the world.
   （中國的人口是世界的人口的四分之一。）

   His dress is **that**（= the dress）of a gentleman, but his speech and behavior are **those**
   　　（= the speech and behavior）of a clown.
   （他的衣著是君子的衣著，可是他的言行卻是小丑的言行。）

4. $\left.\begin{array}{l}\text{that}\cdots\text{this}\cdots \\ \text{those}\cdots\text{these}\cdots\end{array}\right\}$ = the former…the latter（前者…後者）

High and tall are synonyms: **this** (= **the latter** = tall) may be used in speaking of what grows — a tree; **that** (= **the former** = high) in speaking of what does not grow — a mountain.

〔高和高是同義字：後者（高）可被用來說生長的東西 —— 一棵樹；前者（高）說不會生長的東西 —— 一座山。〕

The selfish and the benevolent are found in every community; **these** (= **the latter** = the benevolent) are sought after, while **those** (= **the former** = the selfish) are shunned.

〔自私的人與仁慈的人在每個社會裡都有；後者（仁慈的人）是很受歡迎的，而前者（自私的人）則是人們所躲避的。〕

Health is above wealth, for **this** (= **the latter** = wealth) cannot give so much happiness as **that** (= **the former** = health).

〔健康重於財富，因為後者（財富）不如前者（健康）能給我們那麼多幸福。〕

Work and play are both necessary to health; **this** (= **the latter** = play) gives us rest and **that** (= **the former** = work) gives us energy.

〔工作與遊戲均為健康所必需；後者（遊戲）給我們休息，而前者（工作）使我們奮發。〕

【註】 "**this (these)**…**that (those)**…" 只能指物，不能指人。

指人要用：**the one** (= **the former**) …**the other** (= **the latter**) … (參照 p.140)

My father was quarrelling with the lawyer; **the one** (= **the former** = my father) was cool, and **the other** (= **the latter** = the lawyer) was furious with anger.

（我父親和那位律師在爭吵；我父親很冷靜，而那位律師氣得發狂。）

5. $\left.\begin{array}{l}\text{that which = what} \\ \text{those who = the people who}\end{array}\right.$ （凡…者）

That which (= What) is one man's meat may be another's poison.

（一個人的肉可能是他人的毒藥。）（利於甲未必利於乙。）

That which (= What) is beautiful is not always true. （美的東西未必真實。）

Those who insult themselves will be insulted by others. （人必自侮而後人侮之。）

Those who distrust others are likely to be distrusted themselves.

（凡不相信他人者多半也不被他人相信。）

【註】 $\left.\begin{array}{l}\text{those who} \\ \text{they who}\end{array}\right\}$ + V. (複數) = $\left\{\begin{array}{l}\text{one who} \\ \text{he who}\end{array}\right.$ + V. (單數)

Those who like borrowing, dislike paying. （喜歡借的人不喜歡還。）

= **One who** likes borrowing, dislikes paying.

6. 含有 **this, that, these, those** 的慣用語：

(1) **at this** = on hearing (*or* seeing) this〔一聽（看）到這點…〕

At this he got up angrily and went out. （他一聽到這點就生氣地站起來走了。）

(2) **by this** = by this time （這時候）

It ought to be ready by this. （這事現在就該準備好了。）

⑶ **on** (**upon**) **this** (於是)

On this, we separated. (於是，我們分手了。)

⑷ **with this** (說了這話就…)

With this, she left the classroom. (她說完就離開教室了。)

⑸ **for all that** (**this**) = for all despite (雖然如此；儘管如此)

For all that, he was unhappy. (雖然如此，他還是不快樂。)

⑹ **that is to say** (也就是說；即)

He is a coward; that is (to say), he dares not face danger.

(他是個懦夫；也就是說，他不敢面對危險。)

⑺ **That's it**. (對啦！)

⑻ **That's right**. = That's so. (是的；對的。)

⑼ **That's all**. (只此而已；完了；沒有了。)

⑽ **Is that so?** (是那樣的嗎？)

⑾ **That** (**This**) **will do**. 〔那（這）正合用。〕

⑿ He called ⎱ on her **this day week**.　　 (他**上週**的**今天**拜訪了她。)
　　 He will call ⎰ 　　　　　　　　　　　 (他**下週**的**今天**將拜訪她。)

⒀ **That's that**. (就這麼決定了；不必多講了。)

⒁ **in that** (因為)

⒂ **and all that** (等等)

II. such 的用法：

1. **such** 作代名詞用時，指「如此的人或事物」，主要用於文章中，口語中很少用。

Prosperous men are much exposed to flattery, for **such** (= such men) alone can be made
 to pay for it. (得勢的人極易受人諂媚，因為只有<u>這樣的人</u>才能給與諂媚的代價。)

I am a gentleman, and will be treated as **such** (= a gentleman) .

(因為我是紳士，所以我要受<u>紳士</u>的待遇。)

History as **such** is too often neglected. (歷史<u>本身</u>往往被忽視。)【*此處* as such = in itself】

2. **such** 作主詞補語用時，表示前文提及之內容，句型為 **such** + **連接動詞**（be 動詞,

become 等） + **主詞**

I may have offended him, but **such** was not my intention.

(我可能已冒犯了他，但這不是我的意圖。)

He killed himself. **Such** is the case (*or* **Such** is the fact).

〔他自殺了，事情就是這樣（事實就是這樣）。〕

3. **such** 可用作形容詞，沒有單複數之別，可接任何名詞。

I cannot comply with **such** a request. (我不能聽從這樣的請求。)

I cannot agree to **such** terms. (我不能同意那樣的條件。)

【註 1】 such 應放在 **a**(**n**) 的前面，但放在 **some, any, no, every, all, many, few** 的後面。

I want **such a** man. (我需要這樣的一個人。)

I want **some such** men. (我需要一些這樣的人。)

Can't you think of **any such** man? (你能否想到任何一個這樣的人？)

There is **no such** man that I know of. (據我所知，沒有這樣的人。)

There are **many such** people. (有許多像那樣的人。)

【註 2】　形容詞的 "such" 和副詞的 "so" 的意思大都相等。因此 **such + a + 形容詞 + 名詞**相當於 **so + 形容詞 + a + 名詞**，只是兩者所強調的重點不同而已。

I did not accomplish it $\left\{\begin{array}{l}\text{with } \textbf{such} \text{ ease.}\\ \textbf{so} \text{ easily.}\end{array}\right.$ （我未能如此輕鬆地完成它。）

It is **such** a beautiful day. （這是如此美麗的一天。）── 重點在「一天」（day）

It is **so** beautiful a day. （這一天是如此美麗。）── 重點在「美麗」（beautiful）

4. $\left\{\begin{array}{l}\textbf{such (men) as} = \text{those (men) who（用於人）}\\ \textbf{such}\cdots\textbf{as} = \left\{\begin{array}{l}\text{that}\cdots\text{which}\\ \text{those}\cdots\text{which}\end{array}\right\}\text{（用於物）}\end{array}\right.$　as 是以 such (…) 爲先行詞的關代，做形容詞子句的主詞。

Do not trust **such** men **as** praise you to your face.

= Do not trust **those** men **who** praise you to your face.

（不可信任當面稱讚你的人。＝不可信任那些當面稱讚你的人。）

Such as（= Those who）have plenty will never want for friends.

（富裕的人們絕不會缺乏朋友。）

Such men as（= Those men who）are in the married state wish to get out, and **such as**（= those who）are out wish to get in. 〔已結婚者想脫離，未結婚者想加入（結婚）。〕

He does not read many books, but **such** books **as**（= those books which）he reads he reads carefully.（他並沒讀太多的書，但他卻細心地讀他所讀的書。）

【註】　**such** 代表人做主詞時，**常指複數**（指此種人），所以要用**複數動詞**。如：

Such *as*（= Those *who*）*heard him* **were** full of admiration.
　主詞　　　　　　　動詞

（聽到他的談話的人們都讚賞不絕。）

5. $\left.\begin{array}{l}\text{such}\cdots\text{as}\\ \cdots\text{such as}\end{array}\right\}$ + （代）名詞【主格】= …like + （代）名詞【受格】

此種用法的 as 是做補語的關代，其後面的形容詞子句可省略，僅留做主詞的名詞或代名詞。like 是介系詞，須接受格。

I have never heard of $\left\{\begin{array}{l}\textbf{such} \text{ a great man}\\ \text{a great man } \textbf{such}\end{array}\right\}$ **as** he (*is*).　【a great man such as 中的 such 是 man 的同位語】

= I have never heard of a great man **like** him. （我從未聽過像他這樣偉大的人。）

$\left.\begin{array}{l}\textbf{Such} \text{ men}\\ \text{Men } \textbf{such}\end{array}\right\}$ **as** Napoleon and Bismarck (*are*) are rare. 【若將 as 之後的名詞改爲代名詞，須用 they】

= Men **like** Napoleon and Bismarck are rare. 【若將 like 之後的名詞改爲代名詞，須用 them】

（像拿破崙和俾斯麥這樣的人是少有的。）

6. **such as**（+ 名詞）= for example; for instance （例如像…）

Birds of prey, **such as** the eagle and the hawk, do not lay many eggs.

（肉食鳥如鷹鷲之類都產卵不多。）

He knows many languages, **such as** Chinese, German, and French.

（他會很多語言，例如中文、德文，和法文。）

7. $\left\{\begin{array}{l}\text{such + 名詞 + that}\\[1mm]\text{= so + }\left\{\begin{array}{l}\text{形容詞}\\\text{副　詞}\end{array}\right\}\text{（…）+ that}\end{array}\right\}$ （如此…以致於）　such 是形容詞，so 是副詞，that 是表結果的連接詞。（詳見 p.516）

He is $\left\{\begin{array}{l}\textit{such} \text{ a fool}\\\textit{so} \text{ foolish}\end{array}\right\}$ *that* no one will keep company with him.

（他是如此的愚蠢，以致沒有人願和他作伴。）

Mary is *such* a pretty girl *that* everybody likes her.

= Mary is *so* pretty (*a girl*) *that* everybody likes her.

（瑪麗是如此的漂亮，以致每個人都喜歡她。）

【注意】 such～that…的構句易與 such～as…混淆。必須注意 that 為連接詞，as 為關係代名詞。

He is *such* a nice boy *that* everybody loves him.

（他是個如此好的男孩 —— 因為是好男孩，結果 —— 每個人都愛他。）

【that 是連接詞，沒有代名作用，必須有 him 做 loves 的受詞】

He is *such* a nice boy *as* everybody loves.

（他是像那種被大家疼愛的好男孩。）【as 是關代，有代名作用，做 loves 的受詞】

8. **such that…**（如此…以致於）

such 作為代名詞，可以置於表示結果的 that 子句之前。

His eloquence was *such* (= *such great eloquence*) *that* we were all moved by it.

（他的口才很好，以致於我們全部都被感動。）

【註】 such 做 be 動詞的補語時，也可放在主詞位置。（參照 p.124）

Such was his eloquence *that* we were all moved by it.

9. **such 還可以用作感嘆的意味**，與 what 一樣，接名詞。

We had *such* a pleasant time! = *What* a pleasant time we had!（我們玩得好痛快呀！）

What a grand sight! I never saw *such* a sight in my life.

（多麼壯觀啊！我生平從未見過這麼樣的壯觀。）

He is *such* a liar!（他是這樣的一個騙子！）

10. **慣用語 such and such** 作泛指「**如此如此的**」的意思，形式和 so and so「如此如此；某某」相當。

Tell me to do *so and so* on *such and such* an occasion, and I'll do so.

（告訴我在如此如此的一個時機，做如此如此的一件事，我將照辦。）

III. the same 的用法：same 無論是作代名詞或形容詞用時，**前面都必須加 the**。

1. **the same** 作代名詞用，指和剛剛所提到的**同一個或同樣的**人或事物。指「**同一個**」時，可以說是 it 的加強語氣。

They made a bow to us, and repeated *the same*.（他們向我們鞠躬，而且重複同樣的動作。）

He dived — I did *the same*.（他潛入水中 —— 我也潛入水中。）

"I wish you a Happy New Year!" "(I wish) *The same* to you!"

（「祝你新年快樂！」「你也一樣！」）

I bought a bicycle and had *the same* (= *it*; *the very bicycle*) stolen the next day.

（我買了一輛腳踏車，而那輛腳踏車第二天就被偷了。）【此句中 the same 是 it 的加強語氣用法】

2. **the same** 作為形容詞，表示「**同樣的；同一個的**」，修飾名詞。

We sell them at *the same* price.（我們以同樣的價錢出售它們。）

You get *the same* results under *the same* conditions.

（你在同樣的條件之下，可以得到同樣的結果。）

> 【註】　**the same 表示同一個時**，可以用 **this, these, that, those** 代替 the，此時的 same 具
> 有加強這些指示形容詞的作用。
>
> Afterwards *this same* engineer improved the water-pump.
>
> （後來這同一個工程師改良了抽水機。）

3. $\begin{cases} \text{one and the same} \\ = \text{the very same} \end{cases}$ （完全一樣；就是那個）　是形容詞 the same 加強語氣的慣用法。

These expressions all mean *one and the same* thing.（這些辭句意思都是一樣。）

This is *the very same* tune I heard yesterday.（這就是我昨天聽到的那個曲子。）

> 【注意】　the same 還可作副詞用，表示「**同樣地**」。
>
> These words are pronounced *the same*.（這些字發音相同。）
>
> ※ 作副詞用的 the same 之前加上 **just, all** 等可加強語氣，作「**還是；仍然**」解。
>
> We work hard all right, but we are poor *just the same*.
>
> （我們非常努力工作，但是我們仍然還是窮困的。）
>
> You hate me, but I love you *all the same*.（雖然你討厭我，但是我還是愛你。）

4. $\begin{cases} \text{the same…as…（同樣的）【表種類、意義、數量、性質、程度等的相同】} \\ \text{the same…that…（同一個）【表同一人或同一事物】} \end{cases}$

此用法中的 as, that 是以 the same… 作為先行詞的關係代名詞。

This is *the same* knife *as* I lost.（這把小刀和我遺失的那把一樣。）【不是同一把小刀】

This is *the same* knife *that* I lost.（這就是我遺失的那把小刀。）【是同一把小刀】

> 【註1】　the same…that 中的 same 只是加強其「相同」的語氣而已，即使省略了，也不會
> 改變句意；關代 that 在子句中做受詞時也可省略，但是 the same…as 中的 same
> 不可省略，而且 as 省略會改變句意。
>
> $\begin{cases} \text{This is } \textbf{\textit{the same}} \text{ watch } \textbf{\textit{that}} \text{ I lost.（這只錶就是我遺失的錶。）} \\ = \text{This is } \textbf{\textit{the}} \text{ watch } \textbf{\textit{that}} \text{ I lost.【same 可省略】} \\ = \text{This is } \textbf{\textit{the same}} \text{ watch I lost.【that 可省略而句意不變】} \end{cases}$
>
> This is *the same* watch *as* I lost.【正】（這只錶和我遺失的錶一樣。）
>
> *This is the watch as I lost.*【誤】【same 不可省略】
>
> This is *the same* watch I lost.【正】（這只錶就是我遺失的錶。）【as 省略會改變句意】

> 【註2】　**用於抽象的觀念時同種類和同一事是沒有區別的，所以 as 和 that 也可隨便使用。**
> He has *the same* nice position *as* (or *that*) you have.（他有和你同樣高尚的地位。）
> He answered in *the same* way *as* (or *that*) you did.（他以和你同樣的方式回答。）

> 【註3】　the same 之後的名詞若被省略的話，the same 就成為代名詞。
> This is *the same as* I lost.（這和我遺失的東西相同。）【同樣的東西】
> This is *the same that* I lost.（這就是我遺失的東西。）【同一件東西】

5. $\begin{cases} \textbf{the same} + \textbf{地點} + \textbf{where} = \text{the same} + \text{地點} + \text{that} \\ \textbf{the same} + \textbf{時間} + \textbf{when} = \text{the same} + \text{時間} + \text{that} \end{cases}$

the same…之後可使用關係副詞 when, where 代替 that，引導形容詞子句表示時間或場所。

I met her at *the same* place *where* (or *that*) I met you. (在遇見你的地方，我遇見了她。)

I sat down at *the same* time *when* (or *that*) you stood up.

(我在你站起來的同時，坐了下來。)

※ at the same time (①在同一時間，②可是)

It is impossible to do many things *at the same time*.

(在同一時間做很多事情是不可能的。)

She didn't like to spend any more money. *At the same time*, she wanted to go on the trip. (她不想再花錢，可是她卻想去旅行。)

6. the same…as + 省略句

當 **as**, **that**, **when**, **where** 所引導的子句省略了一部分之後，在 **the same**…之後只能用 **as**，不可用 *that*, *when*, *where*，此時的 as 具有「同樣的」或「同一個」兩種意義，尤其是 as 之後僅剩下名詞或代名詞時，很容易被誤認為是介系詞，須特別注意。

I attend *the same* school $\begin{cases} \textit{that} \text{ he does.} \\ \textit{as} \text{ he (does).} \end{cases}$ (我跟他上同一所學校。)【指同一個】

$\begin{cases} \text{I bought } \textit{the same} \text{ watch } \textit{as} \text{ you have.} \\ \text{I bought } \textit{the same} \text{ watch } \textit{as} \text{ you.} \\ \text{〔我買了一只和你（擁有的）相同的手錶。〕【指相同的】} \end{cases}$

I paid *the same* price $\begin{cases} \textit{that} \text{ I had paid for rice.} \\ \textit{as} \text{ rice.} \end{cases}$

〔我付了和（早先付）米同樣的價錢。〕【price 是抽象名詞，沒有相同和同一個之別】

$\begin{cases} \text{I live in } \textit{the same} \text{ place } \textit{where} \text{ (or } \textit{that}\text{) she lives.} 【正】 \\ \text{I live in } \textit{the same} \text{ place } \textit{as} \text{ she.} 【正】 \\ \text{I live in } \textit{the same} \text{ place } \textit{as} \text{ her.} 【誤】【as 是關係代名詞，不是介系詞】 \\ \text{(我和她住在同一地方。)【同一個】} \end{cases}$

IV. so 的用法：

1. 代替名詞、名詞片語或子句，做下列動詞如：**say, tell, think, hope, expect, suppose, imagine, fear, hear, speak, be afraid, do, see, notice**,…等的受詞。

I haven't called on her yet, but I hope to do **so** soon.

(我還沒有拜訪過她，但我希望不久就拜訪她。)

A: Will he come? (他會來嗎？)

B: $\begin{cases} \text{I think } \textbf{so}. \text{ (我想他會來。)} \\ \textbf{So} \text{ he says. (他說他會來。)} \\ \text{I hope } \textbf{so}. \text{ (但願如此。)} \end{cases}$

A: The new teacher is very strict. (新老師很嚴。)

B: $\begin{cases} \textbf{So} \text{ I've heard. (聽說如此。)} \\ \textbf{So} \text{ I was told. (聽說如此。)} \end{cases}$

A: Is he sick? (他病了嗎？)

B: I'm afraid **so**. (恐怕如此。)

【註1】 so 可以放在句首或句尾。

$$I \begin{cases} believe \\ hope \\ think \\ say \\ suppose \\ \vdots \end{cases} so. = So\ I \begin{cases} believe. \\ hope. \\ think. \\ say. \\ suppose. \\ \vdots \end{cases}$$

但上述動詞之中 see, hear, notice 三個動詞之受詞 so，只能放在句首。

I see so.【誤】	**So** I see.【正】
I hear so.【誤】	**So** I hear.【正】
I notice so.【誤】	**So** I notice.【正】

【註2】 "not" 接在 hope, imagine, suppose, fear, believe, be afraid 等動詞及 perhaps, probably, absolutely 等副詞之後，可以代替否定子句。

A: Will he die?（他會死嗎？）
B: I hope **not**.（= I hope that he will not die.）（我希望他不至於死。）
【比較】I don't hope that he will die.（我不希望他死。）
A: Can you come next week?（下週你能來嗎？）
B: I am afraid **not**.（= I'm afraid that I can't come.）（我恐怕不能來。）

【註3】 在口語中，在 say, tell, do 等動詞之後的 "so" 常用 "that" 或 "it" 代替。
Don't say **that** (*or* **it**). = Don't say **so**.（別那麼說。）
My advice is that you send him an apology, and that you do **that** (*or* **it**) at once.
（我的忠告是你向他道歉，並且即刻去做。）

2. **so 又可做 be 動詞的補語**，不過要注意字序與意義之不同。（參照 p.643）

He is wise. — **So** he is (*or* Yes, he is).（他是聰明的 —— 的確他是聰明的。）
He is wise. — **So** is she (*or* She is, too).（他是聰明的 —— 她也聰明。）

【註1】 在下面各例中，so 為補語，亦即 so 不代表前面的句子或子句，而**只代表其中的一部分**。

Mr. Smith was a student of history and is likely to remain **so**.
【so = a student of history】
（史密斯先生曾是歷史系的學生，而且他很可能繼續下去。）

He was not enthusiastic at first, but became **so** after a little while.
（起初他不熱心，但過一段時間就變得熱心起來了。）【so = enthusiastic】

A: I thought they were intelligent and honest.（我認為他們既聰明又誠實。）
B: **So** they probably were.（他們可能是呀！）

【註2】 **So + 動詞 + 主詞 =「～亦復如此」**（簡略附和句）（此時 so 為副詞）

| I was too. = **So** was I. | He does too. = **So** does he. |
| They did too. = **So** did they. | She will too. = **So** will she. |

He likes it.（他喜歡它。）　　　　　　He must do it.（他必須做那個。）
So do I.（我也喜歡它。）　　　　　　So must she.（她也必須做。）

第三章 不定代名詞（Indefinite Pronouns）

Ⅰ.**定義：不定代名詞是指不定數量的人或物的代名詞**，假如其後接有名詞，即成爲不定形容詞。

If you want **any** money, I will lend you **some**.（假如你需要錢，我可以借給你一些。）
　　　　形容詞　　　　　　　　　　　　　代名詞

Ⅱ.**種類：**

1. 可做代名詞或形容詞者：

some（一些）	any（任何）	both（兩者都）
either（兩者中之任一）	neither（兩者中無一）	all（全部）
one（任何人、某人、某事）	each（各個）	another（另一）
few（極少數）	little（極少量）	many（很多）
much（多量）	other（其他）	such（這樣的）
the same（同樣的）	enough（充分）	several（一些）
more（更多的）	most（大部分的）	

2. 只做代名詞者：

none（無一人；無一物）	nobody（無一人）	nothing（無一物）
someone（某人）	somebody（某人）	something（某物）
anyone（任何人）	anybody（任何人）	anything（任何物）
everyone（每人）	everybody（每人）	everything（每一物）

※ every（每一）只做形容詞，不可做代名詞。

Ⅲ.**不定代名詞的用法：**

1. **some, any** 的用法：（參照 p.171）

⑴ 一般的用法：

some 用於肯定句；**any** 用於疑問句、否定句，或條件句，表示「多少；一些」之意。

A: I want **some** stamps. Have you **any**?（我需要一些郵票，你有嗎？）

B: { Yes, I have **some**.（是的，我有一些。）
　　{ No, I have not **any**.（不，我一張也沒有。）

⑵ 特殊用法：

① **在期望對方答 Yes 時，問句也用 "some"**

Don't you have **some** brothers?（你沒有兄弟嗎？── 你有兄弟吧？）
(= *You have some brothers, don't you?*)

Don't you want **some** money?（你不需要錢嗎？── 你需要錢吧？）
(= *You want some money, don't you?*)

Will you have **some** beer?（要不要來點啤酒？）

Shall I give you **some** wine?（我給你準備些酒好嗎？）

Will you carry **some** of these bottles for me, please?（請爲我拿這些瓶子好嗎？）

Will you lend me **some** money?（你願意借給我一點錢嗎？── 請你借給我一點錢。）
(= *Please lend me some money.*)

② 若 **any** 的意思是「任何」或「任何一個」時，也可用在肯定句裡

You may take **any** of them.（你可以拿其中的任何一個。）

"Which of these pencils do you want?"（「這些鉛筆你要哪一枝？」）

"**Any** will do."（「任何一枝都行。」）

2. **someone, somebody, something, anyone, anybody, anything** 之一般用法上的差別與 **some, any** 一樣。

Somebody has stolen my dog.（有人偷了我的狗。）【肯定句】

If he is **anything** of a gentleman, he will pay the money.【條件句】

（假如他還像個君子，他會付錢的。）【參照 p.132 something of 的用法】

Is there **anything** the matter with you?（你有什麼地方不對勁嗎？）【疑問句】

I don't know **anything** about it.（我對它一無所知。）【否定句】

【註1】 **somebody, anybody, everybody** 為口語，兩字不能分開寫。

someone
anyone } 如果其後接有介系詞片語時，兩個字要分開寫。
everyone

Anyone would like to win in the contest.（任何人都想在比賽中獲勝。）—— 白話

Any one *of the contestants* would like to win.

（任何一個參加比賽的人都想要獲勝。）—— 文言

【註2】 **not any = no; none**

There are **not any** students in the classroom.（教室裡沒有學生。）

= There are **no** students in the classroom.

My brother has some money with him, but I have**n't any**.

= My brother has some money with him, but I have **none**.

（我哥哥身上有錢，而我沒有。）

【註3】 **not anybody (anything) = nobody (nothing)**

I did**n't** see **anybody** there.（我沒有看到有人在那裡。）

= I saw **nobody** there.

The beggar does**n't** have **anything** to eat.（乞丐沒有東西可吃。）

= The beggar has **nothing** to eat.

【註4】 修飾 **something, somebody**…等的形容詞應置於它們的後面。

If there is **anything** wrong, call me up.〔如果有什麼不對的（事故），打電話給我。〕

【註5】 **something, anything, nothing** 可作副詞用。

He was **something** troubled.（他有點兒苦惱。）【something = somewhat】

Is it **anything** like mine?（有一點兒像我的嗎？）

He is **nothing** wiser than before.（他一點也不比以前聰明。）【nothing = not at all】

3. 有關 **something, anything, nothing, somebody**…的慣用語：

⑴ anything but（並不；絕不）

It is *anything but* cheap.（它並不便宜。）

His manners are *anything but* pleasant.（他的態度並不使人愉快。）

I will do *anything* for you *but* that.（除了那件事以外，我願爲你做任何事情。）

She is *anything but* beautiful.（她並不美。）

I can give you *anything but* this pen.

（除了這枝筆，我什麼都可以給你＝我絕不給你這枝筆。）

(2) nothing but（只；不過）

He is *nothing but* skin and bones.（他非常瘦，只有皮包骨。）

It is *nothing but* a joke.（這不過是玩笑而已。）

He is *nothing but* a thief.（除了小偷，他什麼都不是 —— 他只是個小偷。）

(3) do nothing but ＋ 原形動詞（除了…之外什麼都不做；只是）

He *does nothing but* play all day.（他整天除了玩之外什麼都不做。）

(4) have nothing to do but (*or* except) ＋ 原形動詞（除…之外別無辦法）

We *have nothing to do but* wait here.（我們除了在這裡等之外，別無辦法。）

(5) have something to do with（與…有關）

have nothing to do with

doesn't have anything to do with }（與…無關）

He *has something to do with* her.（他和她有些關係。）

He *has nothing more to do with* me.（他和我不再有任何關係。）

It *doesn't have anything to do with* me.（這和我無關。）

(6) be something of ＋ 名詞（稍有）

＝ have something of ＋ 名詞 ＋ in ＋ 代名詞 }（否定、條件時用 **anything** 代替 **something**）

He *is something of* a philosopher.（他略具哲學家之風。）

＝ He *has something of a philosopher in* him.

(7) 有關 **nothing, something, somebody**…的其他慣用語

I received nothing beyond what was due to me.（我不曾接受任何不是我所應得的東西。）

The whole plan has come to nothing.（全部計劃已成泡影。）

He has nothing of the hero in his composition.（他的性格裡沒有一點英雄氣概。）

He has nothing in him.（他是個一無可取的人。）

He is good for nothing.（他毫無用處。）

I can make nothing of it.（我弄不明白它。）

{ He thinks he's (a) somebody but really he's (a) nobody.

（他自命不凡，其實他只是個無足輕重的人。）

He thinks himself to be something when in reality he is nothing.

Money is something, but health is everything.（金錢是重要的，但健康比什麼都重要。）

Is he anybody?（他是個要人嗎？）

He has seen something of life.（他略有閱歷。）

A hundred dollars is nothing to me.（一百元對我算不了什麼。）

{ "Did you mean to insult me?"（「你意思是要侮辱我？」）

"Nothing of the kind (*or* sort)."（「絕無此意。」）

4. **either**, **neither**, **both** 的用法：

代　　　　　名　　　　　詞	形　　容　　詞	副　　　　　詞
either（兩者中任一） 　　　（兩者中每一）｝＋ 單數動詞 neither（兩者中無一） both（兩者都）＋ 複數動詞	either ＋ 單數名詞 neither ＋ 單數名詞 both ＋ 複數名詞	either（也）（用於否定句） neither（也不） both（兩者都）

(1) **either**

　① **either = one** *or* **the other of the two**（兩者中任一）

　　"Which do you prefer, coffee or milk?" "**Either** will do."

　　（「你要咖啡或牛奶？」「隨便哪一樣都可以。」）

　　There are two pencils on the desk, you may use **either**.

　　（桌上有兩枝鉛筆，隨便你用哪一枝。）

　② **either = each of the two**（兩者中的每一）

　　Either of the twins is wise enough.（這雙胞胎的每一個都夠聰明。）

　　There are trees on **either** side of the river.（河的兩岸都有樹。）

　【註1】　**either** 也可做副詞，其意爲「也」，只能用於否定句，且須置於句尾。

　　　　　I don't like tea, and he doesn't, **either**.（我不喜歡茶，他也不喜歡茶。）

　【註2】　**either** 可與 **or** 連用而成對等連接詞，它的意思是「**不是…就是**」。（詳見 p.474）

　　　　　He is **either** in London **or** in Paris.（他不在倫敦就在巴黎。）

(2) **neither**（兩者中沒有一個）

Neither of her parents is alive.（她的雙親都去世了。）

A: Is that a hawk or a kite?（那是一隻鷹還是一個風箏？）

B: It is **neither**.（都不是。）

　　It is an owl.（那是一隻貓頭鷹。）

Neither boy has learned his lesson.（兩個男孩都沒有讀書。）
形容詞

　【註1】　**neither** 除了做代名詞、形容詞之外，**還可以做副詞**，其意思是「也不」

　　　　　（＝ not either）。（詳見 p.643）

　　　　　He will not go, and **neither** will I.（他不願去，我也不願去。）

　　　　　＝ He will not go, and I will not, either.

　【註2】　**neither** 若與 **nor** 連用即成對等連接詞，其意義爲「**既不…也不**」。（詳見 p.468）

　　　　　Neither you **nor** your brother is at fault.（你和你弟弟都沒過失。）

(3) **both**（兩者都）

You can take **both** of them.（兩個你都可以拿去。）

請比較下面例句：

　　He held a gun in **both** of his hands.（他雙手握著一枝槍。）【只有一枝槍】

　　He held a gun in **either** of his hands.（他一手握著一枝槍。）【有兩枝槍】

　　There are trees on **both** sides of the river.（河的兩岸都有樹。）
　　　　　　　　　　　　形容詞
　　＝ There are trees on either side of the river.

【註1】 **both** 之後不可緊接代名詞。

這句 *Both they are diligent.* 是錯誤的，正確的寫法如下：

Both of them are diligent.
They are **both** diligent. （他們兩個都很勤勉。）
They **both** are diligent.

【註2】 **both** 不可放在 **the, these, those, my**…之後，必須放在它們的前面：

These both boys are handsome. 【誤】
Both these boys are handsome. 【正】
His both parents are living. 【誤】
Both his parents are living. 【正】

【註3】 **both** 也可作副詞用。

She can sing and dance **both**. （她能歌又能舞。）

【註4】 **both** 可與 **and** 結合成對等連接詞。

A textbook should be **both** interesting and instructive.
（教科書應當既有趣又有益。）

【註5】 **both**…**not**
not…**both** = one 並非全部否定，而是**部分否定**；換言之，它們的意思不是「兩者都不」，而是「兩者不都」，「兩者中只有一個不」或「並非兩個」。
（詳見 p.658）

Both of them are **not** my students.
（= One of them is my student; the other is not.）
（他們並非兩個都是我的學生，其中之一是我的學生。）
I do **not** know **both** of them. （他倆我並不都認識。）【暗示我只認識其中一位】
（= I know only one of the two, not both.）

5. **any** （三者以上任一）
none （三者以上無一）
all （三者以上全部）

(1) **any** （三者或三者以上的任一個）
You may take **any** of the three. （你可任取三者之一。）
Any of you can do it. （你們之中隨便哪一個都能做它。）

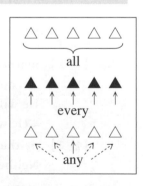

【註1】 **any** 之後接名詞或 **one** 時即為形容詞：

I cannot see **any** difference. （我看不出有什麼分別。）

【註2】 **any** 也可作副詞用：

I will not go to such places **any** more. （我不願再到那種地方去了。）

【註3】 慣用語 “**any and every**” 意思是「隨便什麼都」

I wish to read *any and every* book relating to this subject.
（有關這個課題的任何書我都想讀。）
I wonder if there is a person who knows *anything and everything*.
（我不相信會有任何什麼事都知道的人。）

⑵ **none**（三者或三者以上沒有一個）

　　none 可表示單數的 **no one** 及複數的 **not any persons** 因此是單數兼複數的代名詞（參照 p.143）

　　None of them $\left\{\begin{array}{l} \text{has} \\ \text{have} \end{array}\right\}$ come back yet.（他們之中還沒有一個人回來。）【單複數均可】

　　【註 1】　**none** 用於人或物均可；**no one** 僅用於人，且須接單數動詞：

　　　　　　Have you any children? No, I have **none**.（你有小孩嗎？不，沒有。）【none 指人】

　　　　　　Is there any ink? No, there is **none**.（有墨水嗎？不，沒有。）【none 指物】

　　　　　　It is **none** of your business.（那不干你的事。）【none 指事】

　　　　　　= It is no business of yours.

　　　　　　No one likes to make friends with her.（沒有人喜歡和她做朋友。）

　　【註 2】　**none** 可以作副詞用，意思是「並不」、「絕不」、「一點也不」（= not at all）；

　　　　　　此種用法的 **none** 要放在 "**too**" 或 "**the + 比較級**" 或 "**so**" 前面。

　　　　　　He did it **none** too well (quickly).〔他做得並不好（快）。〕

　　　　　$\left\{\begin{array}{l} \text{He has faults, but I love him \textbf{none the less}.（他雖有缺點，但我仍然愛他。）} \\ \text{= He has faults; \textbf{none the less}, I love him.【none the less 仍然】} \\ \text{= I love him \textbf{none the less} for his faults.} \end{array}\right.$

　　　　　　He is **none** the happier for all his wealth.（他並不因爲有錢而更快樂。）

⑶ **all**（三者或三者以上都）

　　All of us can do it.〔我們所有的人都能做（它）。〕

　　You can not know **all** of it.（你不可能知道它的全部。）

　　All that live must die.（生者必死。）

　　All that glitters is not gold.（閃亮的東西未必全是金子。）

　　【註 1】　**all** 和 **both** 一樣，其後不可緊接代名詞，像下面的句子是錯誤的：

　　　　　　All they are pretty.【誤】

　　　　　　應當改成下面的形式：

　　　　　$\left.\begin{array}{l} \textbf{All} \text{ of them are pretty.} \\ \text{They are \textbf{all} pretty.} \\ \text{They \textbf{all} are pretty.} \end{array}\right\}$（她們都很漂亮。）

　　【註 2】　**all** 之後若接有名詞即成形容詞。

　　　　　　We must defend our country at **all** costs.（我們當不惜任何代價，來保衛我們的國家。）

　　　　　　All men are equal.（人人皆平等。）

　　　　　　He is an honest man beyond **all** doubts.（無疑地他是個誠實的人。）

　　【註 3】　**all** 之後接單數普通名詞時，其意義爲「整個的」；接複數普通名詞時，其意義爲「所有的」。

　　　　　　All the town was destroyed by the earthquake.（全鎮被地震所毀。）
　　　　　　　　單 數

　　　　　　比較下面兩句：

　　　　　　All the schools are closed on national holidays.（在國定假日，所有的學校都放假。）
　　　　　　　　複 數

　　　　　　All the school was flooded.（整個學校都淹了水。）
　　　　　　　　單 數

【註4】 "every" 是對於每一個每一個的總括，比一開始就總括起來的 "all" 的語氣要強一點：

$$\begin{cases} \text{(a) I know all of them.（我都認識他們。）} \\ \text{(b) I know every one of them.（他們每個人我都認識。）【語氣較強】} \end{cases}$$

$$\begin{cases} \text{(a) He told me all about it.（他把那件事的始末都告訴了我。）} \\ \text{(b) He told me everything.（他把每件事都告訴了我。）【語氣較強】} \end{cases}$$

【註5】 **all…not**（或 **not all**）表示部分否定：(詳見 p.658)

Not all good men will prosper.（好人並非都發達。）

All fat men are **not** healthy.（胖的人並非都健康。）【現代美語常將 all…not 視為「全部否定」】
= **Not all** fat men are healthy.

【註6】 **all** 的慣用語：

① all $\begin{cases} = \text{as much as} \\ = \text{everything} \end{cases}$

I give you **all** I have.（我把我所有的都給你。）

I will do **all** I can.（我會盡力做。）

② all in = very tired（很疲倦）

She is **all in**.（她很疲倦。）

③ all but = almost（幾乎）

He is **all but** dead.（他幾乎是死人 —— 奄奄一息。）

④ all in all（a. 完全地　　b. 最愛的　　c. 一般說來）

Trust me not at all, or **all in all**.（要麼根本不相信我，否則就完全相信我。）

She was **all in all** to him.（她是他最愛的人。）

All in all, her condition is greatly improved.（一般說來，她的情況大有進步。）

⑤ all at once $\begin{cases} = \text{suddenly（突然）} \\ = \text{every one at one time（同時；一下子）} \end{cases}$

She cried out **all at once**.（她突然哭了起來。）

Don't do them **all at once**. Save some for later.

（不要一下子就做完。留一些以後做。）

⑥ all right（妥善；無恙）

Everything is **all right**.（一切妥善。）

⑦ all over = finished（結束；遍佈）

The meeting was **all over** when I got there.（當我到達時，這會議已經結束了。）

He has travelled **all over** the world.（他遊遍了全世界。）

⑧ all the same = still; however（仍然；不過）

All the same, I wish you had not done it.（我仍然希望你沒有做那件事。）

⑨ all the same to（對…都一樣）

It is **all the same to** him.（對他而言，這都是一樣的。）

⑩ all alone = completely alone（獨自地）

She did it **all alone**.（那事全都由她一人自己做。）

⑪ all together（全部；一起）

They came **all together**.（他們一起來。）

⑫ all gone $\begin{cases} = \text{nothing left（無物留下）} \\ = \text{nobody left（無人留下）} \end{cases}$

The others had **all gone** by the time I got there.（我到達時，別人都走了。）

There was a little yesterday, and now it is **all gone**.

（昨天有一些，現在全都沒有了。）

⑬ all along $\begin{cases} = \text{all the time; from the beginning（從一開始）} \\ = \text{from end to end（徹頭徹尾）} \end{cases}$

I knew it **all along**.（我從一開始就知道。）

There were trees **all along** the road.（這條路從頭到尾都有樹木。）

⑭ above all（最重要的是）

We should carry the plan out, **above all**.（最重要的是，我們應實現我們的計劃。）

⑮ after all = after all is said and done（畢竟）

After all, man is a selfish being.（人畢竟是自私的。）

⑯ at all 用在疑問、條件、消極及否定句上，作 "in any way"（全然）解

Are you going to give **at all**?（你<u>到底</u>給不給？）

If you give **at all**, give quickly.（你<u>既然</u>要給，就快點給。）

Then you are *not* going to give **at all**.（那麼你是<u>一點也不</u>給的了。）

I can*not* answer this question **at all**.（我<u>一點也</u>答<u>不</u>出這個問題。）

⑰ in all = all together（總共）

There were five of them **in all**.（他們總共有五人。）

⑱ that is all = there is no more（沒有再多的了）

That is all in this classroom.（教室裡的人，就這麼多，沒有再多的了。）

⑲ that is not all = there is some more（並非全部）

That is not all in the house.（在房子裡所看到的，並不是全部，還有一些。）

⑳ once (and) for all（只此一次；斷然地）

Let me tell you this, **once (and) for all**.（讓我斷然地告訴你這件事。）

㉑ for good and all（永遠）

He will not come back **for good and all**.（他永遠不會回來。）

㉒ and all = including（連…一起）

He jumped into the water, clothes **and all**.（他連衣服一起跳進水裡。）

㉓ if at all（如果眞有其事）

I don't think he works much — **if at all**.（我不認爲他做了很多 —— 如果眞有做的話。）

㉔ all the + 比較 = so much the（更…；大大地…）

I feel **all the worse** for the walk.（這個散步使我覺得更不舒服。）

㉕ all + 抽象名詞 = 抽象名詞 + itself（非常的…）（詳見 p.70, 121）
He was **all kindness** in treating us.（他對待我們很親切。）
= He was **kindness itself** in treating us.

6. **each** 和 **every** 的用法：

each	every
1. 可單獨使用	1. 不可單獨使用
2. 可做不定代名詞或不定形容詞	2. 僅做不定形容詞
3. 著重個別	3. 著重全體
4. 用於兩者或兩者以上中的每一個人或物	4. 用於三者或三者以上中的每一個人或物

⑴ **each** 除去做**不定代名詞**之外還可以做**不定形容詞**（後面接單數名詞或 one），甚至**副詞**，請比較下列例句：

① **Each** of the students has his own desk.【代名詞】（每個學生都有他自己的書桌。）

② **Each** country has its own customs.【形容詞】（每個國家都有它的風俗。）

③ They received one dollar **each**.【副詞】（他們每人都拿到一元。）

⑵ **each** 用於兩個或三個以上中的每一個；**every** 只能用於三個以上中的每一個。

There are palm trees on $\left\{ \begin{array}{l} every【誤】\\ each【正】\end{array} \right\}$ side of the road.（路的每一邊都有棕櫚樹。）

$\left. \begin{array}{l} Every【誤】\\ Each【正】\end{array} \right\}$ one of my parents has a car.（我的父母每人有一部車。）

⑶ **every** 是著重許多中的「每一個」、「個個」、「毫無例外」等意思。

Every man desires to live long.（人人都希望長壽。）

Every one must do his duty.（每個人都要盡他的責任。）

【註】 **nearly every + 單數名詞 = most + 複數名詞**

Nearly every student speaks some English.（大部分的學生都能講點兒英語。）

= **Most** student*s* speak some English.

⑷ **not every** 是「不盡然；並非每一個」的意思，為部分否定（**Partial Negation**）；**not any = no** 為「全部否定」（**Complete Negation**）（詳見 p.658）

Not every man can speak and write equally well.【部分否定】

（並不是人人「說」和「寫」都好。）

He does **not** know **anything**.【全部否定】

= He knows **nothing**.（他什麼也不知道。）

⑸ **every other** 是「每隔一個」的意思。

I go to the doctor's **every other** day.（我每隔一天要到醫生那裡一次。）

Write your answer on **every other** line.（每隔一行寫你的答案。）

【參考】 every day（每天）

$\left. \begin{array}{l} \text{every two days}\\ \text{every second day}\\ \text{every other day}\end{array} \right\}$ 每隔一天；每兩天【注意：「每兩天」即是「每隔一天」】

$\left. \begin{array}{l} \text{every four days}\\ \text{every fourth day}\end{array} \right\}$ 每隔三天；每四天

【注意】 $\left.\begin{array}{l}\text{each}\\\text{every}\end{array}\right\}$ ＋ 單數名詞 ＋ and ＋ $\left\{\begin{array}{l}\text{(each)}\\\text{(every)}\end{array}\right.$ ＋ 單數名詞 ＋ 單數動詞

比較： A boy and a girl *are* playing in the backyard.（有一個男孩和一個女孩在後院玩。）

Each boy and (each) girl *wants* to look nice.

（每一個男孩和每一個女孩都想要看起來漂亮。）

Every man and (every) woman *is* at work.（每個男女都在工作。）

7. **one**（任何人，某人，某事）

> one 單數
> ones 複數
> one's 所有格
> oneself 反身代名詞

⑴ **one 的意思較 any one（任何人）的意思稍弱，和 we, you 同樣，用以廣義的指「人」。**
用 one 做主詞，後面的代名詞須用 one('s) 或 oneself 和它相應，但美語中常用 he, him, his, himself。

One should always be prepared for the worst.（人應該時常防備不測的事。）

One must not neglect $\left\{\begin{array}{l}\textbf{one's}\\\textbf{his}【美】\end{array}\right\}$ duty.（人不能忽略自己的責任。）

One is apt to think $\left\{\begin{array}{l}\textbf{oneself}\\\textbf{himself}【美】\end{array}\right\}$ faultless.（人往往以為自己毫無錯誤。）

但 any one, some one, each one, every one, no one, one of ＋ 複數名詞時，其後的代名詞用 he (she), his (her), him (her), himself (herself)。

Any one thinks $\left\{\begin{array}{l}\textit{oneself}【誤】\\\textbf{himself}【正】\end{array}\right\}$ wise.（任何人都以為自己聰明。）

Every one did $\left\{\begin{array}{l}\textit{one's}【誤】\\\textbf{his}【正】\end{array}\right\}$ best.（每個人都盡了全力。）

No one knows what $\left\{\begin{array}{l}\textit{one's}【誤】\\\textbf{his}【正】\end{array}\right\}$ fate will be.（沒有人知道自己的命運將會如何。）

One of the girls left $\left\{\begin{array}{l}\textit{one's}【誤】\\\textbf{her}【正】\end{array}\right\}$ umbrella in the bus.

（女孩中的一位把她的傘留在公車上了。）

⑵ **one 可代替前面已經説過的單數名詞**，以避免重複。

If you need a dictionary, I will lend you **one**（＝ a dictionary）.

（假如你需要一本字典，我可以借給你一本。）

比較： $\left\{\begin{array}{l}\text{I cannot find my hat; I think I must buy }\textbf{one}（＝\text{a hat}）.【不定】\\\text{（我找不到我的帽子；我想我一定要買一頂。）}\\\text{I cannot find my hat; I don't know where I put }\textbf{it}（＝\text{my hat}）.\\\text{（我找不到我的帽子；我不知道我把它放在什麼地方。）【特定，同一物】}\\\text{The hat you bought is cheaper than }\textbf{that}（＝\text{the hat}）\text{ I bought.}\\\text{（你買的帽子比我買的帽子要便宜些。）【特定，同類但不是同一個】}\end{array}\right.$

【註1】 **one 之前可用形容詞 the, this, that, which, any, some, each, every**…等。

Here are three hats. *Which* **one** is yours? *This* **one**, or *that* **one**, or *the* **one** on the peg?

（這裡有三頂帽子。哪一頂是你的？這一頂或那一頂，或是掛在掛鉤上的那一頂？）

【註 2】 **one** 不可代替不可數名詞（物質名詞及抽象名詞）。

If you need money, I will lend you $\begin{cases} \textit{one.} 【誤】 \\ \textbf{some.} 【正】 \end{cases}$

（假使你需要錢，我可以借給你一些。）

【註 3】 在表示序數的後面不可用 **one** 代替前面所說過的名詞。

Since we have finished the first chapter, now we will read the

$\begin{cases} \textit{second one.} 【誤】 \\ \textbf{second.} 【正】 (= \text{the second chapter}) \end{cases}$

（我們既然已唸完第一章，現在我們要唸第二章了。）

【註 4】 慣用語

the little ones = the kids（小孩）

the Holy One = God（上帝）

the Evil One = the devil（魔鬼）

it is all one = it makes no difference（一樣的）

one and all = everybody（衆人）

【註 5】 **one** 也可作形容詞用。

① 在表時間時 "**one**" 可作 "**a certain**" 的意思。

one time = once（某次）

one morning = on a certain morning（某個早上）

【注意】 **one day** 是作過去用，**some day** 是作未來用。

One day he called on me.（從前有一天他來拜訪我。）

I will take you there **some day**.（將來有一天我會帶你去那裡。）

② 附加於人名之上，表示「某人」的意思。（參照 p.61）

I received a letter from **one** Mr. Wang.（我收到一位王先生的來信。）

8. **another, other** 的用法：

⑴ **another** = **different one**

This is not good enough; show me **another**（= a different one）.

（這個不夠好；給我看另一個。）

⑵ **another** = **one more**

If one is not enough, take **another**（= one more）.（假如一個不夠，再拿一個。）

⑶ **another** = **also one**

He is a fool, and his wife is **another**（= also one）.

（他是個傻瓜，他太太也是個傻瓜。）

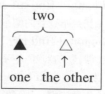

⑷ $\begin{cases} \textbf{one} \cdots \textbf{the other}：\text{one 代替二人或二物中的一個，} \\ \text{the other 代替剩下來的一個。} \\ \textbf{the one} \cdots \textbf{the other}（= \textbf{the former} \cdots \textbf{the latter};\\ \textbf{that} \cdots \textbf{this}）：\text{the one 代替前者，the other 代替後者。} \end{cases}$

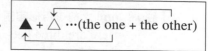

We have two dogs; **one** is white, and **the other** black.

（我們有兩隻狗；一隻是白的，另一隻是黑的。）

We have two dogs, a white one and a black one; **the one**（= the former）is larger than
　the other（= the latter）.（我們有兩隻狗，一隻白的，一隻黑的；白狗比黑狗大。）

(5)　{ **one**…**another** (a second)…**the other** (a *or* the third)（一個…一個…一個）
　　{ **some**…**others**…**still others**（一些…一些…還有一些）

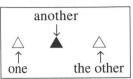

There were three men.　**One** was blind, **another** was
　deaf, and **the other** was lame.
（有三個人，一個是瞎子，一個是聾子，一個是跛子。）
We have plenty of beautiful flowers in our backyard.　**Some** are red, **others** yellow,
　and **still others** white.
（在我們的後院有很多美麗的花。有些是紅的，有些是黃的，還有一些是白的。）

　【註1】　another 是「另外任何一個」，因此至少有三個
　　　　　才能用；如果只有兩個時，只能用 the other。

　【註2】　one…another (a second)…a third…the other
　　　　　(the fourth)（一個…一個…一個…一個）；
　　　　　其餘類推。

1	2	3
△	▲	△

one + another + the other
one + a second + the third
one + another + another…

　【註3】　another, other 之後接名詞或 one, ones 時，即變成形容詞。
　　　　【注意】　① **another 只能接單數名詞或 one**；other 接單複數名詞或 one, ones 均可。
　　　　　　　　② **other 作形容詞用時，在其字尾不能加 s。**
　　　　From that time on he became **another** man.（從那時起，他變成另外一個人了。）
　　　　Her husband is a teacher, and she is **another** one.（她丈夫是個老師，她也是個老師。）
　　　　Put it in your **other** *hand*.（把它放在你的另一隻手中。）
　　　　These oranges are fresher than the **other** *ones*.（這些柳橙比其餘那些新鮮。）

(6)　**one thing**…(*and*) **another (thing)**（…是一回事，…是另一回事）
　　To know is **one thing**, (*and*) to practice is **another**.（知是一回事，行又是另一回事。）
　　To talk is **one thing**, (*and*) to do is **another**.（說是一回事，做又是另一回事。）

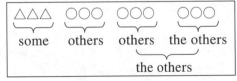

(7)　{ **others** = other people（他人）
　　{ **the others** = the rest（其餘的）
　　Whatever **others** may say, I will do my duty.（不論別人說什麼，我都會盡我的責任。）
　　I don't care what **others** may think of me.（我不在乎別人對我怎麼想。）
　　One of my brothers lives in Taiwan; **the others** are all in my native town.
　　（我有一個兄弟住在台灣；其餘的都在故鄉。）
　　Some of these apples come from America, **the others** from Japan or Korea.
　　（這些蘋果有些是來自美國，其餘的是來自日本或韓國。）

(8)　**有關 other 與 another 的慣用語：**
　　a.　| **other** |
　　　　① the other day = a few days ago（前幾天）
　　　　　I ran into a friend of yours at the zoo **the other day**.
　　　　　（前幾天我在動物園遇見了你的朋友。）
　　　　② every other day (*or* month, year, line…)〔每隔一天（或月，年，行…）〕
　　　　　（參照 p.138 (5) every other）

③ on the other hand（在另一方面；反之）

Father and mother wanted to go for a ride; the children, **on the other hand**, wanted to stay home and play with their friends.

（父母親想要開車去兜風；在另一方面，小孩們想要留在家裡和他們的朋友玩。）

④ some day or other = sooner or later（總有一天；遲早）

Some day or other you will have to repent of it.（總有一天你會後悔。）

⑤ one after the other（二者相繼地）

Her parents died **one after the other**.（她的雙親相繼地死去。）

⑥ one from the other（區分）

⑦ of all others（所有的當中）

⑧ on that day of all others（偏偏在那天）

b. | **another** |

① another day（改天）

② another day or two（再過一、兩天）

③ in another moment（突然）

④ one way and another（用種種方法）

⑤ one way or another（設法；無論如何）

He will accomplish it **one way or another**.（他無論如何都會完成它。）

⑥ one after another（三者以上相繼地）

One after another all his plans have failed.（他所有的計劃，一個接一個地失敗了。）

c.
$$\begin{cases} \textbf{each other} \\ \textbf{one another} \end{cases}$$ （相互）

each other 和 **one another** 是只能做受詞的代名詞片語，舊式的文法規則是 each other 只能用於兩者之間，one another 只能用於三者或三者以上。但是現代英文中已無嚴格限制，通常兩種用法都可替換，只是 each other 較強調「**各個之間**」的個別觀念，而 one another 較強調「**全體之間**」的整體性觀念。

They sat for two hours without talking to $\begin{cases} \textbf{each other.} \\ \textbf{one another.} \end{cases}$

（他們坐了兩小時，相互之間沒有說過話。）

They love $\begin{cases} \textbf{each other.} \\ \textbf{one another.} \end{cases}$ （他們相愛。）

The three men distrusted **each other**.（這三個人彼此互相不信任。）

IV. 做主詞的不定代名詞與動詞的數一致

1. $\begin{cases} \text{one} & \text{any} \\ \text{each} & \text{any one} \\ \text{each one} & \text{either} \\ \text{every one} & \text{neither} \end{cases}$ + of + 複數（代）名詞 + 單數動詞　　【neither, either 在口語中有時用複數動詞】

Each of the three *has* a different instructor.（這三個人每個人有每個人的教官。）

Either of the twins *is* foolish enough to buy a fake diamond.

（這對雙胞胎都很傻，會買到假的鑽石。）

One of the girls *is* going to get married.（那些女孩中有一個快要結婚了。）

2.
$$
\left.
\begin{array}{ll}
\textbf{all}（全部） & \textbf{some}（一些） \\
\textbf{most}（大多數；大部分） & \textbf{the remainder}（其餘的） \\
\textbf{half}（一半） & \textbf{the rest}（其餘的） \\
\textbf{part}（一部分） & \textbf{分數}（幾分之幾）
\end{array}
\right\} + \textbf{of} +
\left\{
\begin{array}{l}
\text{(1)}\textbf{單數（代）名詞後用單數動詞} \\
\text{(2)}\textbf{複數（代）名詞後用複數動詞}
\end{array}
\right.
$$

All of us *are* going to see the game.（我們全都要去看比賽。）

All of his time *was* spent on building model airplanes.（他全部時間都用在做模型飛機。）

3.
$$
\left.
\begin{array}{l}
\textbf{another} \\
\textbf{the other} \\
\textbf{someone} \\
\textbf{no one} \\
\textbf{nobody} \\
\textbf{nothing}
\end{array}
\right\} + \textbf{單數動詞}
$$

Nobody *thinks* that his own dog is a nuisance.（沒有人認爲他自己的狗討厭。）

Someone *has* to lock up the house.（總要有人鎖房子。）

4.
$$
\left.
\begin{array}{l}
\textbf{both} \\
\textbf{some}（指人時） \\
\textbf{others} \\
\textbf{the others}
\end{array}
\right\} + \textbf{複數動詞}
$$

Some *have* come.（有些人已經來了。）

Both *were* there.（兩個都在那裡。）

5. none 表「無一人」時，是指 **no one**（單數），也是指 **not any persons**（複數）；因此，none 做主詞時用**單數動詞**或**複數動詞**均可。

None
$\left\{
\begin{array}{l}
\textit{was} \\
\textit{were}
\end{array}
\right\}$
permitted to enter by this gate.（任何人不准由此門進入。）

None of our party
$\left\{
\begin{array}{l}
\textit{was} \\
\textit{were}
\end{array}
\right\}$
sick.（我們一群人中沒有人生病。）

【註】 現今美語習慣，**none 代表可數的名詞做主詞時用複數動詞，比較普遍。**如用單數動詞時，多將 none 改爲 no one。

There *were* **none** there.【較文言】

There *was* **no one** there.（那裡一個人也沒有。）【較常用】

第四章 疑問代名詞（Interrogative Pronouns）

意義\用法\數格		單　數　與　複　數　同　形		
		主　格	所　有　格	受　格
誰	人	Who	Whose	Whom
什麼	人，事物	What	—	What
哪一個，哪些	人，事物	Which	—	Which

I. 疑問代名詞的用法

1. who, whose, whom 的用法：

⑴ 主格 who 用作主詞或主詞補語。例：**Who** was late?

⑵ 所有格 whose 用以表示「所有者」，多用作疑問形容詞。例：**Whose** dog is that?

⑶ 受格 whom 用作及物動詞的受詞或介系詞的受詞。例：**Whom** do you want to see?

【註 1】 做動詞或介詞的受詞的 "whom" 放在句首時，往往被 "who" 所代替。

Who(m) do you take her to be?（你以為她是誰？）

Who(m) is this letter from?（這封信是由誰寄來的？）

但，若疑問代名詞緊接在介詞之後，則不可用 who 代替 whom。

To **whom** does this book belong?（這本書屬於何人？）

= **Who**(m) does this book belong to?

【註 2】 "whose" 後面的名詞可以略去，作所有代名詞（也叫獨立所有格）用。

Whose book is this?（這是誰的書？）【疑問形容詞】

I don't know **whose** it is.（我不知道是誰的。）【所有代名詞】

2. what 的用法：

⑴ **what 用來指人或事物都可以。**

What do you want?（你要什麼？）

What are you doing?（你在做什麼？）

⑵ **用以指人的 what 是詢問那個人的職業或身份。**

A: **What** is he?（他是做什麼的？）

B: He is a lawyer.（他是個律師。）

而 "who" 則是問那個人的姓名、血緣關係等。

A: **Who** is he?（他是誰？）

B: ⎰ He is Mr. Smith.（他是史密斯先生。）
　　⎱ He is my uncle.（他是我叔叔。）
　　　 He is my English teacher.（他是我的英文老師。）

【註 1】 what 的主格與受格同形而沒有所有格，所以應視 what 在句中的功用而決定其為主格或受格；即 **what 被用為主詞或主詞補語，即為主格**，而被用為及物動詞或介系詞的受詞，即為受格。

【註 2】 what 可當疑問形容詞用。（參照 p.148, 166）

3. **which 的用法：**
   ⑴ **which** 是用以詢問兩件或許多件事物中的「**哪一件**」，指人指物都可以。
      Which is more desirable, health or wealth?（健康或財富，何者更值得希求？）
      Which of your pupils is the most diligent?（你的學生中哪一個最勤勉？）
   ⑵ **which** 之後接名詞（或 **one**）時即成為疑問形容詞。

      Which flower do you like better?（你比較喜歡哪一朵花？）

      【註】　**which** 的主格與受格同形而沒有所有格，所以應視 **which** 在句中的功用而決定
      　　　　其為主格或受格；即 **which** 被用作主詞，即為主格，而被用作受詞，即為受格。
      【注意】　疑問代名詞的單複數是同一形態，所以做主詞時，對**動詞的數**要特別注意。
      　　　　　　Who *is* he?（他是誰？）【單數】
      　　　　　　Who *are* they?（他們是誰？）【複數】
      　　　　　　Which *is* your father?（哪一位是你父親？）【單數】
      　　　　　　Which *are* your brothers?（哪幾位是你的兄弟？）【複數】

II. **有關疑問代名詞應注意的幾點：**

1. **疑問代名詞或「whose + 名詞」，均須放在句首。**
   Who is the gentleman over there?（在那邊的那位先生是誰？）
   Whom do you suppose I met?（你猜我遇到了誰？）
   Whose gloves are these?（這是誰的手套？）
   What does he want?（他要什麼？）
   Which do you like best, coffee, tea, or milk?（你最喜歡什麼，咖啡，茶，或是牛奶？）
   【例外】　疑問代名詞做介詞的受詞時，常被放在介詞的後面。
   　　　　　To whom are you talking?（你在跟誰談話？）
   　　　　　= Whom are you talking to?
   　　　　　In which of the rooms do you live?（你是住在哪一個房間裡？）
   　　　　　= Which of the rooms do you live in?
   　　　　　但兩個字的動詞（像 look at, listen to, depend on…）中的介詞不要分隔。
   　　　　　不說：*To* which of the radio programs are you *listening*?
   　　　　　而說：Which of the radio programs are you **listening to**?（你在聽什麼廣播節目？）
   　　　　　不說：*At* what are you *looking*?
   　　　　　而說：What are you **looking at**?（你在看什麼？）

2. **疑問代名詞或「whose + 名詞」做主詞時，前面不可放助動詞或 be 動詞。**
   Can you swim across the river?【正】（你能游過那條河嗎？）
   助動詞 主詞
   Can which of you swim across the river?【誤】
   　主　詞
   Which of you can swim across the river?【正】（你們哪一個能游過那條河？）
   　主　詞
   Was her child run over by the bus?【正】（她的小孩被公車輾過了嗎？）
   　　　　主詞
   Was whose child run over by the bus?【誤】
   　　　　主詞
   Whose child was run over by the bus?【正】（誰的小孩被公車輾過了？）
   　　　主詞

Did you break the glass?【正】(你把杯子打破了嗎？)
助動詞 主詞

Did who break the glass?【誤】
助動詞 主詞

Who broke the glass?【正】(誰把杯子打破了？)
主詞　動詞

但句首雖是疑問代名詞而不做主詞時，依然要將助動詞放在主詞前面。

Whom you saw?【誤】
受詞 主詞

Whom did you see?【正】(你看見了誰？)
受詞　助動詞 主詞

Which you like best, A, B, or C?【誤】
受詞　主詞

Which do you like best, A, B, or C?【正】(A, B, C 你最喜歡哪一個？)
受詞 助動詞 主詞

3. **疑問代名詞引導名詞子句時，該名詞子句（又稱間接疑問句）不可使用疑問句的形式，要用敘述句的形式（主詞＋動詞…）。**

Who is he?【正】(他是誰？)
I don't know *who is he*.【誤】
I don't know **who he is**.【正】(我不知道他是誰。)【who 是疑代做主詞補語】

What does he want?【正】(他要什麼？)
I will ask *what does he want*.【誤】
I will ask **what he wants**.【正】(我會問他要什麼。)

【例外】　疑問代名詞當主詞時，疑問句的形式等於名詞子句的形式。

Who broke the window?(誰打破了窗子？)
Tell me **who broke the window**.(告訴我誰打破了窗子。)
　　　　　　主詞

What is the matter with him?(他有什麼不對勁？)
I asked him **what was the matter with him**.(我問他有什麼不對勁。)
　　　　　　主詞

4. **以疑問代名詞引導的疑問句，與其他子句結合時有兩種方式。**

⑴ **可以用 yes 或 no 回答者，接在主句之後，其動詞通常為 know, hear, ask, tell 等。**

Do you know who he is?(你知道他是誰嗎？)
Yes, I do. 或 No, I don't.〔是，我知道。(或) 不，我不知道。〕

Have you heard what he wants?(你曾聽說他要什麼嗎？)
Yes, I have. 或 No, I haven't.〔是，我聽說過。(或) 不，我沒聽說過。〕

⑵ **不能以 yes 或 no 回答者，其動詞通常為 think, believe, suppose, guess 等，必須把疑問詞放在句首。**

Who do you think he is?(你認為他是誰？)
I think he is Mr. Smith.(我認為他是史密斯先生。)

> What do you think (*or* suppose) he wants?（你認為他想要什麼？）
> I think (*or* suppose) he wants a watch.（我認為他想要一只錶。）

※ 把疑問詞放在句首，即是把名詞子句分開。

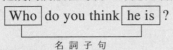

Do you think who he is?【誤】（你認為他是誰了沒有？── 當然沒有這種沒有意義的句子）

因此是否把疑問詞放在句首，完全要看句意而定。

如 say 兩種用法都可：

> Did you say **what you wanted**?（你說過你要什麼嗎？）
> Yes, I did.（是的，我說過。）

> **What** did you say **you wanted**?（你說你要什麼？）
> I said I wanted a pen.（我說我要一枝筆。）

5. **疑問代名詞之後接不定詞即成為名詞片語。**

> what
> whom ⎬ + 不定詞 = 名詞片語
> which

公式：主詞 + 及物動詞 + <u>疑問詞 + 不定詞</u>（受詞）

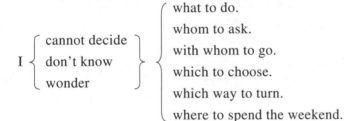

6. **What…for? 或 For what…? 常用來詢問原因或目的，和 Why 相當。** 例如：

What did you get up so early **for**?（你為什麼起得這麼早？）

= **For what** did you get up so early?

= **Why** did you get up so early?

What does he need to learn English **for**?（他為什麼需要學英文？）

= **For what** does he need to learn English?

= **Why** does he need to learn English?

What did she go to New York **for**?（她為什麼去紐約？）

= **For what** did she go to New York?

= **Why** did she go to New York?

What did you always go to the same restaurant **for**?（你為什麼總是去同一個餐廳？）

= **For what** did you always go to the same restaurant?

= **Why** did you always go to the same restaurant?

此種用法的 **what 是疑問代名詞**，做介詞 for 的受詞。

7. $\left\{\begin{array}{l}\textbf{What do you say to} + （動）名詞？\\ = \textbf{What about}\cdots?（= \textit{What do you think about}\cdots?）\\ = \textbf{How about}\cdots?（= \textit{How do you feel about}\cdots?）\end{array}\right\}$ 是用來詢問情形或徵詢意見的

What do you say to this plan?

$= \left\{\begin{array}{l}\textbf{What}\\ \textbf{How}\end{array}\right\}$ **about** this plan?

（這項計劃你覺得如何？—— 你對這項計劃有何意見？）

What do you say to visiting the museum?（我們去參觀博物館，你以為如何？）

$= \left\{\begin{array}{l}\textbf{What}\\ \textbf{How}\end{array}\right\}$ **about** visiting the museum?

8. **疑問形容詞的 what 也常被用來造成感嘆句。**

What eloquence!（多麼善辯的口才呀！）

What a beautiful sunrise!（多麼美的日出呀！）

What an honest boy he is!（他是個多麼誠實的孩子呀！）

【注意】 用作**感嘆形容詞**的 "**what**" 附加在單數普通名詞上用時，後面要加 "**a**"，用作普通疑問形容詞的 "what" 卻不用 "a"。比較下列的例子便知：

普通疑問句	感　嘆　句
What time is it?	**What** a time we had!
（現在幾點？）	（我們玩得多開心哪！）
What book is it?	**What** a book it is!
（這是什麼書？）	（這是一本多麼有趣的書呀！）

9. **No matter** + $\left\{\begin{array}{l}\textbf{who}\\ \textbf{which}\\ \textbf{what}\end{array}\right\}$ = **讓步子句**（參照 p.527）

No matter who may say so, I don't believe it.（不論誰這樣說，我都不相信。）

No matter which book you read, you'll find it interesting.

（不論你讀哪一本書，你將發現它是有趣的。）

No matter what he said, I'll go my own way.

（不論他說什麼，我要怎麼做，就怎麼做。）

第五章 關係代名詞（ Relative Pronouns ）

I. **定義：關係代名詞＝代名詞＋連接詞。亦即關係代名詞兼有代名詞及連接詞的作用。**
例如：

　　This is the hat **that** I bought yesterday.

在上句中，"that" 代表它前面的 "the hat"，同時又用以連接 "This is the hat" 和 "I bought yesterday" 這兩個部分，因此 **"that" 是關係代名詞**，其前面的 "the hat" 就叫先行詞（ Antecedent ）。

II. **種類：**

類別＼格	先 行 詞	主 格	所 有 格	受 格
簡單關係代名詞	有先行詞	**who**	**whose**	**whom**
		which	**of which, whose**	**which**
		that	———	**that**
複合關係代名詞	無先行詞	**what**	———	**what**
		whoever	**whosever**	**whomever**
		whichever	———	**whichever**
		whatever	———	**whatever**
擬似關係代名詞	有先行詞	**as**	———	**as**
		but	———	**but**
		than	———	**than**

【註 1】 簡單關係代名詞和擬似關係代名詞的功用都是引導形容詞子句，修飾它的先行詞，關係代名詞本身在子句中又有代名詞作用，做主詞、做受詞或表所有；**複合關係代名詞的功用在引導名詞子句或副詞子句**，其本身在子句中又有代名詞的作用，複合關係代名詞是先行詞與簡單關係代名詞的合成體，所以無先行詞。

【註 2】 who(m) 在古文中可做「先行詞＋關係代名詞」之用法，通常見於格言中。
　　Who (= He who) never climbs will never fall. （不爬高的人絕不會跌倒。）
　　Whom (= Those whom) the gods love die young. （好人不長壽；紅顏薄命。）
　　此種用法的 who, whom 被稱為獨立關係詞，也可以說是先行詞的省略。

【註3】　通常關係代名詞該緊接著先行詞之後，有時卻被迫分開。

He had three sons, **two of whom** *died in the war.*
（他有三個兒子，其中兩個死於戰爭中。）【two of whom = two of three sons】

He wrote many books, **some of which** *you will read some day.*
（他寫了很多書，有一天你會讀到其中的一些。）【which = many books】

【註4】　先行詞的種類：以片語或子句爲先行詞的形容詞子句，都是補述用法。(參照 p.152, 160)

① 名　　詞　This is the **book** *which I bought.*（這就是我買的書。）

② 代 名 詞　I, *who am your friend*, tell you so.（我 —— 你的朋友 —— 如此告訴你。）

③ 形 容 詞　He was **proud**, *which his brother never was.*
（他生性驕傲 —— 他哥哥從不會如此。）

④ 副　　詞　I found the book **here**, *which was the last place I expected to find it.*
（我在這裡找到了這本書，那是我從未想到會找到它的地方。）

⑤ 片　　語　They tried **to catch the bird**, *which was impossible.*
（他們想捉那隻鳥 —— 這是不可能。）

⑥ 從 屬 子 句　He said **he had read the book**, *which was a lie.*
（他說他唸過這本書 —— 這是一句謊言。）

⑦ 主 要 子 句　**He often comes to see us**, *which shows he is kind to us.*
（他常常來看我們，這表示他對我們很好。）

III. 關係代名詞的用法要點：

關係代名詞必須與先行詞的「人稱」與「數」一致，但與先行詞的格無關。

1. 人稱與數：關係代名詞若在其引導的子句中爲主詞時，其後的**動詞，必須與先行詞的人稱和數一致。**

I, *who am blind*, advise you to use your eyes well.
（我這個盲人勸你們要善用你們的眼睛。）【who 的先行詞是 I，所以動詞要用 am】

The girl *who lives opposite my house* is very pretty.
（住在我家對面的那位女孩很漂亮。）【who 的先行詞是 girl，第三人稱單數，動詞要用 lives】

2. 格：關係代名詞須用何格，視它在其所引導之子句中的結構而定。

He is the man *who wants to see our manager.*【who 做 wants 的主詞，所以是主格】
（他就是要見我們經理的人。）

He is the man *whom our manager plans to interview.*【whom 做 interview 的受詞，所以是受格】
（他就是我們經理打算要面試的人。）

The book *which he sent me* was interesting.（他送我的這本書是有趣的。）

I know a boy *whose name is Billy.*【關係代名詞 whose 是表示所有 (= a boy's)】
（我認識一個男孩，他的名字叫比利。）

That is the girl *whose parents are dead.*（那個女孩的雙親都去世了。）

IV. 簡單關係代名詞的個別用法：

1. **who**, **whose**, **whom**（who, whom 只用於人，whose 用於人和非人）

(1) 主格 who 做主詞：

That is the man ***who*** *teaches me.*（那就是敎我的人。）

(2) 所有格 whose 用以表示「所有者」，具有形容詞的性質，以修飾其後的名詞。

That is the man ***whose*** *son I teach.*（那就是他的兒子被我敎的人。）

(3) 受格 whom 做及物動詞或介系詞的受詞。

That is the man ***whom*** *I teach.*（那就是我所敎的人。）

再做分析如下：

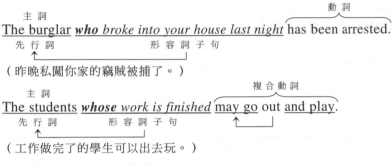

（昨晚私闖你家的竊賊被捕了。）

The students ***whose*** *work is finished* may go out and play.
先行詞　　　形容詞子句

（工作做完了的學生可以出去玩。）

主詞 動詞 直接受詞　　間接受詞
We gave the job to the man ***whom*** *you recommended to us.*
　　　　　　　　　　　先行詞　　　形容詞子句

（我們把那份工作給予你推薦給我們的那個人了。）

2. **which, of which (whose)：用於除了人以外的動物或無生物，即「非人」。**

⑴ **主格 which：**代替「非人」

主詞　　　　　　　　　　　動詞
主格：The river ***which*** *flows through the city* is very long.（流經該城的那條河很長。）
　　　先行詞　　形容詞子句

⑵ **所有格 whose (of which)：**whose 是 who 的所有格，有時也可代替 of which，所以除「人」外，還可代替「非人」。

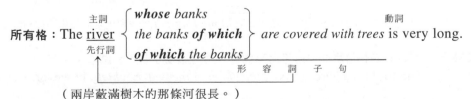

（兩岸蔽滿樹木的那條河很長。）

⑶ **受格 which 代替「非人」：**

主詞　　　　動詞
受格：The river ***which*** *we crossed* is very wide.（我們橫渡的那條河很寬。）
　　　先行詞　形容詞子句

其他例句以供參考：

主詞 動詞　　　受詞
He struck the poor dog ***which*** *had never done him harm.*
　　　　　　　先行詞　　　形容詞子句

（他打那隻從未傷害過他的可憐的狗。）

主詞　　　　　　　　　　　　　　　　動詞
That deer *whose leg had been hurt* couldn't run fast.
先行詞　　形容詞子句

（那隻腿受傷的鹿不能跑得很快。）

主詞　　　　　　　　　　　　　　　　　　　　　動詞
The film *which I watched on television last night* was instructive.
先行詞　　　　　形容詞子句

（昨晚我在電視上看的影片是有教育意義的。）

【註1】 **which** 的兩個所有格 **of which** 與 **whose** 的用法略有不同：

① **of which** 所修飾的名詞應帶有定冠詞 **the**，whose 所修飾的名詞之前不需要定冠詞。

② **of which** 放在被修飾的名詞之前後均可，whose 只能放在名詞之前。

 1. The building
   - *the roof of which we see*
   - *of which we see the roof*
   - *whose roof we see*

 is our school.

 （我們看見那屋頂的房子是我們學校。）

 2. He likes to use words
   - *the meaning of which*
   - *of which the meaning*
   - *whose meaning*

 is clear to him.

 （他喜歡用他明白其意義的字。）

 3. The house
   - *the windows of which*
   - *of which the windows*
   - *whose windows*

 are broken is unoccupied.

 （窗子破了的那棟房子沒人住。）

 【注意】可把 **of which** 放在所修飾名詞的前面，是爲了使 **which** 更靠近其先行詞。

【註2】 **who** 和 **which** 可以用於限定子句（**Restrictive Clause**），也可以用於補述子句（**Continuative Clause**），但做補述子句時，在 **who, which** 和先行詞之間，要用一逗點，至於一些細節容在以後討論（詳見 p.161），先就定義列出下面的例句：

Mr. Smith is the man *who taught me English*.（史密斯先生是教我英文的人。）
　　　　　　　　　　限定形容詞子句

I lived with Mr. Smith, *who taught me English*.（我和史密斯先生同住，他教我英文。）
　　　　　　　　　　補述形容詞子句

【註3】 **which** 在補述用法中還可用來代替一個片語或子句等。例如：

The fool tried hard *to catch the moon in the water*, **which**, however, was found

impossible.（愚人努力在水中撈月，但這是不可能的。）

【這裡的 which 是代表片語 to catch the moon in the water】

I gave my wife a fur coat for her birthday, **which** pleased her a lot.

（我送給我太太一件皮大衣作生日禮物，這使她很高興。）

【這裡的 which 代表子句 I gave my wife a fur coat for her birthday】

3. **that**（主格，受格）

 (1) 只做限定關係代名詞，代替用於限定上的「人」和「非人」。

  I want a man who (*or* **that**) understands English.（我需要一位懂得英語的人。）

  This is the man whom (*or* **that**) I met at my uncle's.（這是我在我叔叔家遇見的人。）

I wish to read a book which (*or* **that**) is both easy and interesting.
（我想讀一本淺易而又有趣的書。）

【注意】that 不能做 whose 的代用，並且 **that** 的前面也不可用介系詞。試比較：

$$\text{the man} \begin{cases} \text{of \textbf{whom} you spoke 【正】} \\ \textbf{whom} \text{ you spoke of 【正】} \end{cases}$$

the man that you spoke of【正】

the man *of that you spoke*【誤】

⑵ 可以用 that 代替 who, whom, which 的地方已如上述，但在**下述的情形通常只能用 that**。

① **當先行詞附有最高級的形容詞的時候。**

He is *the greatest* man **that** ever lived.（他是有史以來最偉大的人物。）

She is *the most beautiful* girl **that** I have ever seen.（她是我所見過最美麗的女孩。）

This is *the most interesting* book **that** I have ever read.（這是我所看過最有趣的書。）

② **先行詞之前有 the only, the same, the very, the first, the last…或 all, only, any,
no, every 的時候**，較常用 that。

Man is *the only* creature **that** is gifted with speech.（唯有人類有語言的天賦。）

This is *the same* watch **that** I lost yesterday.（這就是我昨天丟掉的那只錶。）

This is *the very* room **that** I first met my wife in.

（這就是我初次和我太太相遇的房間。）

He was *the first* man **that** came.（他是最先來的人。）

All **that** glitters is not gold.（光輝燦爛的東西不盡然是黃金。）

Any paper **that** you read will give the same story.

（你所看到的任何報紙都報導相同的新聞。）

No man **that** has common sense can believe it.（有常識的人不會相信它。）

③ **爲加強句中某一部分的語氣而採用 "It is…that" 的構造。**

It is a nightingale **that** is singing over there.（正在那邊唱歌的是隻夜鶯。）

It is not the style, but the sentiment **that** I admire.

（我所讚賞的不是那筆調而是其情操。）

④ **先行詞中含有「人」和「非人」的時候。**

The train ran over *a boy and his dog* **that** were just crossing the track.

（火車輾死了正在穿越軌道的小男孩和他的狗。）

The people and manners **that** one sees there seem to be quite different from those of
any other country.（在那裡所看到的人民與風俗，似乎和任何其他國家的完全不同。）

⑤ **在前面有疑問代名詞的時候，爲了避免 "who…who"，"which…which" 的重複起見，
所以也用 that。**

Who is the man **that** is standing by the door?（站在門旁邊的那個人是誰？）

Who **that** has a sense of honor can do such a thing?

（有廉恥心的人誰會做這種事？）

Which of these steamers is the one **that** plies between Kaohsiung and Makung?

（這些船中哪一艘是通行高雄到馬公的？）

【註】 在先行詞中有 **that** 或 **those** 的時候，關係代名詞最好用 **who** 或 **which**，因為 "that…that"，"those…that" 在語調上不動聽。

That kite *which* Jack made is very beautiful. （傑克做的風箏很美。）

The third door was *that which* we were seeking.

（那第三家正是我們所要找的。）

Heaven helps *those who* help themselves. （天助自助者。）

4. 關係代名詞與介詞：

⑴ 關係代名詞做介詞的受詞時，介詞可置於 **whom** 和 **which** 的前面或後面，但關係代名詞為 **that** 時，則僅能將介詞置於其後。

This is the girl **of whom** I spoke. 【正】

= This is the girl **whom** I spoke **of**. 【正】

= This is the girl **that** I spoke **of**. （這是我曾提過的那個女孩。）【正】

This is the girl *of that* I spoke. 【誤】

Is this the car **for which** you paid a high price? 【正】

= Is this the car **which** you paid a high price **for**? 【正】

= Is this the car **that** you paid a high price **for**? 【正】

（這是你以高價買的那部車嗎？）

Is this the car *for that* you paid a high price? 【誤】

⑵ 像 **during, beyond, except** 或表部分的 **of**，這些介詞通常置於關係代名詞的前面。例如：

The years *during which he was away* were long years to her.

（他離開的期間，對她是一段漫長的歲月。）

He wrote many books, *some of which you will read some day*.

（他寫了很多書，有一天你會讀到其中的一些。）

⑶ 介詞 + **whom**（或 **which**）+ 不定詞 = 形容詞片語

The poor man has no house *in which to live*.

（那窮人沒有可住的房子 —— 那窮人沒有房子住。）

上句也可簡化為：The poor man has no house *to live in*.

The beggar has no money *with which to buy food*. （那乞丐沒錢買食物。）

= The beggar has no money *to buy food with*.

I need a pen *with which to write*. （我需要一枝筆寫字。）

= I need a pen *to write with*.

The selfish guy has few friends *with whom to talk*.

= The selfish guy has few friends *to talk with*.

（那自私的傢伙幾乎沒有可談話的朋友。）

5. 關係代名詞的省略：

在下列的情形下關係代名詞可被省略；尤其在口語中大多被省略。

⑴ 做及物動詞或介詞的受詞時：

The noise *(that) the children made* was intolerable. （孩子們製造的噪音使人不能忍受。）

The dish (*that*) *you have just eaten* contained garlic.（你剛吃的菜含有大蒜。）

Is this the cupboard (*which*) *you keep the linen in*?（這是你放桌巾餐巾的碗櫃嗎？）

The picture (*which*) *you are looking at* was painted by a friend of mine.

（你正在看的那幅畫是我一個朋友畫的。）

【注意】 ① 僅在限定子句裡受格的關係代名詞才可省略，**在補述子句中，關係代名詞雖爲受格也絕不可省略**。見下例：

　　Jane, ***whom*** *Mr. Smith is going to marry*, is twenty-six.【補述子句】

　　（珍二十六歲，將要和史密斯先生結婚。）

　　The girl (*whom*) *Mr. Smith is going to marry* is twenty-six.【限定子句】

　　（史密斯先生要娶的那位女孩是二十六歲。）

② **如果介詞在關係代名詞之前也不能省略。**

　　That is the hotel ***in which*** *we stayed* last summer.

　　（那就是我們去年夏天住的旅館。）

　　That is the hotel (*which*) *we stayed in* last summer.

　　因爲介詞在後面，所以 which 可以省略。

　　Is that the man ***to whom*** *you lent the money*?

　　（那是你要借錢給他的人嗎？）

　　Is that the man (*whom*) *you lent the money to*?

　　因爲介詞在句末，所以 whom 可以省略。

⑵ **在下列特殊句子結構中主格關代也可省略，但現代美語多不省略。**

① **如果句首或句中有 there is, here is, that is, it is 時，主格關代可省略。**

There is a man downstairs (*who*) *wants to see you*.（樓下有個人想見你。）

This is the best dictionary (*that*) *there is* in this library.

（這是本圖書館最好的字典。）

Here is somebody (*who*) *wants to see you*.（這裡有人要見你。）

Who was it (*that*) *said so*?（這樣說的是誰？）

It was Mary (*that*) *said so*.（這樣說的是瑪麗。）

② **that 做主詞補語時**（當補語關代一定要用 that）

He is not the man (*that*) *he was*.

He is not the man (*that*) *he was when I saw him first*.

（他不是我第一次見到的那個人。）

He is all (*that*) *a teacher should be*.（他是個教師的典型。）

He is not the liar (*that*) *he appeared to be*.

（他不是以前所表現的那種說謊者了。）

⑶ **在詩歌或諺語中，往往沒有先行詞**

Who (= *He* who) *never climbs* will never fall.

（不登高的人，就不會跌下來。）

Whom (= *Those* whom) *the gods love* die young.（英才早逝；紅顏薄命。）

V. 複合關係代名詞

在 who, which, what, whose 等關係代名詞上加 (e)ver 即成複合關係代名詞。其本身兼做先行詞及關係代名詞，又因是兩個字所組成，故稱為**複合關係代名詞**。

意義＼格	主　格	所　有　格	受　格
無論誰 任何人	whoever	whosever	whomever
無論何者 任何	whichever	——	whichever
無論什麼 任何	whatever	——	whatever
所有，所為 的事或物	what	——	what

引導名詞子句的複合關係代名詞（複合關係代名詞＝先行詞＋關係代名詞）

what = 先行詞 + which (*or* that)
whoever = any one who (that)
whosever = any one whose
whomever = any one whom
whatever = anything which (that)

whichever = { anything that / any that / either one which / either thing that

引導副詞子句的複合關係代名詞（～ever = no matter～）

whoever = no matter who
whosever = no matter whose
whomever = no matter whom
whichever = no matter which
whatever = no matter what

【註】 what 不可用來引導副詞子句。

1. **what** 的用法：

what 是本身兼做先行詞的關係代名詞，普通和 that (*or* those) which 或 the thing(s) which 是相等的，但有時也用作 all that 的意思。所以 **what 雖然只是一個字，也把它看成是複合關係代名詞**（所謂複合即兩個以上的字所組成，如複合形容詞即兩個以上的字所組成的形容詞）。

Do you understand *what*（= that which）*I say*?（你懂得我所說的嗎？）
I know *what*（= the thing which）*you want*.（我知道你所要的東西。）
He saves *what*（= all that）*he earns*.（他把他的所得全部存起來。）
What has been done, has been done.（既做的事就是做了——已經做了，不可更改。）

【註】 **what** 做附屬疑問代名詞與關係代名詞很相像，要根據上下文意來辨別。
請比較下例：
He did not know **what** I wanted.【what 作「什麼」解時，是附屬疑問代名詞】
（他不知道我要什麼。）
He gave me **what** I wanted.【what = the thing that 時，是複合關係代名詞】
（他給了我所需要的東西。）

2. **what 的慣用語：**

(1) {
　what one is（某人現在的樣子；現在的某人；今日的成就）
　what one has（某人所有的；某人的財產）
　what one was（*or* **used to be**）（某人過去那個樣子）
}

My parents have made me **what I am**.（我之所以有今日是我雙親賜給我的。）

We honour him for what he is, not for **what he has**.

（我們因他的人品而尊敬他，不因他的財富而尊敬他。）

He is not **what he used to be**.（他已非昔日的他了。）

(2) {
　what is called
　what we call
　what you call
} （所謂的）

He is **what is called** a "genius".（他就是所謂的「天才」。）

Most of **what we call** geniuses are successful only because they have made
　extraordinary efforts.（吾人所謂的天才，大部分只是由於格外的努力而成功的。）

She is **what you call** a "new woman".（她就是你所謂的「新女性」。）

(3) **what is (was) +** {
　比較級
　最高級
} （而且；更有進者）（參照 p.654）

He is a good scholar; and **what is better**, a good teacher.

（他是一位好學者；而且猶有進者，是一位好老師。）

He is handsome, clever, and, **what is the best of all**, rich.

（他英俊而聰明，而且最棒的是，他很有錢。）

(4) **A is to B what C is to D**（A 之於 B 猶如 C 之於 D）（參照 p.502）

Reading is to the mind **what** food is to the body.（讀書之於心靈就像食物之於身體。）

Japan is in the East **what** England is in the West.（日本在東方就如同英國在西方一樣。）

(5) {
　what with…and (**what with**)…（半因…半因）—— 表原因
　what by…and (**what by**)…（半靠…半靠）—— 表手段
} （參照 p.469）

What with overwork, and (**what with**) undernourishment, he fell ill.

（半因工作過度，半因營養不良，他生病了。）

What by threats, and **what by** entreaties, he finally accomplished his purpose.

（半靠威脅，半靠懇求，他最後達到了目的。）

(6) {
　and what have you
　= and what not
} （等等）

We have novels, plays, short stories, travelogues, and **what have you**.

（我們有小說、戲劇、短篇小說、遊記等等。）

3. **whoever, whosever, whomever, whichever, whatever 的用法：**

(1) **名詞用法**：whoever, whosever, whomever, whichever, whatever 和 what 一樣，在所
　引導的名詞子句中，有代名作用，所以是**複合關係代名詞**。

Whoever（= Any one who）*comes first* may take it.〔先來的就可以拿它（一個）。〕

I will give a prize to *whoever* writes best.（我要給寫得最好的人一份獎品。）

I will give a prize to *whomever the committee selects*.

（我要給委員會所選出的人一份獎品。）

You may do **whatever** (= anything that) *you like*. (你喜歡什麼就做什麼。)

Here are a gold coin and a Bible. You may choose **whichever** (= either of the two that)
you like. (這裡是一個金幣和一本聖經，你喜歡哪樣就選哪樣。)

Return the book to **whosever** (= anyone whose) *name is on it*.
(把書還給有書上名字的人。)

You had better see the men for yourself and choose **whichever** (= any one of them that)
you like. (這些人你最好自己看看，並且選出你所喜歡的一個。)

(2) **形容詞用法**：whatever 和 whichever 不但可以引導名詞子句，而且還可以修飾子句中的名詞，此時 **whatever 和 whichever 為複合關係形容詞**。(參照 p.166)

Learn **whichever** poem *you find* most interesting. (學習你覺得最有趣的任何詩。)

Eat **whatever** food (= any food that) *you like*. (吃任何你所喜歡的食物。)

(3) **副詞用法**：whoever, whosever, whomever, whichever, whatever 可引導副詞子句表讓步
(參照 p.527)，在子句中有代名作用者，稱為**複合關係代名詞**，有形容詞作用者，稱為**複合關係形容詞**。

Whatever (= No matter what) *your problems are*, they can't be worse than mine.
(不論你的問題是什麼，總不會比我的更嚴重。)

Whoever (= No matter who) *may desert you*, I will help you to the last.
(不論誰置你於不顧，我一定幫助你到底。)

Whichever (= No matter which) *you may take*, I will have no objection to it.
(不論你選哪一個，我絕不反對。)

Whatever difficulties *he may meet with*, he will not be discouraged.

= *No matter what* difficulties *he may meet with*, he will not be discouraged.
(他無論遭到什麼困難，他都不會洩氣。)

【註】引導名詞子句和副詞子句的複合關係代名詞或複合形容詞容易弄混，請看下面的比較：

引　導　名　詞　子　句	引　導　副　詞　子　句
whoever = any one who	whoever = no matter who
whichever = any that	whichever = no matter which
whatever = anything that	whatever = no matter what

Whoever (= Any one who) *says so* is a liar. (誰這樣說就是一個說謊者。)
　　　　　　　—— 名　詞　子　句 ——

Whoever (= No matter who) *may say so*, it is a lie. (不論誰這樣說，那是謊言。)
　　　　副　詞　子　句

He succeeds in **whatever** (= anything that) *he undertakes*.
　　　　　　　　　　—— 名　詞　子　句 ——
(他在他從事的任何事業上總是成功的。)

Whatever (= No matter what) *he may undertake*, he succeeds in it.
　　　　副　詞　子　句
(不論他從事任何事業，他總是成功的。)

VI. 準關係代名詞（Quasi-Relative Pronouns）：

as, but, than 等原來是連接詞引導副詞子句，現多當關係代名詞來解釋，這種語詞稱作**準關係代名詞**，也有人譯成**擬似關係代名詞**。

以 **as** 當連接詞分析：

He is *as* brave a soldier *as any soldier who* ever lived.（他的英勇不下於古今任何軍人。）

※ 在 as 和 than 後 what 可省略，故本句 = **He is as brave a soldier as ever lived**.

以 **as** 當關係代名詞分析：

He is *as* brave a soldier *as ever lived*.

1. **as 的用法**：as 原來是連接詞，但為了省略它後面的代名詞起見，它本身就兼有代名詞的作用而成為關係代名詞。其**用法有下列三種**：

⑴ **前面有 as 的時候**，引導形容詞子句的關係代名詞用 **as**（不用 who, that…）

As many children *as came* were given some cakes.

= All the children *that came* were given some cakes.

（所來的那許多孩子們都被給了一些蛋糕。）

再看下例：

He is *as* diligent a man *as ever lived*.（他是有史以來最勤勉的人。）

⑵ **前面有 such 的時候**，引導形容詞子句關代用 **as**（不用 that, who…）

I will provide you with *such* things *as you may need*.

（我要供給你一些你可能會需要的東西。）

He does not possess *such* a mind *as is necessary to a scientist*.

（他缺乏科學家所必須具備的頭腦。）

Such as praise you to your face cannot be trusted.（當面稱讚你的人不可靠。）

【Such as = Those who】

⑶ **前面有 the same 的時候**，引導形容詞子句的關代通常用 **as**（用 that 時意義不同。詳見 p.127）

I have bought *the same* bicycle *as you have*.（我買了跟你一樣的腳踏車。）

主詞　動詞　　　　　　　　　S.　V.
Bees like *the same* odors **as** *we do*. (蜜蜂喜歡的氣味跟我們一樣。)
先行詞　關代
形容詞子句

【注意】 the same 之後的關係代名詞也可用 that，但兩者含意不同。(參照 p.127)

the same…as（ 指同樣或同類的 ）

the same…that（ 指同一個 ）

This is *the same* watch **as** I lost. (這與我遺失的錶是同樣的 —— 不同一只。)
This is *the same* watch **that** I lost. (這就是我遺失的那只錶 —— 同一只。)

(4) 作為代替整個句子的關係代名詞：(詳見 p.499)

I helped him with his homework, **as** was my duty. (我幫助他做功課，這是我的職責。)

He was late for school, **as** was usual with him. (他上學遲到，他通常如此。)

As is often the case, the girl forgets to bring her dictionary.
(那女孩忘記帶字典，這是常有的事。)

【註】 先行詞是句子時，**as** 或 **which** 都可以引導非限定形容詞子句，但要注意用法的不同：

① **as** 子句可以放在句首，居於先行詞之前，結構上很像副詞子句，**which** 則不能放在句首。

As【正】
Which【誤】 } was natural, he married her. (他娶了她是很自然的事。)

② 當關係代名詞是一般動詞的主詞（ 非 be 動詞 ）時，只能用 **which**。

He saw the girl, { *as*【誤】
which【正】 } delighted him.【as 只能做 be 動詞的主詞】

He saw the girl, { **as**【正】
which【正】 } he had hoped (he would).
【as 和 which 都可做動詞的受詞】

He married her, { **as**【正】
which【正】 } was natural.
【as 和 which 都可做 be 動詞的主詞】

2. **but 的用法：but** 本身含有否定的意思，其作用相當於 "**that…not**"，它前面的主要子句須有否定的字（ 如 **no, not, scarcely, hardly**…等 ）。這樣一來，由於前後的雙重否定就演變成肯定，所以含有關係代名詞 but 的句子，其含意即等於一個有形容詞 every 的肯定句，不過用 but 的語氣較強罷了。

　　　　　　　　S.　V.
There is *no rule* **but** *has exceptions*. (沒有規則是沒有例外的。)
先行詞　關代
形容詞子句

= There is no rule **that** *has not exceptions*.

= Every rule has exceptions.

再參考下例：

There is *no* man ***but errs***. (沒有人不犯錯的。)

= There is no man *who does not err*. = Every one errs.

【注意】 下面兩句中的 **but** 不是關係代名詞而是純粹的連接詞，引導表結果的副詞子句。

(詳見 p.519)

No one is so old ***but he may learn***.

= No one is so old *that* he may *not* learn.

直譯：沒有人是太老了而不能學習。

意譯：無論年紀多大都能學習。

Nothing is so hard ***but it becomes easy by practice***.

= Nothing is so hard *that* it does *not* become easy by practice.

直譯：沒有事情是那麼的困難而不能藉著練習而變得容易的。

意譯：無論多麼困難的事情經由練習都會變得容易。

※ 因爲 but 前後兩部分均爲完整的子句，**but** 前又無先行詞，意義上又表結果，
　所以它是純粹的連接詞而不是關係代名詞。

3. **than** 的用法：先行詞有比較級形容詞修飾時，關係代名詞應該用 **than**（不用 that, who…)。

主詞
Children should not have *more* money ***than is needed***. (孩子們不應該有超出需要的錢。)
　　　　動　詞　　　　　　先 行 詞　關代
　　　　　　　　　　　　　　　　形容詞子句

There is *more* money ***than is needed***. (有超過需要的錢。)

【註】 **than** 接在比較級或副詞之後，是連接詞，引導副詞子句。(詳見 p.200, 503)

I never saw a *taller* man ***than he***. (我從未見過一個比他更高的人。)

She danced more *beautifully* yesterday ***than the day before***.

(她昨天跳舞比前天跳得更美。)

VII. 關係代名詞的二種用法：

1. **限定用法（Restrictive Use ）**：是用形容詞子句把其先行詞限定於某一個特殊型態。

譬如： *People are fools.* 是一般敘述，*people* 是指所有的人，當然不通，要改成下面的句子才合理。

People ***who do such things*** are fools. (做這種事情的人是傻瓜。)

句中的 who do such things 是用來限定是什麼樣的人才是傻瓜。這樣的子句就叫限定子句。

再看下一句：

The man is coming to tea. (那人要來喝茶了。)

一見到上句，我們必定會直覺地問道：「那人是誰？」所以要用一個限定子句來說明是什麼人來喝茶。

The man ***who wrote this poem*** is coming to tea. (寫這首詩的人要來喝茶了。)

※ 在口語中百分之九十的關係子句都屬於限定子句。

2. **補述用法（Continuative Use ）**：用以補充説明先行詞的意思。

John, ***who returned yesterday***, is coming to see me. (約翰來看我，他是昨天回來的。)

上句中的 who returned yesterday 是對約翰的補充說明，在全句中並不十分重要，去掉它也不影響全句的完整。

所以在口語中常分成下面兩句來表達：

John returned yesterday; he is coming to see me this evening.

【類例】 Her husband, *who is older than she is*, is a bank manager.

（她丈夫是個銀行經理，他年紀比她大。）

Love, *which is a wonderful feeling*, comes to everyone at some time in his life.

（愛情，一種奇異的感覺，人一生當中總要碰上一次的。）

【註1】 限定用法和補述用法（非限定用法）形容詞子句的比較：

(a) I want a man *who understands English*. （我需要一個懂英文的人。）

(b) I will engage Mr. Smith, *who understands English*.

（我要聘請史密斯先生，他懂英文。）

(a) 句是限定子句，表示我需要的是那一種人。

(b) 句則是補述子句，只提供一些有關史密斯先生的事情。

如果去掉 (a) 句的關係子句 who understands English 就影響 (a) 句的意義的完整；去掉 (b) 句的則無大礙。

(c) He has two sisters, *who work in the Ministry of Education*.

（他有兩個姊姊，她們在教育部工作。）

(d) He has two sisters *who work in the Ministry of Education*.

（他有兩個在教育部工作的姊姊。）

(c) 句是補述子句，表示他只有兩個姊姊。

(d) 句是限定子句，表示他至少還有一個姊姊在別處工作。【總共至少有三個姊姊】

(e) My father *who is now in Tainan* will return to Taipei soon. 【誤】

（我在台南的爸爸快回台北了。）

(f) My father, *who is now in Tainan*, will return to Taipei soon. 【正】

（我爸爸快回台北了，他現在在台南。）

(e) 句是限定子句，表示「我在台南的爸爸」，難道我還有在台中或高雄的爸爸？因此句意不合理。

(f) 句是補述用法，「他現在在台南」只是對這句話的主題加以補充說明。

以上是就意義上的分別，下面再看構造上的不同：

限　定　用　法	補　述　用　法
1. 關係代名詞之前沒有逗點	關係代名詞之前有逗點
2. 做受格的關係代名詞可省略	關係代名詞不可省略
3. 可用 that	不能用 that
4. 控制關係代名詞的介詞最好置於　子句末端並省掉該關係代名詞	該介詞很少放在子句末端

限定： This is the man *I spoke to you about*. （這就是我跟你提到的那人。）

補述： This is Mr. Roberts, *about whom I spoke to you*.

（這位是羅勃茲先生，就是我曾跟你提過的那位。）

※ 以片語或子句作為先行詞的關係代名詞所引導的形容詞子句全都是補述用法，其關係代名詞通常是 which 和 as。（詳見 p.152, 160）

【註2】 補述用法的形容詞子句，常常可以分解作對等子句或副詞子句，也就是在意義上相當於對等子句或副詞子句。但究竟該分解為何種子句，必須由前後句意來加以判斷。

① 分解成對等子句：

I met Mr. B, **who** (= *and he*) told me the news.
（我遇見了某乙，他告訴我這個消息。）

I went to view the river, **which** I found (= *and I found it*) greatly swollen.
（我去視察河流，我發覺河水大漲。）

② 分解成副詞子句：用以表<u>理由、目的、讓步</u>等。

I will let off this man, **who** (= *because he*) has been sufficiently punished already. （我願釋放這個人，因為他所受的處罰已經足夠了。）【**表理由**】

A man was sent, **who** should (= *so that he might*) deliver the message.
（派出一個人，以便能傳遞這個訊息。）【**表目的**】

The man, **who** (= *though he*) was very poor, never complained of his lot.
（這個人雖然窮，但從未抱怨過自己的命運。）【**表讓步**】

VIII. 關係代名詞的總結：

綜合前面所講的有關關係代名詞的種種，我們做一總結。如下表：

類別 先行詞 作用	限　定　用　法		補述用法（非限定用法）	
	人	物	人	物
主　　詞	who; that	which; that	…, who…,	…, which…,
受詞　動　詞	(whom); (that)	(which); (that)	…, whom…,	…, which…,
受詞　介　詞	(whom)…介詞 (that)…介詞	(which)…介詞 (that)…介詞	…, 介詞 + whom…, …, who(m)…介詞	…, 介詞 + which…, …, which…介詞
所　有　格	whose	of which; whose	…, whose…,	…, of which…, …, whose…,

【注意】 ① 上表中分號兩邊的關係代名詞可互換使用。
　　　　 ② 圓括弧內的關係代名詞可以省略，而且最好是省掉。
　　　　 ③ that 只能用於限定子句，不能用於補述用法。

IX. 關係代名詞應注意事項：

1. **注意沒有逗點分開的插入語：**關係代名詞與動詞之間，常常有一個插入語，有時有逗點分開，有時則沒有，插入語裡的動詞常常是 believe, think, suppose, imagine, guess, say 等。(參照 p.651)

We feed children who | *we think* | are hungry.

（我們把食物給那些我們認為飢餓的孩子吃。）

This is the man who | *I believe* | is honest. （這是一位我相信是誠實的人。）

2. **關係代名詞的重複與雙重限制**

(1) 兩個以上的形容詞子句可用對等連接詞連接，共同修飾一個先行詞。

This is the paper (*which*) *I read every day* **and** *which I find so enjoyable.*

（這就是我每天閱讀的報紙，並且我覺得該報很有趣。）

We found a dog *which was running toward us* **and** *which I thought was Rover.*

（我們發現一隻向我們跑來的狗，而我想牠是洛佛。）

You have many people around you *who are kind to you* **but** *whom you will soon forget.*

（你周圍有許多對你親切的人，但你卻會很快遺忘那些人。）【whom 是 who 的受格】

(2) 兩個形容詞子句也可以不用對等連接詞，而同時修飾一個先行詞，短的形容詞子句在前，長的在後，此種用法稱為**雙重限制**（Double Restriction）。

Is there anything *that you cooked* **which** *we can eat*?
（你烹飪的食物，有沒有什麼我們可以吃的？）

There is nobody *that I know of* **whom** *you can trust.*
（我所認識的人當中，沒有一個是你可以信任的。）

She is the only girl *I ever saw* **whom** (or ***that***) *I would marry.*
（她是我目前所看到的唯一想娶的女孩。）【第一個關代在子句中做受詞時可省略】

【註】 嚴格說來，雙重限制並不是兩個形容詞子句分別修飾同一個先行詞，而是第二個形容詞子句修飾整個先行詞和第一個形容詞子句，這就是此種用法中不需要對等連接詞的理由。

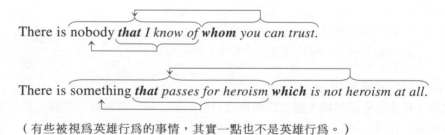

There is nobody ***that*** *I know of* ***whom*** *you can trust.*

There is something ***that*** *passes for heroism* ***which*** *is not heroism at all.*

（有些被視為英雄行為的事情，其實一點也不是英雄行為。）

請立刻做　練習一～六

第四篇　形容詞（**Adjectives**）

第一章 形容詞的種類

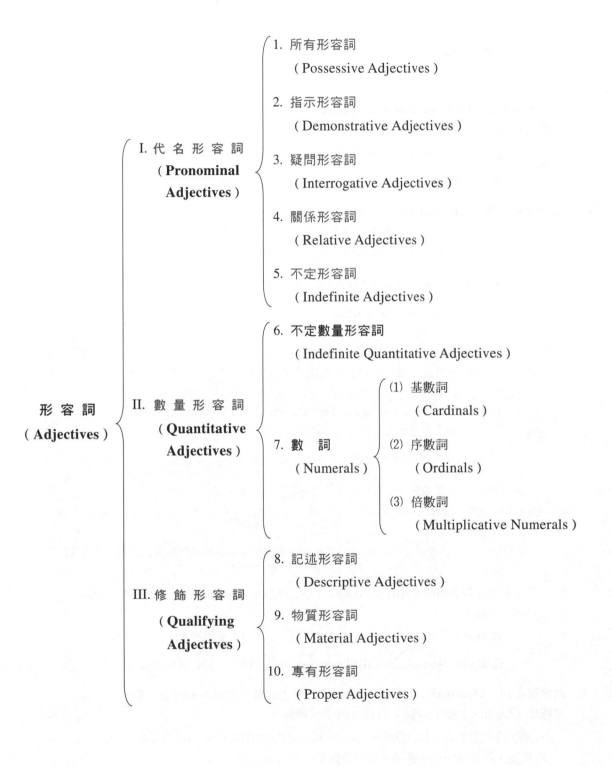

形容詞
（**Adjectives**）

I. 代 名 形 容 詞
（**Pronominal
Adjectives**）

1. 所有形容詞
（Possessive Adjectives）

2. 指示形容詞
（Demonstrative Adjectives）

3. 疑問形容詞
（Interrogative Adjectives）

4. 關係形容詞
（Relative Adjectives）

5. 不定形容詞
（Indefinite Adjectives）

II. 數 量 形 容 詞
（**Quantitative
Adjectives**）

6. 不定數量形容詞
（Indefinite Quantitative Adjectives）

7. 數　詞
（Numerals）

(1) 基數詞
（Cardinals）

(2) 序數詞
（Ordinals）

(3) 倍數詞
（Multiplicative Numerals）

III. 修 飾 形 容 詞
（**Qualifying
Adjectives**）

8. 記述形容詞
（Descriptive Adjectives）

9. 物質形容詞
（Material Adjectives）

10. 專有形容詞
（Proper Adjectives）

第二章 分 論

I. 代名形容詞（**Pronominal Adjectives**）：**由代名詞轉換而來的形容詞稱作代名形容詞。**

  1. 所有形容詞（**Possessive Adjectives**）：人稱代名詞的所有格，具有形容詞的性質修飾後面的名詞，所以又稱所有形容詞，**共有 my, your（你的）, his, her, its, our, your（你們的）, their 八個字。**

   Is this **your** friend?（這是你的朋友嗎？）

  2. 指示形容詞（**Demonstrative Adjectives**）：指示代名詞 this, that, these, those 後接名詞時，即為指示形容詞。

   指示 ⎰ 代名詞： **This** is my dictionary.（這是我的字典。）
   　　 ⎱ 形容詞： **This** dictionary is mine.（這本字典是我的。）

  3. 疑問形容詞（**Interrogative Adjectives**）：疑問代名詞 what, which, whose 後接名詞時，即為疑問形容詞。疑問形容詞和疑問代名詞一樣，可引導疑問句或名詞子句。（參照 p.144）

   疑問 ⎰ 代名詞： **What** is that bird?（那隻鳥是什麼？）
   　　 ⎱ 形容詞： **What** bird is that?（那是隻什麼鳥？）

   　　　　　 Do you know **what** day it was?（你知道那是星期幾嗎？）
   　　　　　 └── 名詞子句 ──┘

  4. 關係形容詞（**Relative Adjectives**）：關係代名詞 what, whose, which 及 ～ever 之後接名詞時，即為關係形容詞。關係形容詞和關係代名詞一樣，可引導形容詞子句。（參照 p.149）

   關係 ⎰ 代名詞： He spoke to me in French, **which** I do not understand.
   　　 ⎪ 　　　　　（他用法文和我交談，那個我不懂。）
   　　 ⎱ 形容詞： He spoke to me in French, **which** language I do not understand.

   　　　　　　　（他用法文和我交談，那種語言我不懂。）

   但是 what 做關係形容詞和做關係代名詞一樣，可引導名詞子句。（what 做關係形容詞或疑問形容詞的區別，在 p.156）

   　　　　　 I will give you **what** books I possess.（我會把我所有的書給你。）
   　　　　　 └── 名 詞 子 句 ──┘

  5. 不定形容詞（**Indefinite Adjectives**）：不定代名詞 some, any, one…之後接名詞時，即為不定形容詞。

   不定 ⎰ 代名詞： **Some** are my students.（有一些是我的學生。）
   　　 ⎱ 形容詞： **Some** man called you yesterday.（昨天有個人打電話給你。）

II. 數量形容詞（**Quantitative Adjectives**）：用來表示**數**（Number）、**量**（Quantity），或**程度**（Degree）的形容詞，可劃分為下列兩種：

   ⎰ 1. 不定數量形容詞（Indefinite Quantitative Adjectives）：約略地表示數的多少。
   ⎱ 2. 數詞（Numerals）：表示一定的數目。

（I）不定數量形容詞（**Indefinite Quantitative Adjectives**）：

表　　數　　者	表量或程度者
附加在複數普通名詞之前	附加在物質或抽象名詞之前
many	much
few, a few	little, a little
a (good, large, great) number of	a (good, great) deal of
several	
a lot of ; lots of ; plenty of	
enough	
some ; any ; no ; all	

上表中沒有中線分隔的，表數、表量均可。

1. "**many**" 和 "**few**" 的用法：

⑴ many 和 few 是用在複數**可數名詞**（即普通名詞與集合名詞）**之前**表「**多**」和「**少**」的。

He has **many** friends, but **few** true ones.（他有很多朋友，但忠實的卻很少。）

【註】 many 之後若無名詞，則作爲代名詞。

Many of them were very tired.（他們當中有很多人都非常累了。）
代名詞

⑵ **many a**, **a great (good) many**：

① **many a** 和 **many** 同義，但 many a 語氣比較強，並且**要與單數名詞及單數形動詞連用**。

Many a student **has** fallen a victim to this vice.（很多學生染上這種惡習。）
= **Many** students **have** fallen a victim to this vice.

Many a prisoner **has** been set free.（很多犯人已經獲釋。）
= **Many** prisoners **have** been set free.

② **a great (good) many** 後面若只是接複數名詞時，不可加 **of**；如果其後接代名詞或所有形容詞時，則須加 **of**。

A great many <u>enemy planes</u> were shot down.（許多敵機被擊落。）
複數名詞

A good many of <u>them</u> surrendered.（他們當中很多人投降。）
代名詞

A great many of <u>my friends</u> went abroad.（我的許多朋友都出國了。）
所有形容詞 + *n.*

⑶ **as many** 與 **so many** 均等於 **the same number of**（同數的）之意：

These are not all the books I have. There are **as many** more upstairs.

（我所有的書不只如此。樓上還有一樣多的。）

We waited about ten minutes; it seemed to me **as many** hours.

（我們等了大約十分鐘；對我而言好像是十個小時。）

He regards his children as **so many** encumbrances.【前有 as, like 時，只用 so many】
（他把他的孩子看成是同樣多的累贅。）

> He worked like an ant.（他像螞蟻似地工作。）
> They worked like **so many** ants.（他們像那樣多的螞蟻一樣地工作。）

⑷ **so many** 的用法也有和 **such and such** 的用法相似，**用來約略地指「多少」的**。

In Japan, they do not say that a room is **so many** feet long or wide, but that it has **so many** mats.（在日本，房間的大小他們不說多少呎長或多少呎寬，而說多少榻榻米。）

⑸ **few** 相當於「**不多；少**」，**可由 hardly any 或 almost no 所取代，含否定的意味。**
a few 相當於 some，**意指「爲數雖不多，但總是還有幾個」，含肯定的意味。**

① The composition is well written; it has **few** mistakes.（這篇作文寫得很好；錯誤不多。）
② The composition is well written, but it has **a few** mistakes.
（這篇作文寫得很好，但是有幾個錯誤。）

> 【註】 **except** 含否定意味，故與 few (little) 連用。
> **besides** 含肯定意味，故與 a few (a little) 連用。
> I have **few** friends **except** you.（我除了你以外幾乎沒有別的朋友——意即不能捨你。）
> I have **a few** friends **besides** you.（我除了你以外還有一些朋友——意即捨你不足惜。）

⑹ **含有 many, few 的慣用語：**
① as many again（加倍的）
② many a time = on many occasions（不知多少次）
③ be one too many（多餘的；礙手礙腳的）
④ be one too many for（勝過）
⑤ the many = the majority（多數人）
⑥ the few = the minority（少數人）
⑦ not a few = quite a few = not few = many（不少）
⑧ only a few = but few = few（很少；不多）
⑨ no fewer than = as many as（不少於；多達）
⑩ every few minutes (hours, days)〔每隔幾分鐘（小時；天）〕
⑪ a man of few words（沉默寡言的人）

The teacher demands that he go away; he **is one too many** here.
（老師命令他走開；他在這兒礙手礙腳。）
In most countries, **the many** have to labor for **the few**.
（大部分的國家裡，多數人要爲少數人服務。）
There are **not** (*or* **quite**) **a few** theaters in this city.（這個城市有不少戲院。）
There are **only a few** such men.（這樣的人很少。）

2. "much" 和 "little" 的用法：

⑴ **much 和 little 附加在物質名詞上表示量，附加在抽象名詞上表程度。**

This ore contains **much** silver, but **little** gold.（這礦石含很多的銀，但很少的金。）
He has **much** skill in teaching, but **little** patience with his students.
（他教學很熟練，但對於學生欠缺耐心。）

【註】 much 後不接名詞時，作為代名詞；另外 much 也可做副詞。

I don't eat **much** for lunch.（我中餐吃得不多。）
　　　　　　代名詞

He is **much** taller than I.（他比我高多了。）
　　　副詞

⑵ **as much** 有「**同量**」（the same amount of）的意思，也可移作「**同一事情**」的意思用。

表同量： He earns twice **as much** money as I.（他賺的錢是我的兩倍。）
　　　　 = He earns as much money again as I.
　　　　 He bought two pounds of sugar and **as much**（= two pounds of）tea.
　　　　（他買了兩磅糖和兩磅茶葉。）

表同樣的事： I was not in the least surprised, for I had fully expected **as much**.
　　　　　　（我一點也不驚訝，因為我已完全料到會這樣。）

注意下面幾個習慣的用法：

It was **as much as**（= **all**）he could do to catch up with the rest of the class.
（要趕上班上其他同學，他已盡全力了。）

She gave me a look **as much as**（= **as if**）to say, "Leave me alone."
（她看了我一眼，好像要說「別管我」。）

She can **not so much as**（= **not even**）write her own name.
（她連自己的名字都不會寫。）

He is **not so much** a scholar **as** a writer.（與其說他是位學者，不如說他是位作家。）
= *He is* **not** *a scholar*, **but rather** *a writer*.
= *He is a writer* **rather than** *a scholar*.

⑶ 　{ **little**（不多；很少）
　　 a little（一些） } + 不可數名詞

　{ He grows worse; there is **little** hope of his recovery.
　　（他的病情逐漸惡化；痊癒的希望<u>不多</u>。）
　　 He is not much better, but there is **a little** hope.（他雖不太好，但尚有<u>少許</u>希望。）

　{ This ore contains silver, besides **a little** gold.
　　（這礦石除含有<u>少許</u>金之外，還有銀。）
　　 It contains much silver, but **little** gold.（它含銀甚多，但含金<u>不多</u>。）

【註】 與動詞如 **know, think, dream, imagine, realize, expect, etc.** 一起用的 **little** 為
副詞，相當於 "**not at all**" 之意。

When I came to this country, I **little** thought that I should stay so long.
（當我來到這個國家時，我<u>一點也沒</u>想到會停留這麼久。）

Little did I dream of hearing such exquisite music.【本句為倒裝句，詳見 p.629】
（我<u>一點也沒</u>夢想到能聽到這樣優美的音樂。）

(4) **含 much 和 little 的慣用語：**

① much the same（差不多）

② make (think) much of（尊重；重視）

③ be much of（有…氣概）

④ see much of（常常碰面）

⑤ much more（更加）

⑥ much less（更不）

⑦ not so much…as（與其說是…不如說是）

⑧ not a little = quite a little = (very) much（不少）

⑨ only a little = but little = little（很少）

⑩ little by little = gradually（漸漸地）

⑪ make (think) little of（不重視；輕視）

⑫ for a little = for a while（暫時）

⑬ after a little = after a while（過了一會兒）

⑭ little (small) hours（半夜一、兩點鐘）

⑮ little ones（孩子們）

He **is much of** a knight.（他有騎士的精神。）

Do you **see much of** your uncle?（你常見到你叔叔嗎？）

I don't like painting, **much less** dancing.（我不喜歡繪畫，更不喜歡跳舞。）

He made **not a little**（= much）contribution to the prosperity of our town.
（他對我們鎮上的繁榮貢獻良多。）

There is **only a little**（= little）money left.（只剩下很少的錢。）

3. "several" 的用法：

several 只可形容可數的複數名詞，相當於「數個」。

He has been in **several** countries, and knows **several** languages.
（他到過幾個國家，且通幾國語言。）

I repeated my questions **several** times.（我把我的問題重複了幾次。）

【註】 several 之後無名詞時是做代名詞。

Several of them are absent.（他們當中有幾位缺席。）

4. "enough" 的用法：

(1) **enough** 可放在名詞的前後。

We have **enough** books. = We have books **enough**.（我們有足夠的書。）

We have **enough** time. = We have time **enough**.（我們有足夠的時間。）

(2) **enough** 的後面若跟 **for**…或 **to**…大都表示「足夠」的意思。

I have **enough** money **for** the purpose.（我有<u>夠用</u>的錢去達到這個目標。）

There was **enough** noise **to** wake the dead.（這般的喧鬧<u>足以</u>吵醒死人。）

【注意】enough 除了做形容詞，還可以**做名詞、副詞**。

　　名詞：You have done **enough** for him.（你為他做的已經足夠了。）

　　副詞：I can never thank you **enough**.（我感激不盡。）

※ 如 **enough** 做副詞來修飾形容詞或副詞時，要置於被修飾的形容詞或副詞的後面。

He is old **enough** to do for himself.（他已到了自立的年齡了。）

He will learn it soon **enough**.（他很快就能學會它。）

⑶ **be + 形容詞 + enough to = be so + 形容詞 + as to**

My brother **is tall enough to** touch it.（我哥哥夠高，能碰得到它。）

= My brother **is so tall as to** be able to touch it.

5. "some" 和 "any" 的用法：（參照 p.130）

⑴ **some 和 any 修飾可數單數名詞，表示「某一個」或「任何一個」；修飾可數複數名詞和不可數名詞，表示「一些；有些」。**

I cannot see **any** similarity between these two pictures.

（我看不出這兩幅畫有任何相似之處。）

Please bring me **some** milk.（請替我帶些牛奶來。）

He gives Mary **some** beautiful dolls.（他給瑪麗一些漂亮的洋娃娃。）

【註】 some 與 any 後沒有名詞時是做代名詞，此外 some 和 any 也可做副詞。

Some of them are my students.（他們當中有一些是我的學生。）
代名詞

Is your mother **any** better?（你的母親好一點了沒？）
副詞

⑵ **some 通常用於肯定句**，如果用於疑問句時ⓐ表示期待對方的**肯定回答**ⓑ向對方**推薦事物**ⓒ與 will you…? 連用表示**請求**。

Have you **some** relatives in Taiwan?（你在台灣有親戚嗎？）

Yes, I have.（是的，我有。）

Won't you have **some** coffee?（你不喝點咖啡嗎？）

Will you write **some** letters to me?（請寫一些信給我好嗎？）

⑶ **some 和 any 的慣用語：**

① some day（將來有一天）

② some day (time) or other（遲早）

③ any more = any longer（再）

④ at any rate = at any cost = in any case（無論如何）

If you don't follow your father's advice, you will be sorry for it **some day or other**.
（你如果不聽你父親的勸告，遲早會後悔的。）

I don't want to speak to him **any more**.（我再也不想和他說話了。）

We have to help him to finish this mission **at any rate**.

（無論如何，我們都必須幫助他完成這項任務。）

6. "no" 的用法：

⑴ **no 修飾單數可數名詞等於 not a (an)；no 修飾複數可數和單數不可數名詞等於 not any。**

There is **no** place like home.（沒有像家這麼溫暖的地方。）

= There is **not a** place like home.

John has **no** money to go to the movies.（約翰沒錢去看電影。）

= John does**n't** have **any** money to go to the movies.

They have **no** high schools in their hometown.（他們的家鄉沒有高中。）

= They don**'t** have **any** high schools in their hometown.

(2) **be no** + 名詞（補語）中 no 為「絕非；絕不是」的意思，和「be not a + 名詞」的語氣不同。
【比較】

> He **is no** gentleman. (他絕不是紳士。── 他不配稱為紳士。)
> He **is not a** gentleman. (他不是紳士。── 他是××。)
> 二句比較可知 no + 名詞是表示強烈的否定。

(3) **no** 的慣用語：

① no longer = not…any longer (不再)

② no more = no longer (不再)

③ no more = dead (死了)

④ by no means (絕不)

⑤ in no time = very quickly (很快；立刻)

⑥ no end (非常地；無限地)

⑦ no doubt (無疑地)

⑧ no wonder (難怪)【是 It is no wonder that 簡化而來】

⑨ no end of (大量；很多)

⑩ no sooner…than (一…就~)

⑪ There is no + V-ing = It is impossible to + V. (原形) (…是不可能的)
　　　　　　　　　　　= We cannot + V. (原形) (參照 p.439)

We saw him **no more**. (我們再也沒看過他。)

No wonder she didn't want to meet me. (難怪她不想見到我。)

He is **by no means** a clever boy. (他絕不是個聰明的男孩。)

No sooner had I left **than** he came. (我一離開他就來了。)

> **There is no telling** when lasting peace will come.
> = *It is impossible to tell when lasting peace will come.*
> = *We cannot tell when lasting peace will come.* (永久和平何時來臨是不可能知道的。)

7. "**all**" 的用法：(參照 p.135)

(1) all 修飾複數名詞表「全數的；所有的」，**修飾不可數名詞表「整個的；全部的」**。

All men are brothers. (四海之內皆兄弟。)

His brother has spent **all** his money on gambling. (他哥哥把全部的錢都花在賭博上。)

He works hardest in **all** the family. (他是全家人中最努力工作的。)

(2) **all** 要放在定冠詞、指示詞、所有格，及基數的前面。

All these books are very interesting. (所有的這些書都很有趣。)

All my teachers are very kind to me. (我所有的老師都對我很好。)

All five men are hard workers. (五個人都很努力工作。)

【註】 all 之後沒有名詞時作代名詞用，此外 all 也作副詞用。

　　　All of my students are very naughty. (我的學生都很頑皮。)
　　　代名詞

　　　The birthday cake is **all** eaten. (生日蛋糕全部吃光了。)
　　　　　　　　　　　副詞

(3) **all 的慣用語：**

① all over（完畢；遍及）

② all right（很好；無恙）

③ in all directions（向四面八方）

④ after all（畢竟；終究）

⑤ once (and) for all（斷然；只此一次）

My uncle has travelled **all over** the world several times.

（我叔叔環遊世界好幾次了。）

"Shall I send for a nurse?" "It's **all right**."（「我叫人去請個護士來好嗎？」「我沒事。」）

(II) **數詞（Numerals）**：包括⑴基數詞（Cardinal Numerals）；⑵序數詞（Ordinal Numerals）；⑶倍數詞（Multiplicative Numerals）。

【註】數詞表：

阿 拉 伯 數　　字	羅　　馬 數　　字	基　　　數	序　　　數	簡　　體
0	×	nought (zero)	×	×
1	I	one	first	1st
2	II	two	second	2nd
3	III	three	third	3rd
4	IV	four	fourth	4th
5	V	five	fifth	5th
6	VI	six	sixth	6th
7	VII	seven	seventh	7th
8	VIII	eight	eighth	8th
9	IX	nine	ninth	9th
10	X	ten	tenth	10th
11	XI	eleven	eleventh	11th
12	XII	twelve	twelfth	12th
13	XIII	thirteen	thirteenth	13th
14	XIV	fourteen	fourteenth	14th
15	XV	fifteen	fifteenth	15th
16	XVI	sixteen	sixteenth	16th
17	XVII	seventeen	seventeenth	17th
18	XVIII	eighteen	eighteenth	18th
19	XIX	nineteen	nineteenth	19th
20	XX	twenty	twentieth	20th
21	XXI	twenty-one	twenty-first	21st
32	XXXII	thirty-two	thirty-second	32nd
43	XLIII	forty-three	forty-third	43rd
54	LIV	fifty-four	fifty-fourth	54th
65	LXV	sixty-five	sixty-fifth	65th
76	LXXVI	seventy-six	seventy-sixth	76th

87	LXXXVII	eighty-seven	eighty-seventh	87th
98	XCVIII	ninety-eight	ninety-eighth	98th
100	C	a (*or* one) hundred	one hundredth	100th
201	CCI	two hundred and one	two hundred and first	201st
400	CD	four hundred	four hundredth	400th
500	D	five hundred	five hundredth	500th
900	CM	nine hundred	nine hundredth	900th
1,000	M	one thousand	one thousandth	1,000th
1,001	MI	one thousand and one	one thousand and first	1,001st
1978	MCMLXXVIII	one thousand nine hundred and seventy-eight	one thousand nine hundred and seventy-eighth	1978th
2,000	MM	two thousand	two thousandth	2,000th
10,000	X̄	ten thousand	ten thousandth	10,000th
100,000	C̄	one hundred thousand	one hundred thousandth	100,000th
1,000,000	M̄	one million	one millionth	1,000,000th

	BRITISH SYSTEM（英制）	AMERICAN SYSTEM（美制）
1,000,000,000	one thousand million	one billion
1,000,000,000,000	one billion	one trillion
1,000,000,000,000,000	one thousand billions	one quadrillion
1 + 18 zeros	one trillion	one quintillion
1 + 24 zeros	one quadrillion	one septillion
1 + 30 zeros	one quintillion	one nonillion

【注意】記數法普通有三種：①數學上用阿拉伯數字②鐘錶上用羅馬數字③英文用基數記數。

用阿拉伯數字記數時，通常自末端起每隔三位用一逗點（comma），例如 1,347 或 3,587,245 等。但記年號時不用逗點，如 1982（一九八二年）。此外，**不論是用阿拉伯數字或羅馬數字記數，其讀法和用英語基數記數的讀法相同。**

1. 基數詞（Cardinal Numerals）

(1) **由 1 到 100 的基數詞**

① 除 eleven, twelve 外，13 到 19 字尾是 "teen"。thirteen, fourteen, etc.

② 從 20 到 90 表十位數字的字尾是 "ty"。thirty, forty, etc.

③ 從 21 到 99 應在十位數與個位數之間加一連字號（hyphen）"-"。twenty-one, thirty-two, ninety-nine, etc.

(2) **hundred 的後面須加 and**（但美式英語可省略 and），**如果沒有 hundred，要在 thousand 的後面加 and。**

139　one hundred **and** thirty-nine

205 two hundred **and** five

1,028 one thousand **and** twenty-eight

3,004 three thousand **and** four

【注意】 一百用 one hundred 或 a hundred 都可以，一百萬用 one million 或 a million 均可，只有一千要用 **one thousand** 不能用 *a thousand*。

(3) **自 1,000 到 1,999 的數字有兩種讀法：**

1,456 { **one thousand four hundred and fifty-six**
　　　　　{ **fourteen hundred and fifty-six**

【註】 一千到兩千之間的數字也可讀成：

1,200 twelve hundred

1,600 sixteen hundred

其餘類推

(4) 英語中沒有「萬」字，所以只得在 **thousand** 前加上十位數或百位數的字，說「萬」為 ten thousand，「十萬」為 one (a) hundred thousand。

12,642 **twelve** thousand six hundred and forty-two

263,975 **two hundred and sixty-three** thousand, nine hundred and seventy-five

456,789,123 four hundred and fifty-six million, **seven hundred and eighty-nine** thousand, one hundred and twenty-three

(5) **年號的讀法有三種**

　　　　{ **twenty eleven**
2011 { **two thousand eleven**
　　　　{ **two thousand and eleven**

不過**第一種讀法最普遍**，如果有月日其讀法如下：

2011 年 11 月 17 日 **November (the) seventeenth, twenty eleven**（美國）
　　　　　　　　　　 (the) seventeenth of November, twenty eleven（英國）

【注意 1】 在個人的信裡或日記或記錄簿裡，按月，日，年的順序可用數字表示幾年幾月幾日。例如 2011 年 11 月 17 日（November 17, 2011）用數字表示則為 11/17/11（= eleven-seventeen-eleven）。

【注意 2】 「紀元前 100 年」寫成 100 B.C. 是 Before Christ（基督誕生以前）的縮寫。「公元 2011 年」可寫成（A.D. 2011, 2011 A.D.），A.D. 是拉丁文 Anno Domini（in the year of our Lord 主耶穌基督紀元）的縮寫，但 A.D. 通常被省略掉。

(6) **時間的讀法**

三點鐘 = three o'clock

五點半 = five thirty = half past five

九點三刻 = nine forty-five = a quarter to (before, of) ten

上午七點二十分 = seven twenty a.m.

下午八點十分的火車 = the 8:10 p.m. train

(7) **汽車牌照號碼、電話號碼、貨幣的讀法**

21638 = two one six three eight

850324 = eight five 0 / o / three two four

$7.35（七元三角五分）= seven dollars thirty-five cents = seven thirty-five

$20（二十元整）= twenty dollars even

£ 2（兩鎊）= two pounds

NT $123（新台幣一百二十三元）= one hundred and twenty-three (N.T.) dollars

⑻ **住址的讀法**

426 Maple Avenue = four twenty-six Maple Avenue

1400 16th St. = fourteen hundred, sixteenth Street

⑼ **百分比、折扣、度數的讀法**

20% = twenty percent

0.4% = point (*or* decimal) four percent

八折 = twenty percent discount

九五折 = five percent discount

-20°（零下二十度）= twenty degrees below zero

75°F. = seventy-five degrees Fahrenheit

27°C. = twenty-seven degrees centigrade / Celsius

⑽ **度量衡的讀法**

長度　8 ft. 6 in. = eight feet six inches

面積　16×9 feet = sixteen by nine feet = sixteen feet by nine

體積　$6'' \times 4'' \times 3\,\tfrac{3}{4}''$ = six inches by four by three and three-fourths

液重　4 gal. 3 qt. 2 pt. = four gallons three quarts two pints

重量　10 lb. 6 oz. = ten pounds six ounces

　　　　45 kilos = forty-five kilograms

⑾ **算術式的讀法**

$4+3=7$　　Four and three is (makes, equals; are, make, equal) seven.

　或爲　　Four plus three is (makes, equals) seven.

$7-4=3$　　Seven minus four is (equals, leaves) three.

　或爲　　Four (subtracted) from seven is (equals, leaves) three.

$4 \times 3 = 12$　　Four times three is (makes, equals; are, make, equal) twelve.

　或爲　　Four multiplied by three is (equals, makes) twelve.

$12 \div 3 = 4$　　Twelve divided by three is (equals, makes) four.

　或爲　　Three into twelve is (equals, makes) four.

$2:4=3:6$　　Two is to four as three is to six.

　或爲　　The ratio of two to four equals the ratio of three to six.

$(7+6\tfrac{3}{8}-3.88 \times 4) \div 2\tfrac{1}{5}$ = seven plus six and three-eighths minus three point eight eight

　　　　　　　　multiplied by four, all divided by two and a fifth

$x^2 = x$ square 或爲 x squared

$y^3 = y$ cube 或爲 y cubed

$z^4 = z$ (raised) to the fourth (power)

$a^2 + 2b = 6$　　a squared and two times b makes six.

$a^3 - 4b = 8$　　　*a* cubed minus four times *b* equals eight.

$2^5 = 32$　　　　Two raised to the fifth power is thirty-two.

　　或爲　　　　Two raised to the power of five is thirty-two.

$\sqrt{270}$ = the square (*or* second) root of 270

$\sqrt[3]{400}$ = the cube (*or* third) root of 400

⑿ **hundred, thousand, dozen (12), score (20)** 等字的前面雖有大於二的定數詞後面也不加
"**s**"，如果前面無數詞，僅表約略的多數時，其複數形往往與 of 連用。

（單數）
- two **dozen** pencils（兩打鉛筆）
- three **hundred** soldiers（三百名士兵）
- three **hundred** of them（他們之中的 300 人）

（複數）
- We consume **dozens** of eggs every day.（我們每天吃好幾打的蛋。）
- **Scores** of ships were wrecked in the storm.（這次的暴風雨破壞了好幾十艘船。）

※ 有時 **a dozen, a score** 也用來表示約略的「**許多**」。
The tile broke into **a dozen** pieces.（這磁磚碎成了很多片。）
I have tried **a score** of times.（我已經試過許多次了。）

⒀ **a couple of** 可代 **two** 使用
I stayed only **a couple of** days.（我只停留了兩天。）

⒁ **million** 爲名詞、數詞，後加 **s** 與不加 **s** 均可，如做形容詞修飾名詞或**後還有數字時**，取單數
形式。
Taiwan has a population of over twenty-three **million(s)**.（台灣有兩千三百多萬人口。）【名詞】

Taiwan has more than twenty-three **million** inhabitants.
（台灣有兩千三百多萬居民。）【形容詞】
Tokyo has a population of nearly twelve **million** nine hundred thousand.
（東京將近有一千兩百九十萬人口。）

⒂ **billion** 與 **trillion** 英美兩國代表的數字不同，見下表：

十億	【英】one thousand million	【美】one **billion** = 1 + 9 zeros
百億	【英】ten thousand million	【美】ten **billion** = 1 + 10 zeros
千億	【英】one hundred thousand million	【美】one hundred **billion** = 1 + 11 zeros
一兆	【英】one **billion**	【美】one **trillion** = 1 + 12 zeros
百萬兆	【英】one **trillion**	【美】one quintillion = 1 + 18 zeros

⒃ 基數 "0" 的不同讀法
① 在數學上
.03 = point **nought** three
② 在數學上或溫度上
.03 = point **zero** three
It's five degrees below **zero**.（氣溫是零下五度。）
③ 電話上，數學上
Dial 7050 /ˈsɛvən o faɪv o / and ask for extension 90 / naɪn o /.
〔撥 7050 再轉（分機）90。〕
603.09 = / sɪks o θri pɔɪnt o naɪn /　　*雙斜線表讀音

④ 在運動比賽時

nil / nɪl /, **nothing** 零

The result of the match was 4 : 0〔four (goals to) **nil**〕.（比賽結果四比零。）

Brazil won 4 : 0〔four (to) **nothing**〕.（巴西以四比零獲勝。）

love 【在網球比賽時】零分

Norway leads by 30 : 0 (thirty **love**) in the first game of the second set.

（挪威在第二場第一局以三十比零領先。）

(17) **以基數代替序數的讀法**

No. 2（讀 number two）= the second

Book IV（讀 book four）= the fourth book

Lesson V（讀 lesson five）= the fifth lesson

Chapter III（讀 chapter three）= the third chapter

P. 7（讀 page seven）= the seventh page

Line 8（讀 line eight）= the eighth line

World War II（讀 World War two）= the Second World War

(18) **以複數形基數構成的慣用語**

The guests departed **by twos and threes**.（客人三三兩兩地離開了。）

Ten to one he forgets it.（他十之八九忘了。）

There are **thousands of** apples in our garden.（在我家花園裡有好幾千顆蘋果。）

in one's teens（在某人十幾歲時）　　in one's thirties（在某人三十幾歲時）

2. **序數詞**（Ordinal Numerals）：first, second, third…表示順序的數字稱爲序數詞。

(1) **序數詞只須在基數詞的字尾加上 "th" 即成，但 first, second, third 是例外**，而且字尾上加 th 的在拼法上還有需要變更的地方：

基　數	序　數
five	fifth
eight	eighth
nine	ninth
twelve	twelfth
twenty	twentieth
thirty	thirtieth

(2) **序數詞的寫法**

① 1～19 各基數的字尾加 "th" 即成序數，但有七個例外，first, second, third, fifth, eighth, ninth, twelfth。

② 20, 30,…90 各十位基數的字尾 y 改成 "ieth" 即成序數，twenty → twentieth, thirty → thirtieth,…ninety → ninetieth。

③ 自 21 以後的多位數的序數，是將最後一個數字用序數，前面的各數字（即十位數、百位數等）用基數，21 → twenty-first, 22 → twenty-second, 23 → twenty-third,…100 → (one) hundredth, 101 → (one) hundred and first, 110 → (one) hundred and tenth, 1000 → (one) thousandth,…

(3) **序數詞的簡體**

first = 1st　　　eleventh = 11th　　　twenty-first = 21st

second = 2nd　　twelfth = 12th　　twenty-second = 22nd

third = 3rd　　thirteenth = 13th　　twenty-third = 23rd

fourth = 4th　　fourteenth = 14th　　twenty-fourth = 24th

以此類推可以做所有的序數詞。

【注意】　序數詞的前面必須附以**定冠詞**。如：**the** first, **the** second 等，而 **a second,
a third** 等則是用作 **another** 的意思。

(4) **序數詞的用法**

① 做形容詞：Sunday is **the first** day of the week.（星期日是一星期的第一天。）

② 做名　　詞：**The first** is better than this.（第一個比這個好。）
名　　詞

③ 做副　　詞：He **first** went to Keelung, and then to Taipei.（他先到基隆，然後到台北。）

④ 日期多用序數：

$$5 月 10 日 = \begin{cases} \textbf{the tenth} \text{ of May} \\ \textbf{the } 10\textbf{th} \text{ of May} \\ \text{May } \textbf{the tenth} \\ \text{May } 10\textbf{th} \\ \text{May ten} \\ \text{May } 10 \end{cases}$$

⑤ 帝王等的「第幾世」是在專有名詞的後面，用羅馬數字表示的，但讀起來須插入一個
定冠詞 the。

Charles I = Charles **the First**（查理一世）

Henry VIII = Henry **the Eighth**（亨利八世）

⑥ **分數的表示法：**

a. 分子用基數，分母用序數。

b. **分子大於 2 時，分母須加 "s" 以形成複數。**

c. 分母與分子之數目較大時，分子（基數）over（*or* by）分母（基數）。

d. 1/2 用 half，1/4 可用 quarter 來表示。

1/2 = a half（*or* one half）

1/3 = a third（*or* one third）

2/3 = two thirds

1/4 = a quarter（*or* one fourth）

3/4 = three quarters（*or* three fourths）

9/10 = nine tenths

2 7/8 = two and seven eighths

319/456 = three hundred and nineteen **over**（*or* by）four hundred and fifty-six

(5) **序數前面無所有形容詞時，通常要有冠詞 "the"。**

The second girl from the left is Mary.（左邊算來第二個女孩是瑪麗。）

【例外】

① 序數作副詞用時，無冠詞。　　He came **first**.（他來得最早。）

② 序數的意義為 another 時，前面要用不定冠詞 a (an)。

A second（= Another）girl came into the room.（另一個女孩走進了房間。）

③ 考試（賽跑等）獲得的名次其序數不要冠詞。

He stands **first** in his class.（他在班上成績第一。）

(6) **用序數詞所做的慣用語：**

　　John came *first*.（= John was the first to come.）（約翰來得<u>最早</u>。）

　　I *first* learned English, *and then* German and French.

　　（我<u>最初</u>學英文，<u>然後</u>才學德文和法文。）

　　Business *first* and pleasure *afterwards*.（<u>先</u>做事<u>而後</u>玩樂。）

　　I found it rather difficult *at first*, but soon got used to it.

　　（<u>起初</u>我覺得它很困難，但不久就習慣了。）

　　First come, *first served*.（<u>捷足先登</u>；<u>先到者優先</u>。）

　　I met him *a second time*（= again）.（我<u>再度</u>遇到他。）

　　Don't give it *a second thought*.（別<u>再去想</u>它。）

　　You'll need *a second*（= another）*pair* of shoes.（你需要<u>另一雙</u>鞋子。）

　　America is *second to none* in natural resources.

　　〔美國的天然資源<u>不亞於</u>（= 勝過）任何國家。〕

　　I liked English *from the first*.（我<u>從一開始</u>就喜歡英文。）

　　It looked like an island *at first sight*.（<u>乍看起來</u>，它像是一個島。）

　　He was only ten years of age when he went to America *for the first time*.

　　（他<u>第一次</u>到美國時才十歲。）

　　If you want me to trust you, *first of all*, be honest.（你如果要我信任你，<u>首先</u>要誠實。）

　　I have known him, *first and last*, for ten years.（我認識他<u>總計</u>已有十年。）

3. **倍數詞（Multiplicative Numerals）：** 常用的有 half（一半），double（兩倍），treble（三倍）等。

(1) **half 的用法：** half 除當形容詞用，還可用為名詞、代名詞、副詞。

① **half 做形容詞**

a. **表示「一半」有 half a, a half, half the 及 a half a + 名詞的四種表示法，**
　　half a + 名詞，是一般用法，a half a + 名詞，是較粗俗的用法。

> He ran $\left\{\begin{array}{l}\textbf{a half} \\ \textbf{half a}\end{array}\right\}$ mile in half an hour.（他半小時跑了半哩路。）

　　I have read **half** the book.（我已讀完了這本書的二分之一。）

　　【注意】 a half moon（上弦月或下弦月），a half sister (brother)（異父或異母的姊妹
　　　　　　或兄弟）是固定用法，不可寫成 *half a moon* 或 *half a sister*。

b. **表示「多少又一半」用 and a half。**

　　Mr. Smith went to New York two **and a half** months ago.

　　（史密斯先生兩個半月前到紐約去了。）

　　【注意】 <u>比較下列二種用法</u>，可知在此種表示法中，**half 有名詞或形容詞**的作用。

> $\left\{\begin{array}{l}\text{two miles } \textbf{and a half} \\ \text{two } \textbf{and a half} \text{ miles}\end{array}\right.$（兩哩半）
>
> $\left\{\begin{array}{l}\text{three pounds } \textbf{and a half} \\ \text{three } \textbf{and a half} \text{ pounds}\end{array}\right.$（三磅半）
>
> $\left\{\begin{array}{l}\text{four hours } \textbf{and a half} \\ \text{four } \textbf{and a half} \text{ hours}\end{array}\right.$（四小時半）

② **half** 做名詞時，可有複數形態

To know one thing well is better than knowing many things by **halves**.

（徹底知道一事，勝過一知半解地知道很多事。）

Two **halves** make a whole.（兩個一半成為整體。）

③ **half** 做代名詞，形式為 **half of a** (**the**)

half the sum = **half** of the sum（半額）
形容詞　　　　　代名詞

half one's pay = **half** of one's pay（某人薪水的一半）
形容詞　　　　　　代名詞

half a pound = **half** of a pound（半磅）
形容詞　　　　　代名詞

half a mile = one **half** of a mile（半哩）
形容詞　　　　　　代名詞

half the distance = one **half** of the distance（距離的一半）
形容詞　　　　　　　代名詞

※ 此種用法後面接的動詞，**須視其代替之名詞的意義是複數或單數來決定**。（參照 p.142）

Half (of) the apples **were** eaten.（半數的蘋果被吃掉了。）

Half (of) the apple **was** eaten.（半個蘋果被吃掉了。）

④ **half** 做副詞

His homework is not yet **half** done.（他的功課尚未完成一半。）

Mary has **half** as many books again as I have.（瑪麗的書是我的一倍半。）

This is **half** as much again as that.（這個是那個的一倍半。）

The husband is **half** as old again as his wife is.（丈夫的年紀是妻子的一倍半。）

I am **half** as old again as you.（我的歲數<u>比你大半倍</u> = 我的歲數<u>是你的一倍半</u>。）

※ half as $\left\{ \begin{array}{c} \text{many} \\ \text{much} \end{array} \right\}$ again as（一倍半）

= half as $\left\{ \begin{array}{c} \text{many} \\ \text{much} \end{array} \right\}$ as（半倍）+ as $\left\{ \begin{array}{c} \text{many} \\ \text{much} \end{array} \right\}$ again as（加一倍）

(2) **double**（= **twofold**）**的用法**：可做形容詞、名詞、副詞、動詞。

① double 做形容詞

Mrs. Brown is a woman of **double** character.（布朗太太有雙重人格。）

Travel subserves the **double** end of health and culture.（旅行有助於健康和修養的雙重目的。）

A transitive verb sometimes takes a **double** object.（及物動詞有時需要兩個受詞。）

※ **double** 當作「加倍的」解表比較時，可放在 **the** 或所有格形式的前面。

The ship has **double the** capacity of that.（這艘船的容量是那艘船的兩倍。）

He is **double her** age.（他的歲數比她大一倍。）

The college had **double** (treble, quadruple, etc.) **the** number of expected applicants.

〔申請那所大學學生的人數為預期的兩倍（三倍、四倍等）。〕

② double 做名詞

Twenty is the **double** of ten.（二十是十的兩倍。）

③ double 做副詞

This river is **double** as broad as that one.（這條河是那條河的兩倍寬。）

④ double 做動詞

The classrooms of the school **doubled** in one year.（這學校的教室一年內加了一倍。）

⑶ **treble**（ = **threefold**）的用法：可做形容詞、動詞。

① treble 做形容詞

His salary is **treble** mine.（他的薪水是我的三倍。）

② treble 做動詞

The price of the bicycle has **trebled**.（腳踏車的價格漲了三倍。）

【注意】 treble 和 triple 可互換，但 treble 比較普通。可是有一些一定要用 triple，如：
the triple alliance（三國同盟）。

⑷ **倍數常用的表達法：**

I bought it at **half** the usual price.（我用平常價格的一半買下它。）

The salesman earns **half** my salary.（這銷售員的收入是我薪水的一半。）

I had to pay **double**（ = twice）the usual fare.（我不得不付平常車資的兩倍。）

My brother owns **double** my books.（我哥哥擁有的書是我的兩倍。）

I offered him **treble** the sum.（我向他出的價是總額的三倍。）

His age is **treble** my age.（他的年齡是我的三倍。）

That window is **three times** the size of this.（那個窗子是這個窗子的三倍大。）

⑸ **倍數副詞**（**Adverbial Multiplicative**）：表示倍數的副詞。

half（一半）

once = one time（一倍；一次）

twice = two times（兩倍；兩次）

thrice = three times（三倍；三次）

four times（四倍；四次）　　　 five times（五倍；五次）…etc.

倍數副詞的表達法：表示「什麼是什麼的幾倍」。

公式：
$$\begin{cases} \cdots\text{times as + 形容詞或副詞 + as}\cdots \\ = \cdots\text{times the + 名詞 + of + }\cdots \end{cases}$$

My living room is **half** as large as yours.（我的客廳只有你的一半大。）

= My living room is **half** the size of yours.

China is **twenty times** as large as Japan.（中國是日本的二十倍大。）

= China is **twenty times** the size of Japan.

They have **twice** as many ships as we have.（他們船的數量是我們的兩倍。）

= They have **twice** the number of our ships.

He is **twice** as old as you. （他的年齡是你的兩倍。）

= He is **twice** your (own) age.

【注意】　上四例的第二種結構與以前講的 half the sum 等，皆是省略了 of。

half (of) the sum （總額的一半）

twice (of) the sum （總額的兩倍）

Ⅲ. **修飾形容詞（Qualifying Adjective）**：用於敘述人或事物的性質或狀態的形容詞，稱作修飾形容詞。**可再分為記述形容詞（Descriptive Adjective）、物質形容詞（Material Adjective）、專有形容詞（Proper Adjective）三種。**

1. **記述形容詞**：是用來說明事物的種類、性質，或狀態的形容詞，大部分記述形容詞有比較級、最高級等變化。

He is a **diligent** student. （他是個勤奮的學生。）

She is a **kind** woman. （她是位仁慈的婦人。）

It is a **long** sentence. （它是個很長的句子。）

I'm very **glad** to see you again. （我很高興再次見到你。）

【註1】　英文形容詞中**記述形容詞佔最多**，又可把它歸納成兩類：

① **含有判斷（主觀性質）的形容詞**，如：

clever, beautiful, foolish, wise, kind, cruel, good, bad, honest, right, wrong, diligent, lazy, etc.

② **純描述（客觀性質）的形容詞**，如：

long, short, big, small, green, blue, square, round, wide, narrow, deep, shallow, high, low, etc.

【註2】　**記述形容詞包括由動詞轉成的形容詞**（即作形容詞用的現在分詞、過去分詞，與動名詞）。

① 現在分詞

an interesting story （有趣的故事）　　　a flying bird （飛鳥）

running water （流動的水）　　　a confusing plot （令人困惑的情節）

② 過去分詞

lost treasure （失去的寶藏）　　　a broken leg （跌斷的腿）

a drunken soldier （喝醉的士兵）　　　a wounded arm （受傷的手臂）

③ 動名詞

a resting room （休息室）　　　a sleeping car （臥車）

a walking stick （手杖）　　　a swimming pool （游泳池）

【註3】　**記述形容詞中有些是合併其他詞類而形成，稱為複合形容詞（Compound Adjectives）**，如：（參照 p.450）

① **形容詞 + 名詞-ed**

a small-sized box = a box of small size （小型的箱子）

high-prized goods = goods with high prize （極受讚賞的商品）

② **形容詞 + 動詞-ing**

a slow-burning candle = a candle that burns slowly （慢慢燃燒的蠟燭）

an odd-looking man = a man who looks odd （長得很奇怪的人）

③ **名詞 + 過去分詞（被動）**

a hunger-weakened man = a man who is weakened by hunger

（因飢餓而虛弱的人）

④ **名詞 + 形容詞**

fire-resistant cloth = cloth which can resist fire （防火布）

2. **物質形容詞**：是由當作表示材料的名詞轉用而來，**有時在物質名詞之後加 "en" 或 "y" 做形容詞**，即表示其物質名詞之屬性或作比喻使用。例如說「金質的」要用 "gold" 而不能用 "golden"，**"golden" 通常表抽象的意味**，指「金黃色的」或「寶貴的」。(參照 p.100)

物質名詞做形容詞者	物質名詞 + en 或 y 者 (表抽象意味者)
a **gold** watch (金錶)	a **golden** opportunity (千載難逢的機會)
a **silver** spoon (銀湯匙)	a **silvery** voice (銀鈴似的聲音)
a **stone** wall (石牆)	a **stony** heart (鐵石心腸)
a **rain** coat (雨衣)	a **rainy** day (雨天)

【例外】但也有少數物質名詞，在字尾上加 en 或 y 而表材料形容詞的。

an **earthen** vessel (陶器)　　　　an **oaken** bucket (橡木桶)
a **wooden** ship (木船)

也有些物質名詞，字尾沒加 en 或 y 而用來表抽象的、比喻的。

an **iron** will (鋼鐵般的意志)

3. **專有形容詞**：是由專有名詞所做成的形容詞，都用**大寫**字母起首。

Victorian order (維多利亞勳章)
Platonic love (柏拉圖式的戀愛；純潔的愛)
Buddhist temple (佛寺)

上面 Victorian 來自 Queen Victoria (維多利亞女王)。Platonic 來自希臘哲學家 Plato (柏拉圖)。Buddhist 來自 Buddha (佛陀)。

【註】 都市的名稱用作形容詞時，一般都不用改變。

像：Beijing dialect (北京話)　　　Taipei Station (台北車站)

除去上述以**人名、地名**所做成的專有形容詞以外，還有**大部分的專有形容詞是由國名演變而來的**，詳見下表：(為了便於記憶，將其劃分為三個類型)

A. 字尾為 sh, ch, ss 者

專 有 名 詞 (Proper Noun)	形 容 詞 (Adjective) (Language)	全 體 人 民 (People) (Collective)	個　　　人 (Individual)	
			單　　數 (Singular)	複　　數 (Plural)
Britain (不列顛；英國)	**British**	the British Britons	a Briton	Britons
Denmark (丹麥)	**Danish**	the Danes	a Dane	Danes
England (英國)	**English**	the English	an Englishman	Englishmen
Finland (芬蘭)	**Finnish**	the Finns	a Finn	Finns
Ireland (愛爾蘭)	**Irish**	the Irish	an Irishman	Irishmen
Poland (波蘭)	**Polish**	the Poles	a Pole	Poles
Scotland (蘇格蘭)	**Scotch** **Scottish** **Scots**	the Scotch the Scots Scotsmen	a Scotchman a Scot a Scotsman	Scotchmen Scots Scotsmen
Spain (西班牙)	**Spanish**	the Spaniards	a Spaniard	Spaniards
Sweden (瑞典)	**Swedish**	the Swedes	a Swede	Swedes
Turkey (土耳其)	**Turkish**	the Turks	a Turk	Turks
Wales (威爾斯)	**Welsh**	the Welsh Welshmen	a Welshman	Welshmen
France (法國)	**French**	the French	a Frenchman	Frenchmen
Holland (荷蘭)	**Dutch**	the Dutch	a Dutchman	Dutchmen
Switzerland (瑞士)	**Swiss**	the Swiss	a Swiss	Swiss

【註】　我們普通稱英國爲 Great Britain（包含 England, Scotland, Wales）和 Northern
　　　　Ireland 的 United Kingdom（聯合王國），所以正式的說起來，非說「大不列顛及北愛
　　　　爾蘭聯合王國」（**the United Kingdom of Great Britain and Northern Ireland**）
　　　　不可，並且有關英國全體的事情，形容詞又必須用 "British" 一詞，像 the British
　　　　Ambassador（英國大使），the British Navy（英國海軍）。

B. 字尾爲 **an** 者

專 有 名 詞 （Proper Noun）	形 容 詞 （Adjective） （Language）	全 體 人 民 （People） （Collective）	個　　人（Individual）	
			單　　數 （Singular）	複　　數 （Plural）
Africa（非洲）	**African**	the Africans	an African	Africans
America（美國）	**American**	the Americans	an American	Americans
Asia（亞洲）	**Asian**	the Asians	an Asian	Asians
Australia（澳洲）	**Australian**	the Australians	an Australian	Australians
Belgium（比利時）	**Belgian**	the Belgians	a Belgian	Belgians
Brazil（巴西）	**Brazilian**	the Brazilians	a Brazilian	Brazilians
Canada（加拿大）	**Canadian**	the Canadians	a Canadian	Canadians
Europe（歐洲）	**European**	the Europeans	a European	Europeans
Germany（德國）	**German**	the Germans	a German	Germans
Hungary（匈牙利）	**Hungarian**	the Hungarians	a Hungarian	Hungarians
Italy（義大利）	**Italian**	the Italians	an Italian	Italians
Korea（韓國）	**Korean**	the Koreans	a Korean	Koreans
Mexico（墨西哥）	**Mexican**	the Mexicans	a Mexican	Mexicans
Norway（挪威）	**Norwegian**	the Norwegians	a Norwegian	Norwegians
Rome（羅馬）	**Roman**	the Romans	a Roman	Romans
Russia（俄國）	**Russian**	the Russians	a Russian	Russians

C. 字尾爲 **ese** 者

China（中國）	**Chinese**	the Chinese	a Chinese	Chinese
Canton（廣東）	**Cantonese**	the Cantonese	a Cantonese	Cantonese
Japan（日本）	**Japanese**	the Japanese	a Japanese	Japanese
Portugal（葡萄牙）	**Portuguese**	the Portuguese	a Portuguese	Portuguese
Taiwan（台灣）	**Taiwanese**	the Taiwanese	a Taiwanese	Taiwanese
Vietnam（越南）	**Vietnamese**	the Vietnamese	a Vietnamese	Vietnamese

D. 幾個國家的字尾變化不規則：

Greece（希臘）	**Greek** **Grecian**	the Greeks	a Greek	Greeks
Israel（以色列）	**Israeli**	the Israelis	an Israeli	Israelis
Pakistan（巴基斯坦）	**Pakistani**	the Pakistanis	a Pakistani	Pakistanis
Arabia（阿拉伯）	**Arabic** **Arabian**	the Arabs	an Arab	Arabs

【說明】　第一欄是國名或省名。
　　　　　第二欄是形容詞，同時也作該國的語言的名稱用。
　　　　＊但 Canadian, African, American, Asian, European, Mexican, Roman,
　　　　　Australian, Belgian 等只作形容詞用，不能代表該國的語言。
　　　　　第三欄是指全國國民的統稱。
　　　　　第四欄是指個人的稱謂。

比較下面例句：

Japanese houses are usually made of wood. ······························· 【形容詞】
（日本房屋通常是木製的。）

Japanese is difficult to learn. ······································· 【單數名詞（語言）】
（日文很難學。）

The Japanese are said to be diligent. ····························· 【複數名詞（全體）】
（據說日本人很勤勉。）

Japanese were among them. ··· 【複數名詞（個人）】
（其中有日本人。）

A Japanese is coming to see me this afternoon. ············· 【單數名詞（個人）】
（今天下午有個日本人要來看我。）

【註1】 Grecian 主要是指古希臘，如：a Grecian urn（一個希臘古甕）。

【註2】 Arabic 用於 Arabic numerals（阿拉伯數字），the Arabic language（阿拉伯語言）。
He speaks Arabic fluently.（他能流利地說阿拉伯語。）
Arabian 用於 Arabian brown（阿拉伯的褐色），an Arabian camel（阿拉伯的駱駝），
an Arab(ian) horse（阿拉伯馬）。

【註3】 以下專有形容詞含有特別的意思。
French leave（不告而別）
French crown（禿頭）
French kiss（舌吻）
French window（落地窗）
French toast（以牛奶雞蛋炸出之土司）
Indian file（縱隊）
Indian summer（秋老虎；返老還童）
Indian gift（期待還禮之贈品）
Irish promotion〔愛爾蘭式的升遷（表降級）〕
Irish potato〔白馬鈴薯（與 sweet potato 不同）〕
Dutch comfort（烈酒；不令人感激的安慰）
Dutch treat (party)〔各自付帳（的宴會）〕
Dutch uncle（嘮叨的老人）
Dutch courage（酒後之勇；虛勇）

※ 英國和荷蘭早期因海外殖民地之爭，經常發生戰爭，英國人就造了許多話，來諷刺
荷蘭人。長久使用之下，就成了各含特別意義的慣用語了。

第三章 形容詞的用法與位置

形容詞用以修飾名詞或代名詞時，有兩種基本用法：

1. 限定用法：通常放在被修飾的名詞或代名詞的前面。
2. 敘述用法：放在補語的位置。

I. **限定用法（Attributive Use）**：形容詞緊靠著所修飾的（代）名詞之前後，以直接修飾該（代）名詞時，稱為限定用法。

This is a **beautiful** rose.（這是一朵美麗的玫瑰花。）

John is an **honest** boy.（約翰是個誠實的男孩。）

Let me tell you something **interesting**.（我來告訴你一些有趣的事。）

【注意】 大部分的形容詞可用於限定用法，亦可用於敘述用法，但**下列形容詞只有限定用法**而無敘述用法：

wooden（木製的）	woolen（毛料的）	golden（金色的）	drunken（喝醉的）
elder（年長的）	upper（上面的）	former（以前的）	leaden（鉛製的）
latter（後半的）	outer（外面的）	inner（內在的）	utmost（最大的；極度的）
mere（僅僅）	only（唯一的）	utter（完全的）	beaten（被打敗的）
main（主要的）	certain（某一）	very（同一的；恰好的）	

【註】 **字尾為 en**（名詞 + en = 形容詞或 p.p. 字尾為 en 當形容詞）或**表比較的形容詞**，大多只能做限定用法，放在名詞的前面。

① woolen, drunken, golden, leaden,…

② elder, inner, former, utmost,…

The plan was an **utter** failure.（這項計劃完全失敗了。）

My brother will come back from America in the **latter** part of the year.
（我哥哥將在今年的下半年從美國歸來。）

(I) **限定用法的形容詞**通常放在名詞或代名詞之前，但**在下列情形時，應置於被修飾字的後面**：

1. **仿照法文的成語**
   governor-**general**（總督）　　　　　　poet **laureate**（桂冠詩人）
   consul-**general**（總領事）

2. **something, anything, everything, nothing, everyone, anybody,… + 形容詞。**

   There is something **peculiar** about him.（他有些特別的地方。）

   Is there anything **wrong** with your watch?（你的錶有什麼問題嗎？）

3. **為區別專有名詞**，而將形容詞放在後面。
   Alexander **the Great**（亞歷山大大帝）　　George **the Fifth**（喬治五世）
   Asia **Minor**（小亞細亞）　　　　　　　　John Smith, **Jr**.（小約翰史密斯）

4. 前有**限定最高級**或 **all, every, only, the few** 等的形容詞，則以 **ible** 或 **able** 做字尾的形容詞，放在名詞後。但 **possible** 例外，可放在前後。

They are on the best terms **imaginable**. (他們十分要好。)

I have tried all (*or* every) means **imaginable**. (我已試過所有想到的方法了。)

【例外】 The car ran at the highest speed **possible**. (那部車以可能的最高速度行駛。)
= The car ran at the highest **possible** speed.

5. **在名詞之後的數詞 + 名詞 + old, long, high, wide, deep, etc.**

> **a** girl three years **old** (三歲大的小女孩)
> = **a** girl of three years **old**
> = **a** three-year-**old** girl

It is a room (*which is*) twelve feet **wide** and fifteen feet **long**.
(那是一個十二呎寬十五呎長的房間。)

6. **修飾指示代名詞 those 的形容詞放在它後面。**

Those **present** were all surprised at the news. (在場的人得知那個消息都非常驚訝。)

Among those **invited** were some women. (在受邀的人當中有些婦女。)

7. **akin** (近似的), **alive** (活著的), **alone** (單獨的), **present** (在場的), **else** (其他的), **here**, **there** 必須置於被修飾的名詞的後面。

Man **alone** has the gift of speech. (唯有人類有說話的天賦。)

All the people **present** burst into tears. (所有在場的人都突然大哭。)

The house **here** is for rent. (這裡房子要出租。)

The people **there** have many peculiar customs. (那裡的人有很多特別的習俗。)

He is the greatest man **alive**. (他是當今世上最偉大的人。)

Was anybody **else** absent? (還有誰缺席了？)

Who **else** has come? (還有誰來了？)

8. **為加強語氣或音調美可把限定形容詞放在後面。**

比較 { A man, *poor but contented*, is to be envied. (貧窮但知足的人會令人羨慕。)
A *poor but contented* man is to be envied. }

比較 { The boy, *wise and diligent*, is Mary's brother. (這個聰明又勤勉的男孩是瑪麗的弟弟。)
The *wise and diligent* boy is Mary's brother. }

9. **名詞 + 形容詞片語或子句**

(1) **介詞片語**

The house *on the corner* is the home of Mayor Williams.
(在轉角處的房子是威廉斯市長的家。)

(2) **分詞片語**

The boy *wearing the red shirt* is Tom. (穿紅色襯衫的男孩是湯姆。)

(3) **不定詞片語**

The books *to be read this semester* are listed here. (這學期要讀的書都列在這裡。)

(4) **形容詞子句**

Men *who are wise* seldom speak. (聰明的人很少說話。)

10. **其他一些置於後位的常用語**

> God **Almighty**（全能的上帝），time **immemorial**（太古），a notary **public**（公證人），the body **politic**（國家），an heir **apparent**（法定繼承人），court **martial**（軍事法庭），blood **royal**（王族；皇家），a sum **total**（總計）

(II) 可置於被修飾字前後的一些特別的限定形容詞

1. **last**, **next**, **following** 修飾表時間的名詞時。

My brother came to see me ⎰ on Sunday *last*.
⎱ *last* Sunday.　（我弟弟上週日來看我。）

We are going to have an English test ⎰ on Monday *next*.
⎱ *next* Monday.　（我們下星期一將舉行英文測驗。）

He said he would go to Taipei ⎰ on the day *following*.
⎱ the *following* day.　（他說他隔天要去台北。）

2. 形容詞 **enough** 可置於名詞的前後來修飾它。（參照 p.170）

I have ⎰ *enough* money ⎱ to buy a car.（我有足夠的錢買部車。）
　　　⎱ money *enough* ⎰

(III) 同種類的形容詞之排列

兩個以上的同類形容詞並列，用以修飾同一個名詞時，**通常按照字的長短，將較短的形容詞放在較長的形容詞之前**，但有時也按形容詞與所修飾的名詞之關係，**將關係較密切者放在最接近名詞的地方。此時可將各字用逗點或連接詞 "and" 連接起來。**

He is a *tall*, *strong*, and *intelligent* boy.（他是一位既高且強壯，而且又聰明的男孩。）

He was a *learned*, *valiant* and *much-loved* king.

（他是一位既有學問又英勇，而且受人民愛戴的國王。）

> 【註】**如果幾個形容詞關係很密切就去掉逗點或 and。**
> It is a *short black silk* coat.（那是一件短的黑色絲質大衣。）
> I will take *those first three honest young* fellows.
> （我願意錄取那前三位誠實的年輕人。）
> The *lame and blind old* man was led by a *pretty little* girl.
> （那個跛腳又瞎眼的老人由一位漂亮的小女孩帶路。）
> It is an *easy and interesting French* novel.（那是一本易懂而又有趣的法國小說。）

(IV) 不同種類的形容詞之排列順序

兩個以上屬於不同種類的形容詞用來修飾同一名詞時，其排列順序大致如下：

> 代名形容詞 + 數量形容詞 + 性狀形容詞 + 名詞

<u>Those</u> <u>five</u> <u>fine</u> <u>old</u> <u>red</u> <u>dilapidated</u> <u>brick</u> houses are unsafe.

（那五棟美麗的荒廢的紅磚舊房子是不安全的。）

再細分如下：

I		II		III						
代 名 形 容 詞		數量形容詞		性 狀 形 容 詞						
1	2	3	4	5	6	7	8	9	10	11
前置冠詞的形容詞（放在冠詞前的形容詞）	冠　詞指示形容詞所有形容詞不定形容詞	序 數	基 數	性質狀態形容詞	大小長短形狀	新舊溫度	顏色	國　籍	材料	名詞動名詞
all both such what ⋮	the, a(n), your, Tom's, this, that, those, another, some, any, ⋮	first second third fourth fifth next last ⋮	one two three four five many few ⋮	kind fine good sick ⋮	large small big long short round ⋮	old new young cool hot ⋮	red blue white green ⋮	Chinese English Japanese American ⋮	iron brick stone silk ⋮	boy house book vase fishing ⋮

舉例：

⑵ the ⑶ first ⑷ two children（頭兩個孩子）

⑵ the ⑶ last ⑸ important ⑹ big meeting（最後一個重要的大型會議）

⑵ those ⑸ very interesting ⑺ medieval castles（那些很有趣的中世紀的城堡）

⑵ that ⑸ very well-mannered ⑺ young child（那個很有禮貌的年齡很小的小孩）

⑵ that ⑺ warm ⑻ red ⑽ silk dress（那件暖和的紅色絲質洋裝）

⑵ my ⑺ oldest ⑻ gray ⑽ tweed suit（我最舊的灰色粗花呢的西裝）

⑵ a ⑺ freezing ⑼ New England winter（一個冰冷的新英格蘭冬天）

⑵ the ⑸ best ⑺ modern ⑼ American music（最好的現代美國音樂）

⑷ many ⑸ interesting ⑺ old ⑾ history books（很多有趣的舊歷史書籍）

⑷ very few ⑸ beautiful ⑺ old ⑼ Chinese vases（很少的漂亮的中國古花瓶）

⑴ all ⑵ the ⑷ six ⑸ strong ⑺ young ⑼ American ⑾ boy students
（所有六個年輕力壯的美國男學生）

⑵ the ⑶ first ⑷ two ⑸ fine ⑹ big ⑺ old ⑻ red ⑼ Jamaican ⑽ stone ⑾ plantation houses
（頭兩棟漂亮的大的舊牙買加的紅石頭農場房子）

【註 1】 如 **gold watch**（金錶），**boy scout**（童子軍）等（名詞＋名詞）時，中間不可插入其他修飾語。

【註 2】 形容詞前有 **so, as, too, how, however, no more, no less** 等修飾時，則把 **a(n)** 放在形容詞後。
No more ridiculous a thing has ever happened here.
（這裡不曾發生比這更荒謬的事。）

II. **敘述用法（Predicative Use）**：形容詞如用作補語而間接地修飾（代）名詞，稱爲敘述用法。

(I) **做主詞補語的用法：**

It is *nice and warm* today.（今天天氣好又暖和。）

The rose is *beautiful* and smells *sweet*.（玫瑰花漂亮而且聞起來又香。）

【比較】　　限 定 用 法　　　　　　　敘 述 用 法

John is an **honest** man.　　　John is *honest*.

She is a **happy** woman.　　　She is *happy*.

【注意】下面是一些省略的用法：

> Tom came home very *tired*.（湯姆回家時很疲倦。）
> = Tom was very tired when he came home.
>
> She married *young*.（她很年輕就結婚。）
> = When she got married, she was young.
>
> I came back from each of my journeys *a little different*.
> = Every time I came back from my journey, I felt a little different.
> （每次我旅行回來，總覺得有些不同。）

(II) **做受詞補語的用法：**

I found the book *difficult*.（我覺得這本書很難。）

I saw a dog *sleeping* by the door.（我看到一隻狗在門旁睡覺。）

(III) **獨立片語的用法：**是補述用法的形容詞子句省略關代和 be 動詞而來的。（參照 p.160）
Contrary to our expectation, he was born of a poor family.
（出乎我們意料的是，他出身於貧寒家庭。）
Effective on the first of July, the library will close at 7 p.m.
（七月一日生效，本圖書館下午七時關閉。）

(IV) **下列是只能做敘述用法而不能做限定用法的形容詞：**

afraid（害怕的）	alike（相像的）	alive（活的）
alone（單獨的）	asleep（睡著的）	ashamed（慚愧的）
awake（醒著的）	aware（知道的）	content（滿足的）
drunk（喝醉的）	ill（生病的）	liable（易遭受…的）
subject（易於）	sunk（沉沒的）	sure（確定的）
unable（不能的）	well（健康的）	worth（值得的）

※ 通常 a 字母開頭的字，只能做敘述用法的形容詞，如 afraid, awake, alike 等。

> I'm *afraid* to die.（我怕死。）
> I'm *afraid* of the dog.（我怕狗。）
> I'm *afraid* that he will not come.（我怕他不來。）

Both Tom and John are *alike* in many ways.（湯姆和約翰有很多地方很像。）

He lives *alone* in the country.（他單獨住在鄉下。）

> The baby fell fast *asleep*.（這嬰兒熟睡了。）
> She felt *sleepy*.（她覺得很想睡。）

He's *ashamed* at being *unable* to answer the question.（他因無法回答問題而感到慚愧。）

He was *ill* last week.（他上週生病了。）

【註1】 I caught the fish *alive*.（我活捉了那條魚。） **alive 是限定形容詞**，但我們也可以解釋成是敘述用法的形容詞，理由是我們可把 I caught the fish alive. 變成 I caught the fish which is *alive*. 像這樣的字還有 **asleep, alone**…。

【註2】 只可做敘述用法而不可做限定用法的形容詞之前不可用 *very*，要用 much, very much 或其他的副詞。

錯　誤	正　確
very alike	(very) much alike
very awake	wide awake
very asleep	fast (*or* sound) asleep
very drunk	dead (*or* blind) drunk

【註3】 有些形容詞雖有限定、敘述兩種用法，但意思各不相同。

- the **present** king（現在的國王）【限定用法】
- The king was *present*.（國王有出席。）【敘述用法】
- the **late** Mr. Smith（已故的史密斯先生）【限定用法】
- I was *late* for school.（我上學遲到。）【敘述用法】
- a **certain** American（某一位美國人）【限定用法】
- It is *certain* that he will succeed.（他一定會成功。）【敘述用法】
- **ill** news（壞消息）【限定用法】
- She is *ill*.（她生病了。）【敘述用法】

ill 在敘述用法時意思是「有病的；生病的」，而在限定用法時意思是「壞的；邪惡的」。因此，「生病的男孩」不可寫成 *an ill boy*，須用 sick 代替 ill，寫成 **a sick boy**。

III. 將形容詞轉成名詞的用法：

(I) 國名的形容詞做國語的名稱和國民的統稱的用法：

像 the Chinese, the Japanese…在第二章裡的專有形容詞一節已有詳述，此地從略。

（參照 p.184, 185）

(II) **the + 形容詞**（含用作形容詞的現在分詞、過去分詞等）**= 名詞**，可分為下列四種：

（參照 p.104）

1. **作為複數普通名詞**表示「…人們」。

The rich（= Rich people）sometimes envy the happiness of *the poor*（= poor people）.（有錢人有時也羨慕窮人的快樂。）

The learned are apt to despise *the ignorant*.（有學問的人往往會輕視無知的人。）

The plain was covered with *the dead* and *the dying*.（平原上佈滿了已死或將死的人。）

【註】 **成對使用時可省略冠詞：**

Rich and poor, *young and old* were gathered there.

（不論貧富、老少，全都聚在那裡。）

其他例子：

the brave, the (wise, foolish, idle, diligent, deaf, blind, dumb, lame, living, missing, strong, weak, sick, wounded), etc.

2. **作為單數普通名詞**表示「人」。

The deceased had made a will.（死者已立下遺囑。）

The accused was acquitted of the charge.（被告已被宣告無罪釋放。）

其他例子：

the condemned（死刑犯），the employed（受雇者），the beloved（心愛的人），

the assured（被保險人），the Almighty（萬能之神；上帝）= God, etc.

3. **作抽象名詞用**：

There is but one step from *the sublime*（= sublimity）to *the ridiculous*

（= ridiculousness）.（高尚和荒謬相去只一步。）

The beautiful（= Beauty）is not always the good, and *the good*（= goodness）is

not always *the true*（= truth）.（美不一定是善，善不一定是眞。）

4. **用以表現一部分時**：

the white of the eye（白眼球）　　　*the yellow* of an egg（蛋黃）

the middle of the river（河流中部）　*the thick* of the forest（森林密處）

(III) **成為正式名詞而有複數和所有格等變化的形容詞**

a white（白人），a native（當地人），a noble（貴族），a lunatic（瘋子），

a criminal（罪人）等。

常取複數形的：

the ancients（古人），the moderns（現代人），eatables（= edibles）（可吃的東西），

valuables（貴重的東西），daily necessaries（日用品），chemicals（化學藥品）等。

(IV) **有些形容詞可做動詞或介詞的受詞**

It will not take long.（時間不會太久的。）

at large（逍遙法外）　　in full（詳細地）　　　of old（從前）

in short（簡言之）　　　in general（一般而言）　in vain（徒勞無功）

for certain（確定地）　　in particular（特別地）　before long（不久）

like mad（瘋狂地）　　　of late（最近）

IV. 有些形容詞可轉變成副詞的用法：

(I) **加強語氣：修飾其他的形容詞，本身卻失去原來的意義。**

The night was *bitter*（= *bitterly*）cold.（晚上非常寒冷。）

The stove was *red* hot.（火爐是熾熱的。）

He came home *dead* tired.（他回到家來，累得要死。）

其他例子：

sound asleep（熟睡），dead sure（鐵定），awful sick（病得嚴重），

a real good time（好時光）

(II) **修飾全句：**

sure enough = certainly ; in fact（確實地）

I said it would happen, and **sure enough** it did happen.

（我說它會發生，而它確實眞的發生了。）

V. **形容詞做準介詞的用法**：worth, like, near, opposite 這四個形容詞有介詞性質，和介詞一樣，常接有受詞。

Our house is **near** the lake.（我們家靠近那個湖。）

We stayed in the hotel **nearest** the station.（我們住在最靠近車站的一家旅館中。）

The picture is quite **like** him.（這張照片跟他很像。）

This book is **worth** reading.（這本書值得一讀。）

The building **opposite** the church is a high school.（教堂對面的建築物是一所中學。）

VI. **非人稱形容詞和人稱形容詞**：非人稱形容詞（**Impersonal Adjective**）不能用來修飾人，只能修飾事物；人稱形容詞（**Personal Adjective**）才可修飾人。（一般形容詞可修飾人或事物）

We are necessary to do this.【誤】【necessary 屬於非人稱形容詞，不能用來修飾人】

It is necessary for us to do this.【正】（我們做這件事是必要的。）

1. **常用的非人稱形容詞：**（限於括弧內的意思）

wonderful（很棒的）	boresome（令人厭煩的）	convenient（方便的）
dangerous（危險的）	delightful（令人愉快的）	difficult（困難的）
disagreeable（不同意的）	easy（容易的）	frightful（可怕的）
hard（堅硬的；困難的）	harmful（有害的）	healthful（有益健康的）
impossible（不可能的）	necessary（需要的）	painful（痛苦的）
possible（可能的）	shameful（可恥的）	tiresome（令人厭倦的）
satisfactory（令人滿意的）	troublesome（麻煩的）	useful（有用的）
boring（令人厭煩的）	amusing（令人覺得好玩的）	amazing（令人驚訝的）
confusing（令人困惑的）	convincing（令人信服的）	interesting（有趣的）
surprising（令人驚訝的）	exciting（令人興奮的）	

2. **常用的人稱形容詞：**

free（自由的）	healthy（健康的）	wonder-struck（深感驚訝的）
troubled（困擾的）	surprised（感到驚訝的）	amused（感到有趣的）
amazed（感到驚訝的）	convinced（相信的）	confused（感到困惑的）
bored（感到無聊的）	delighted（感到愉快的）	frightened（受到驚嚇的）
harmed（受傷害的）	interested（感興趣的）	ashamed（慚愧的）
tired（疲倦的）	satisfied（滿意的）	excited（興奮的）

VII. Be + 形容詞 + 介詞 = 及物動詞

be fond of = like（喜歡），be afraid of = fear（害怕），be ignorant of = don't know（不知道），be aware of = realize（了解），be expressive of = show（顯示），be sure of = believe（確信）

I **am fond of**（= like）classical music.（我喜歡古典音樂。）

He **is aware of**（= realizes）his own intelligence.（他知道他自己很聰明。）

第四章 形容詞的比較

I. 形容詞的等級及不可比較的形容詞

(I) 爲表現性質的程度，形容詞可以做比較；比較分三級：

1. 原級（**Positive Degree**）：不與其他的事物比較的原級形容詞。
   The lion is **strong**.（獅子很強壯。）
   This flower is **beautiful**.（這朵花很美麗。）

2. 比較級（**Comparative Degree**）：表現二者中的一個比其他一個在程度上更進一層。
   The lion is **stronger** than the tiger.（獅子比老虎強。）
   This flower is **more beautiful** than that.（這朵花比那朵花好看。）

3. 最高級（**Superlative Degree**）：表現三個以上的事物在程度上最高的一個。
   The lion is **the strongest** of all animals.（獅子是所有動物中最強的。）
   This is **the most beautiful** flower I ever saw.（這是我所見過的花當中最美麗的。）

(II) 有些沒有比較級的形容詞：（因本身程度就達到極限）

1. 表「**絕對、完整**」等：absolute, full, empty, whole, entire, complete, certain,…
2. 表「**最佳、獨特**」等：supreme, perfect, excellent, unique, only, universal, ideal,…
3. 表「**主要、基本**」等：chief, main, fundamental, essential, basic,…
4. 表「**生、死**」等：mortal, living, dead, fatal, immortal,…
5. 表「**形態**」：circular, round, square（方的）, flat,…
6. 表「**時間**」：weekly, temporary, permanent, eternal, perpetual, everlasting,…
7. 表「**物質**」：golden, silk, woolen,…

II. 形容詞比較級和最高級的構成

(I) 規則變化：

1. **單音節的字在字尾加 er 及 est。**

（原級）	（比較級）	（最高級）
old	older	oldest
kind	kinder	kindest
tall	taller	tallest
young	younger	youngest

   【注意】false（錯的；假的），just（公正的），wrong（錯誤的），real（真的），雖爲單音節，通常加 more, most。

2. **單音節的字其最後字母爲 e 時，只加 r 及 st。**

free	freer	freest
fine	finer	finest
wise	wiser	wisest
large	larger	largest

3. **單音節的字其最後一個字母爲子音而其前又爲短母音時，便重複這字尾的子音字母，然後再加 er, est。**

big	bigger	biggest
hot	hotter	hottest
fat	fatter	fattest

thin	thinner	thinnest
thick	*thicker*	*thickest*

4. 二音節的字如發音方便的話，也加 er, est，尤其字尾爲 er, ow, ple, ble 等時，但也有例外，例如：**clever** 的比較級爲 **cleverer**，但 **proper** 的比較級卻爲 **more proper**。

narrow	narrower	narrowest
sober	soberer	soberest
simple	simpler	simplest
gentle	gentler	gentlest

5. 單音節及二音節的字尾爲子音 + y 時，先將 y 變成 i 再加 er, est。

dry	drier	driest
angry	angrier	angriest
merry	merrier	merriest
early	earlier	earliest
ugly	uglier	ugliest
lovely	lovelier	loveliest
heavy	heavier	heaviest
easy	easier	easiest
happy	happier	happiest
healthy	healthier	healthiest
*shy	shier / *shyer*	shiest / *shyest*
*sly	slier / *slyer*	sliest / *slyest*

※ 但字尾爲母音加 y 時 y 不變，直接加 er, est。

gay	gayer	gayest
gray / grey（灰色）	grayer / greyer	grayest / greyest

6. 二音節字中特別由 **ful**, **less**, **able**, **ous**, **ive**, **ing** 等結尾的字，及三音節以上的字，通常加 **more**, **most** 在原級的前面。

beautiful	more beautiful	most beautiful
laughable	more laughable	most laughable
useless	more useless	most useless
famous	more famous	most famous
active	more active	most active
interesting	more interesting	most interesting
diligent	more diligent	most diligent
leisurely	more leisurely	most leisurely
satisfactory	more satisfactory	most satisfactory
difficult	more difficult	most difficult

【註1】 **trustworthy**（值得信任的）**雖爲三音節，但卻加 er, est。**

trustworthy	trustworthier	trustworthiest

【註2】 有些形容詞既可以在字尾加 er, est，又可在前面加 more, most 來做比較級與最高級：

pleasant	pleasanter / more pleasant	pleasantest / most pleasant
common	commoner / more common	commonest / most common
polite	politer / more polite	politest / most polite
handsome	handsomer / more handsome	handsomest / most handsome

【註3】 原爲加 er, est 變成比較級與最高級的二音節形容詞，**增加了否定的字首（如 un-）**後，雖然變成了三個音節，**其比較級與最高級依然是在字尾加 er, est。**

happy	happier	happiest
unhappy	unhappier	unhappiest
easy	easier	easiest
uneasy	uneasier	uneasiest

【註4】 上述均爲優等比較；至於**劣等比較，是在一切原級形容詞之前加 less, least 而造成**比較級與最高級。

kind	優等：kinder	kindest
	劣等：less kind	least kind
useful	優等：more useful	most useful
	劣等：less useful	least useful

優等：She is **taller** than you.（她比你高。）
劣等：You are **less tall** than she.（你沒有她高。）

優等：He is **more diligent** than his brother.（他比他哥哥用功。）
劣等：His brother is **less diligent** than he.（他哥哥沒有他用功。）

7. 一些複合形容詞的比較：

bad-tempered	worse-tempered	worst-tempered
cold-blooded	more cold-blooded	most cold-blooded
fine-looking	finer-looking	finest-looking
good-hearted	better-hearted	best-hearted
well-known	better-known	best-known
hard-working	harder-working	hardest-working

(II) **不規則變化：**

1. **不規則的字例：**

good / well	better	best

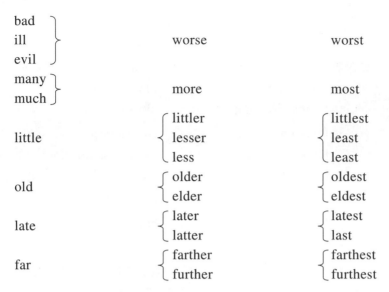

bad		
ill	worse	worst
evil		
many	more	most
much		
little	littler / lesser / less	littlest / least / least
old	older / elder	oldest / eldest
late	later / latter	latest / last
far	farther / further	farthest / furthest

2. **一些不規則變化的形容詞之正確用法：**

⑴ **good, bad; well, ill**

good 的反義字為 bad，well 的反義字為 ill。

Don't be a **bad** boy. Try to be a **good** boy. (不要做壞孩子。要做好孩子。)

Is he **well**? (他身體好嗎？) ＊well 作「健康的」解，只能做敘述用法形容詞，不能直接修飾名詞。

He has been **ill** since a few days ago. (幾天前他就生病了。)

But he is a little **better** today. (但他今天好一點了。)

⑵ **elder, eldest; older, oldest**

> elder, eldest 是用來表示家族關係的**長幼順序，只做限定用法。**
>
> older, oldest 表示年齡的比較、事物的新舊，限定用法、敘述用法均可。
>
> My **elder** brother is three years **older** than your younger sister.
>
> (我哥哥比你妹妹大三歲。)
>
> His **eldest** son is the **oldest** student in our school. (他的大兒子是我們學校最年長的學生。)
>
> My coat is **older** than yours. (我的外套比你的舊。)
>
> 【註】美語中亦有用 older (oldest) brother (sister,…) 代替 elder (eldest) brother (sister,…)。

⑶ **later, latest; latter, last**

later, latest 指**時間**的先後；latter, last 指**順序**的先後。

She came **later** than usual. (她比平常晚來。)【時間】

This station will give you the **latest** news. (本台將提供您最新的消息。)【時間】

He will be free in the **latter** part of the week. (他本週的下半週有空。)【順序】

His **latest** book may be his **last** one. (他最新的書可能是他最後的一本書了。)【順序】

其他例子：

a **later** edition (較近的版本)

the **latest** Paris style (最新的巴黎款式)

the former and the **latter** (前者與後者)

the first and the **last** (最先與最後)

one's **latest** work（某人最新的作品）

one's **last** work（某人最後的作品）

【注意】 the last ＋ 名詞（最不可能的…；最不願意的…）【後面須接不定詞（片語）或形容詞子句，參照 p.664】

He is **the last** person that I want to see.

（他是我最不想看見的人。）不可譯成「他是我想見的最後的人。」

⑷ **farther**, **farthest**; **further**, **furthest**

farther, farthest 原則上是指「距離」或「時間」的比較，表「**更遠**」；further, furthest 指「程度」表「**更進一步**」；實際上在口語中，兩者常相互通用，且後者有代替前者的趨勢。

Kaohsiung is **farther** from Taipei than Keelung.（從台北到高雄比到基隆遠。）

The **farthest** planet from the earth is Pluto.（離地球最遠的行星是冥王星。）

I have nothing **further** to say on the subject.（對該主題我沒有什麼要說的了。）

Have you any **further** need of me?（你還有要我幫忙的嗎？）

⑸ **little-less-least** 是關於量的，是 **much-more-most** 的相反字；**little-littler-littlest** 表示大小時，就等於 **small-smaller-smallest**；*little-lesser-least* 很少使用，現在的用法相當於 minor（次要的）。

例如：lesser nation（次要的國家），lesser writer（二流作家）。

⑹ **nearest**, **next**

nearest 指「距離」，next 指「位置」。

Which is the **nearest** road to the station?（去車站最近的路是哪一條？）【距離】

His seat is **next** to mine.（他的座位在我的隔壁。）【位置】

⑺ **last**, **next**

last 放在表時間的名詞之前時，表「過去」，它的意思是「昨」、「上」、「去」；next 放在表時間的名詞之前時，表「未來」，它的意思是「第二（天）」、「下（月）」、「明（年）」。

last evening（昨晚），last week（上週），last year（去年）。

next week（下週），next year（明年）。

【注意】「昨天早晨」非 last morning，而是 yesterday morning。

【註 1】 last, next 放在表時間的名詞之前時，其間的 on, in 須省略。

He fell ill
{
on **Sunday last**. 【正】
last Sunday. 【正】（他上星期日生病了。）
on last Sunday. 【誤】
}

【註 2】 next Sunday 是從現在算起的「下一個星期日」，the next 是從過去某時算起的「次一個星期日」；二者區別與 tomorrow（明天），the next day（第二天）的區別一樣。

{
He said, "I will leave Taipei **next** Sunday."
He said he would leave Taipei *the next* Sunday.
}

III. 形容詞的比較方式

(I) 二人或二物相比的結果可能有 **1.** 相等、**2.** 超過、**3.** 不如，三種。

1. 相等

(1) …as + 原級 + as…

She is **as** beautiful **as** her mother (*is*).（她和她的母親一樣漂亮。）

I am **as** interested in English **as** you (*are*).（我對英文和你一樣有興趣。）

(2) …as + 原級 + 名詞 + as…

She has **as** much money **as** I (*have*).（她有和我同樣多的錢。）

【註】 如果變成否定句，第一個 as 可改爲 so。

She is **not so** beautiful **as** her mother.（她不像她母親那樣漂亮。）

【注意】 **not so much as = not even**（連…都不）

He can **not so much as** spell his own name.（他連自己的名字都拼不出來。）

= He can **not even** spell his own name.

(3) 複數形主詞 + 連綴動詞 + { the same / similar / alike / different

These books	**are**	**the same**.（一樣）
These two chairs	**look**	**similar**.（相似）
These two brothers	**seem**	**alike**.（相像）
Those buildings	⋮	**different**.（不同）

(4) 單數形主詞 + 連綴動詞 + { the same as / similar to / like / different from } + （代）名詞

This book		**the same as**	that one.
This chair	**is**	**similar to**	that one.
This man		**like**	his brother (*or* that one).
This building		**different from**	that building (*or* that one).

2. 超過 —— 優等比較

(1) …比較級 + than…

John is **taller than** Jack.（約翰比傑克高。）

Health is **more important than** wealth.（健康比財富更重要。）

It is **colder** this year **than** (*it was*) last year.（今年比去年冷。）

【注意 1】 I am taller than *him*. 是非正式用法（此時 than 被視爲介詞）。正式用法爲 I am taller than **he** (*is*). 但有時 than 後亦可用受格的 him，不過意義不同，如：

I like you better than **he** (*likes you*).（我喜歡你甚於他喜歡你。）【主格】

I like you better than (*I like*) **him**.（我喜歡你甚於我喜歡他。）【受格】

第二人稱的 you 是主、受格同形，因此主格時後面加 do 以便判別。

I love her better than **you do**.（我愛她甚於<u>你愛她</u>。）【主格】

I love her better than **you**.（我愛她甚於<u>我愛你</u>。）【受格】

【注意 2】 不可弄錯比較對象，如「台灣的氣候比日本的氣候更熱。」如何譯成英文？

The climate of Taiwan is hotter *than Japan*.【誤】

> The climate of Taiwan is hotter than **that of** Japan.【正】
> 不可將台灣的氣候與日本本身比較，應是氣候與氣候的比較才是，故 Japan 前應加 that of，that 是 the climate 的代名詞。

【註 1】 有時用 **of the two** 代替 than，不過要在比較級前加 **the**。

Which is the more useful (*metal*), iron or gold?（鐵和金，哪一個是比較有用的？）

Iron is **the more useful** (*metal*) **of the two**.（鐵是兩者中比較有用的。）

Iron is a more useful metal than gold.（鐵是比金更有用的金屬。）

Iron is more useful than gold.（鐵比金更有用。）

【註 2】 比較級上可以附加表示優劣程度或差別的字眼，像 much (*or* far), a great deal, a little，以及數詞等。

This is much (*or* far) bigger than that.（這個遠比那個大。）

This is a great deal better than that.（這個比那個好多了。）

This is by far the better of the two.（這個是那兩個中較好的一個。）

He is a little taller than I.（他比我高一點。）

He is three years older than I.（他大我三歲。）

= He is older than I by three years.

※ 原級之前不可用 **much**，要用 **very**；比較級之前不能用 **very**，要用 **much** 或 **far**…等。

Gold is very valuable, but iron is much more useful (*than gold*).（參照 p.251）

（金是很貴重的，但鐵比金有用多了。）

【註 3】 …more～than…（與其説…不如説…）

同一人或物，比較其兩種性質或狀態時，不管形容詞是單音節或多音節，一律用 more～than 表示之。

He is wiser than you.（他比你更聰明。）

是 He 和 you 二人比較同一性質 wise 的程度，這是一般常見的句子，wise 的比較級用 wiser 不可用 more wise。

> 但如果說，「<u>與其說他誠實不如說親切</u>。」這時所比較的是同一人的二種不同性質「誠實」和「親切」的程度，譯成英文應為：
> He is **more** kind **than** honest.【正】
> He is *kinder than honest*.【誤】
> { She is **more** wise **than** diligent.（<u>與其說她勤勉不如說聰明</u>。）
> { = She is wise **rather than** diligent.

(2) 比較級 + and + 比較級 (越來越…)

She is growing **fatter and fatter**. (她變得越來越胖了。)

It is getting **colder and colder**. (天氣變得越來越冷了。)

(3) the + 比較級…, the + 比較級… (越…，就越…)

The more he has, **the more** he wants. (他擁有的越多，想要的就越多。)

The more he reads, **the less** he understands. (他越讀越不明白。)

The older we grow, **the poorer** our memory will become.

(我們年齡越大，記憶力就越差。)

(4) all (*or* so much) the + 比較級形容詞或副詞 (更加；反而)

He is **all the happier** for his poverty. (他因貧窮而更加快樂。)

He likes her **all the better** for her freckles. (他因她的雀斑而更喜歡她。)

I like him **all the more** because he has a few faults.

(我因為他有一些缺點而更喜歡他。)

(5) none the + 比較級 (沒有更；並不更)

＊none (在 the + 比較級, too, so 前) = not at all (參照 p.135)

I am **none the worse** for a single failure. (我並沒有因一次的失敗而更糟。)

He is **none the happier** for his wealth. (他並不因財富而更愉快。)

You have faults, but I love you **none the less** (= all the same) .

(你雖然有缺點，但我依然愛你。)

3. 不及 —— 劣等比較

(1) …less + 原級 + than… (= not so + 原級 + as…)

Helen is **less busy than** Mary. (海倫沒有瑪麗忙。)

= *Helen is not so busy as Mary*. (= 海倫不像瑪麗那樣忙。)

You are **less careful than** he. (你比他不細心。)

= *You are not so careful as he*. (= 你不像他那樣細心。)

(2) ┌ no more than = only (只)
　　└ not more than = at most (最多)

He is **no more than** a puppet. (他<u>只</u>是個傀儡罷了。)

I have **no more than** ten dollars in my pocket. (我口袋裡<u>只</u>有十塊錢。)

I have **not more than** ten dollars in my pocket. (我口袋裡<u>最多</u>也<u>不過</u>十塊錢。)

(3) ┌ no more…than = not…any more than (和…一樣不…)
　　└ not more…than = not so…as (沒有到…的程度；不像…那樣…)

He is **no more** generous **than** John. (他<u>和</u>約翰<u>一樣不</u>大方。)

= *He is **not** generous **any more than** John*.

He is **no more** a fool **than** John. (他<u>和</u>約翰<u>一樣不</u>是傻瓜。)

= *He is **not** a fool **any more than** John*.

He is **not more** generous **than** John. (他<u>沒有</u>約翰大方。)

= *He is **not so** generous **as** John*. (= 他<u>不像</u>約翰<u>那麼</u>大方。)

She is **not** cleverer **than** her sister. (她<u>沒有</u>她姐姐<u>那樣</u>聰明。)

= *She is **not so** clever **as** her sister*.

(4) $\left\{\begin{array}{l}\text{no less than = as much (}or\text{ many) as（多達；…那樣多）}\\ \text{not less than = at least（最少）}\end{array}\right.$

$\left\{\begin{array}{l}\text{He has \textbf{no less than} five children.（他有五個孩子之多。）}\\ = He\ has\ \textbf{\textit{as many as}}\ five\ children.\end{array}\right.$

He has **no less than** five children. （他有五個孩子之多。）
= *He has **as many as** five children.*

He stayed in Taipei **no less than** ten days. （他在台北停留了十天之久。）
= *He stayed in Taipei **as long as** ten days.*

He has **not less than** five children. （他至少有五個孩子。）
= *He has **at least** five children.*

He stayed in Taipei **not less than** ten days. （他在台北至少停留了十天。）
= *He stayed in Taipei **at least** ten days.*

(5) $\left\{\begin{array}{l}\text{no less…than = as…as（和…一樣）}\\ \text{not less + 原級 + than = perhaps + 比較級 + than（至少不比…差；也許比…更…）}\end{array}\right.$

He is **no less** busy **than** a bee. （他像蜜蜂一樣的忙。）
= *He is as busy as a bee.*

He is **not less** busy **than** his elder brother. （他也許比他哥哥更忙些。）
= *He is perhaps busier than his elder brother.*

【注意】牢記 no（在比較級前）= not at all 便可分辨上述各項用法。

4. 含有比較級的幾個慣用語：

He will succeed **sooner or later**. （他遲早會成功的。）

Men are **more or less** selfish. （人多少有些自私。）

It was **none other than** Smith. （那就是史密斯自己。）

He knows German, **much more** English. （他懂德文，英文更不用說了。）

He does not know English, **much less** German. （他不懂英文，德文更不必說了。）

There is **no more**. （沒有剩的了。） = *There is none left.*

He is very ill; I am afraid he will soon be **no more**. （他病得很重；恐怕他很快就要死了。）

Say it **once more** (= *once again*). （再說一遍。）

The doctor has advised him to give up smoking **more than once**.
（醫生不只一次地勸他戒煙。）

5. 不用比較級形容詞的比較：

(1) He *is* four months *senior to* me. （他比我大四個月。）

= *He is older than I by four months.*

= I *am* four months *junior to* him. （我比他小四個月。）

= *I am younger than him by four months.*

【註】**senior** 和 **junior** 也可作名詞用，例如：

He is my *senior* by four months. （他大我四個月。）

I am his *junior* by four months. （我小他四個月。）

(2) He is *superior to* me (= *better than I*) in English. （他的英文比我好。）

= I am *inferior to* him (= *worse than he*) in English. （我的英文不如他。）

(3) This *was* an event *anterior* (or *prior*) *to* (= *earlier than*) World War II.
（這是第二次世界大戰以前的事。）

The event *was posterior to* (= *later than*) his death. （這件事發生在他死後。）

⑷ prefer to + 原形…rather than + 原形 = prefer + （動）名詞 + to + （動）名詞

I *prefer to* read *rather than* talk.（我寧願讀書也不願聊天。）

= I *prefer* reading *to* talking.

⑸ (be) preferable to（勝於…）

Silence is sometimes *preferable to* talk.（沉默有時勝過說話。）

Death is *preferable to* dishonor.（寧死而不受辱。）

(II) 三人或三物以上相比的結果即產生了一個最高級；其表達方式如下：

1. 用最高級形容詞表示最高級：

⑴ **優等比較**（最…）

①
$$\cdots\text{the} + 最高級（+ 單數名詞或 one）+ \begin{cases} \text{of (}or\text{ among)} + 人或物（複數） \\ \text{in} + 場所（單數） \end{cases}$$

Iron is *the most useful* $\begin{cases} of \\ among \end{cases}$ all metals.（鐵是一切金屬中最有用的。）

He is *the youngest boy* $\begin{cases} of \\ among \end{cases}$ them.（他是其中年紀最小的男孩。）

The Yangtze Kiang is *the longest river in* China.

（長江是中國最長的河。）

②
$$\begin{cases} \cdots\text{the} + 最高級 + 單數名詞 \\ \cdots\text{one of} + \text{the} + 最高級 + 複數名詞 \end{cases} + \text{that}\cdots\text{(ever)}$$

He was *the greatest musician* that ever lived.（他是有史以來最偉大的音樂家。）

John is *the best tennis player* that we have in our school.

（約翰是我們學校最佳網球員。）

She is *the most beautiful girl* that I have *ever* seen.

（她是我所見過最美麗的女孩。）

He was *one of the greatest presidents* that we have had.

（他是我們最偉大的總統之一。）

③
$$\cdots\text{be} + \begin{cases} \text{one of} \\ \text{among} \end{cases} + \text{the} + 最高級 + 複數名詞（表若干最高級中之一）$$

She is *one of the most beautiful girls* in our school.

（她是我們學校最漂亮的女孩之一。）

Paris is *among the greatest cities* in the world.（巴黎是世界上最大的都市之一。）

（= Paris is *one of the greatest cities* in the world.）

比較下面兩句：

New York is *the greatest among* all cities in the world.

（紐約是全世界所有的都市中最大的。）

Rome is *among* (or *one of*) *the greatest cities* in the world.

（羅馬是全世界最大的都市之一。）

⑵ **劣等比較**（最不…）

$$\text{···the + least + 原級（+ 單數名詞或 one）} \begin{cases} \text{+ of (or among) + 人或物（複數）} \\ \text{+ in + 場所（單數）} \end{cases}$$

Grammar is *the least interesting of* (or among) all the subjects.

（文法是所有的科目中最無趣的。）

Jack is *the least diligent* boy *in* his class.（傑克是班上最不用功的男孩。）

2. **在下列的情形下，雖是最高級其前也不用 "the"。**

⑴ **最高級之前有所有格形容詞時。**

She is **my (John's)** youngest sister.〔她是我（約翰的）最小的妹妹。〕

⑵ **最高級副詞之前不用 the。**

I like apples **best** of all fruits.（所有水果中，我最喜歡蘋果。）

【比較】　This is **the best** of all.（這是所有當中最好的。）

⑶ **most 若作「大部分」或「大多數」解時，則不用 the。**

Most people think so.（大部分的人都這麼想。）

Most learned men are modest.（大部分有學問的人都謙虛。）

【比較】　**The most** learned man（= *Even the most learned man*）among them could not

answer the question.（他們當中，即使是最有學問的人也答不出這個問題。）

本句的 most learned（最有學問的）是形容詞 learned 的最高級，所以要加 the。

⑷ **most = very 時，也不加 the。**（參照 p.262）

He is a **most**（= *very*）proud man.（他是個非常驕傲的人。）

I am **most**（= *very*）grateful to you.（我非常感激你。）

They are all **most**（= *very*）beautiful girls.（她們都是非常漂亮的女孩。）

⑸ **絕對最高級之前不加 the。**

所謂「絕對最高級」就是沒有明確的和其他人或物相比，而是用來加強「very + 原級」的
最高級。

This method is **simplest and easiest**.（這個方法最簡易不過了。）

= This method is **very simple and easy**.

He is **calmest** when he is all by himself.（他獨自一人時非常冷靜。）

= He is **very calm** when he is all by himself.

3. **很多情形可用原級和比較級表最高級而不影響其義。**

原　級：He is *as poor as* a church mouse.（他像教堂老鼠一樣窮。）【比喻他很窮】

比較級：A church mouse is *not poorer than* he.（教堂老鼠並不比他窮。）

比較級：Iron is *more valuable than* gold.（鐵比金更有價值。）

原　級：Gold is *not so valuable as* iron.（金不如鐵那樣有價值。）

原　級：Some grains are at least *as nutritious as* rice.

（一些穀類至少也像稻米一樣的有營養。）

比較級：Rice is *not more nutritious than* some other grains are.

（稻米並不比其他穀類更營養。）

最高級：Rice is *not the most nutritious* of all grains.

（稻米並不是所有穀類當中最有營養的。）

最高級：The Yangtze Kiang is *the longest* river in China.
（長江是中國最長的河流。）

比較級：The Yangtze Kiang is *longer than* any other river in China.
（長江比中國任何其他的河流都長。）

原　級：No other river in China is *as long as* the Yangtze Kiang.
（在中國沒有其他的河流像長江一樣長。）

最高級：Time is *the most precious of* all things.（時間是一切事物中最寶貴的。）

比較級：
Time is *more precious than*
any other thing (*or* anything else).
（時間比其他任何東西都可貴。）
all other things.

Nothing is *more precious than* time.（沒有東西比時間更可貴。）

原　級：Nothing is *so precious as* time.（沒有東西像時間這樣可貴。）

最高級：Taipei is *the largest* city in Taiwan.（台北是台灣最大的城市。）

比較級：Taipei is *larger than* any other city in Taiwan.（台北比台灣任何其他城市大。）

原　級：No other city in Taiwan is *so large as* Taipei.
（在台灣沒有別的城市像台北這樣大。）

4. **最高級形容詞的慣用語：**

⑴ at first（起初）
At first you may find it hard, but it will soon become easy.
（起初你可能覺得它難，但它很快就會變得容易了。）

⑵ at last（最後）
Here we are at our journey's end *at last*.（我們終於到了旅程的終點。）

⑶ at (the) latest（最遲）
I shall be back by Wednesday *at (the) latest*.（最遲我星期三就回來。）

⑷ at (the) most（最多）
I can pay only fifty dollars *at (the) most*.（我最多只能付五十元。）

⑸ at least（至少）
There were *at least* fifty people there.（那裡至少有五十個人。）

⑹ at best（充其量不過）
He is a second-rate actor *at best*.（他充其量只不過是個二流演員。）

⑺ at *one's* best（全盛時期）
The cherry-blossoms are *at their best*.（櫻花正在盛開著。）

⑻ do *one's* best（盡力）
I will *do my best* to help you.（我會盡力幫助你。）

⑼ for the most part（多半；大部分）
These animals are *for the most part* found in the desert.（這些動物多半出現在沙漠中。）

⑽ make the most (*or* best) of（善加利用）
You should try to *make the most of* your leisure time.（你應該善加利用空閒時間。）
He has a very small income, but he knows how to *make the best of* it.
（他收入微薄，但他知道如何善加使用。）

⑾ not in the least = not at all（一點也不）

He was ***not in the least*** injured.（他一點都沒受傷。）

⑿ at (the) worst（最壞也不過）

We shall lose ***at worst*** only a little money.（我們最壞也不過損失一些錢而已。）

IV. 常用於修飾各等級形容詞的副詞：

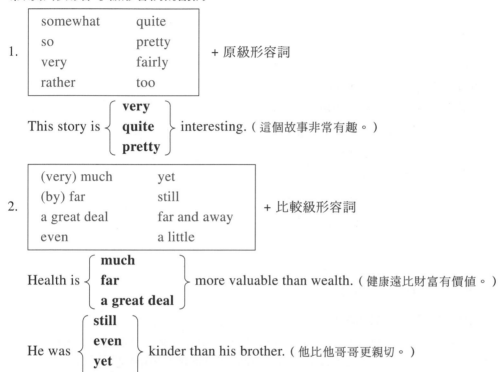

1.

somewhat	quite
so	pretty
very	fairly
rather	too

＋ 原級形容詞

This story is { **very** / **quite** / **pretty** } interesting.（這個故事非常有趣。）

2.

(very) much	yet
(by) far	still
a great deal	far and away
even	a little

＋ 比較級形容詞

Health is { **much** / **far** / **a great deal** } more valuable than wealth.（健康遠比財富有價值。）

He was { **still** / **even** / **yet** / **much** } kinder than his brother.（他比他哥哥更親切。）

This apple is **far and away** sweeter.（這個蘋果甜多了。）

3.

the very
much the
by far the
far and away the

＋ 最高級形容詞

Gold is { **the very** / **much the** / **by far the** / **far and away the** } most valuable of all metals.（金是所有金屬中最珍貴的。）

This is **the very** largest baseball diamond in the world.（這是世界上最大的棒球場。）

V. 有關比較級應注意事項：

1. **兩者之間的比較要用比較級，三者以上用最高級。**

Of the **two** brothers, he is **the cleverer** one.（他們兩兄弟當中，他是較聰明的一位。）

Of the **three** sisters, she is **the most** beautiful.（她們三姊妹中，她是最漂亮的。）

Tom had a **better** horse than Frank had.（湯姆的馬比法蘭克的馬好。）

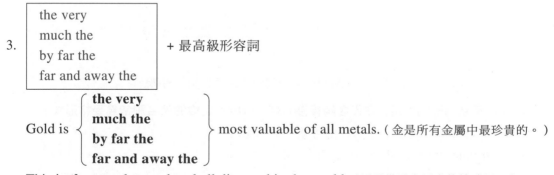

2. 使用比較級時，必須把本身除外，常與 other 或 else 連用。

This book is more interesting than $\left\{\begin{array}{l}\textbf{any other} \text{ book.}\\ \textbf{any} \text{ book } \textbf{else.}\end{array}\right.$ （這本書比<u>其他</u>任何的書都有趣。）

$\left\{\begin{array}{l}\text{He is more diligent than } \textit{any boy} \text{ in the class. 【誤】}\\ \text{He is more diligent than } \textbf{any other} \text{ boy in the class. 【正】}\\ \text{（他比班上}\underline{\text{任何其他}}\text{的男孩更勤勉。）}\end{array}\right.$

但當本身已除外，則不必再加 other 或 else。

$\left\{\begin{array}{l}\text{New York is larger than } \textit{any other} \text{ city in Asia. 【誤】} \text{【}\textit{紐約不在亞洲之內，當然不需加}\text{ other】}\\ \text{New York is larger than } \textbf{any} \text{ city in Asia. 【正】}\\ \text{New York is larger than } \textbf{any other} \text{ city in America. 【正】}\end{array}\right.$

$\left\{\begin{array}{l}\text{I am taller than } \textit{any other} \text{ boy in your class. 【誤】}\\ \text{I am taller than } \textbf{any} \text{ boy in your class. 【正】}\\ \text{I am taller than } \textbf{any other} \text{ boy in my class. 【正】}\end{array}\right.$

$\left\{\begin{array}{l}\text{I am the tallest boy in } \textit{your} \text{ class. 【誤】【句意不合理】}\\ \text{I am the tallest boy in } \textbf{my} \text{ class. 【正】}\end{array}\right.$

3. 比較級不可重複使用。

$\left\{\begin{array}{l}\text{He is } \textit{more} \text{ cleverer than you. 【誤】}\\ \text{He is } \textbf{cleverer} \text{ than you. 【正】}\end{array}\right.$

4. 句意相當或同類的東西才能比較。

$\left\{\begin{array}{l}\text{Most of the highways in America are wider } \textit{than Europe.} \text{ 【誤】【}\textit{公路不能和歐洲相比}\text{】}\\ \text{Most of the highways in America are wider than } \textbf{those} \text{ in Europe. 【正】}\\ \text{（美國大部分的公路都比歐洲的寬。）}\end{array}\right.$

$\left\{\begin{array}{l}\text{You are a little fatter } \textit{than I saw you last.} \text{ 【誤】【句意不合理】}\\ \text{You are a little fatter than (}\textit{you were}\text{) when I saw you last. 【正】}\\ \text{（你比我上次見到你時更胖一點。）}\end{array}\right.$

＊as 或 than 之後有副詞子句時，可將前面相同的主詞及動詞等省略。

5. **than 與不及物動詞連用，在代名詞後接 all 時，than 之後的代名詞常為受格形式。**

He is wiser than us all. （他比我們都聰明。）【不用 *we all*】

He is stronger than us all. （他比我們都強壯。）

6. **than 之後的主詞和動詞與前面相同時，可省略，但動詞片語中的介詞不可省**，以免其後的名詞（受格）被誤解為主格。

He has done better than (*he did*) last time. （他已經做得比上次好了。）

Some people think much more about their rights than (*they do*) *about* their duties.

（有些人考慮自己的權利，比考慮自己的義務多得多。）　　think

She was much more afraid of the teacher than (*she was afraid*) *of* the principal.

（她怕老師更甚於怕校長。）

第五章 容易錯用的形容詞

※ 表示最重要者

1. ｛ amiable 和藹可親的；好脾氣的
   ｛ amicable 友善的（= friendly）

2. ｛ ancient 古代的
   ｛ antiquated 落伍的

3. ｛ ashamed 慚愧的【通常指人】
   ｛ shameful 可恥的【通常指事物】
   ｛ shy 害羞的

4. ｛ asleep 睡著的【只可做敘述用法或放在被修飾的名詞之後】
   ｛ sleeping 睡著的【只可做限定用法】

5. ※ ｛ *bimonthly* ①兩個月一次的
   ②一個月兩次的
   semimonthly 半個月一次的；一個月兩次的

6. ｛ bored 覺得無聊的
   ｛ boresome 令人厭煩的
   ｛ boring 無聊的

7. ｛ big （體積）大 ↔ *little* 小的【指面積、體積、數量較尋常爲小，不含感情意味】
   ｛ large （面積）大 ↔ *small* 小的【指形狀小、數量少、微小、弱小等，含感情意味】
   ｛ great 大的；偉大的【數量、程度】↔ *small*, *little*
   ｛ lofty = noble, very high 高尚的

8. ｛ correct 正確的
   ｛ corrective 矯正的

9. ｛ clear 清楚的
   ｛ clean 乾淨的

10. ｛ cold 寒冷的
    ｛ cool 涼快的

11. ｛ colorful 多彩多姿的
    ｛ colored 彩色的

12. ｛ comic 喜劇的
    ｛ comical 滑稽的

13. ｛ comparable 可比較的
    ｛ comparative 比較上的

14. ｛ constructional 構造上的
    ｛ constructive 有建設性的

15. ｛ costly （合理的）昂貴的
    ｛ dear （不合理的）昂貴的

16. ｛ cultural 文化的
    ｛ cultured 有教養的

17. ｛ cheap 便宜的【品質不佳】
    ｛ inexpensive 不貴的【品質不低於其價格】

18. ｛ courageous 勇敢的
    ｛ encouraging 激勵的

19. ｛ contradictory 矛盾的
    ｛ contrary 相反的

20. ※ ｛ *credible* 可信的 ↔ *incredible* 不可置信的
    credulous 輕信的 ↔ *incredulous* 不輕信的
    creditable 值得讚揚的

21. ｛ ceremonious 拘泥形式的
    ｛ ceremonial 儀式上的

22. ｛ contemptuous 表示輕蔑的；傲慢的
    ｛ contemptible 卑劣的

23. ｛ childish 幼稚的【指不良的性質】
    ｛ childlike 天眞的【指可愛的性質】

24. ※ ｛ *continual* 不斷的【中間有稍歇的】
    continuous 不斷的【中間無停頓的】

25. ｛ complete 完全的【完全無缺的，指量而言】
    ｛ perfect 完美的【無缺點的，指質而言】
    ｛ thorough 完全的；徹底的

26. ｛ content 滿足的【只可做敘述用法】
    ｛ contented 滿足的【可做限定用法，亦可做敘述用法】

27. ｛ confused 感到困惑的【指人】
    ｛ confusing 令人困惑的【指物】

28. ※ ｛ *considerate* 體貼的
    considerable 相當大的

29. ｛ delicious 美味的
    ｛ delightful 令人愉快的

30. ｛ dangerous 危險的
    ｛ in danger 在危險中

31. ※ ｛ *dependent* 依賴的
    dependable 可信賴的；可靠的

32. { dead 死的
   deadly 致命的
   deathly 如死一般的

33. { decided 無疑的；確定的
   decisive 決定性的；果斷的

34. { dislike 不喜歡（*v.*）
   unlike 不像（*adj.*）

35. ※ { *disinterested* 公正無私的
   uninterested 不感興趣的；不關心的

36. { desirable 令人渴望的；想要的
   desirous （人）對事物渴望的

37. { different 不同的
   indifferent 漠不關心的

38. { economic 經濟上的
   economical 節儉的

39. { exceeding 非常的
   excessive 過度的

40. { eminent 有名的；卓越的
   imminent 逼近的

41. { endurable 可忍受的
   enduring 持久的

42. { empty 空無一物的
   vacant （有設備而無人佔用的）空的

43. { eventual 最後的；結果的
   eventful 多事的；多事故的

44. { exhausting 令人精疲力盡的
   exhausted 精疲力盡的
   exhaustive 徹底的；無遺漏的

45. { ex-(president) 前任的（總統）
   late (president) 已故的（總統）

46. { funny 好笑的
   queer 奇怪的

47. { favorable 有利的
   favorite 最喜愛的

48. { former 早先的；前任的
   formal 正式的

49. { foremost （品質上的）第一
   first （次序上的）第一

50. { forced 被迫的；強迫的
   forcible 強有力的；能說服的

51. { former （兩者中之）前的
   first-mentioned （三者以上中的）前的

52. { hard 困難的；堅硬的
   hardy 能吃苦耐勞的；耐寒的

53. ※ { *human* 人類的
   humane 人道的

54. ※ { *honorable* 值得尊敬的；高尚的
   honorary 名譽上的（不受薪的）

55. { healthful （氣候環境方面）有益健康的
   wholesome （食品等）有益健康的；衛生的
   well 健康的【只可做敘述用法】
   healthy 健康的【可做限定用法亦可做敘述用法】

56. { happy 快樂的；幸福的
   merry 愉快的；快樂的（充滿笑聲和歡樂的）
   lucky 幸運的

57. { homelike 像在家似的；舒適的；友好的
   homely 樸素的；醜的

58. { high 高的【指體積大，不能生長之物及程度性的高】↔ *low* 低的
   tall 高的【指生物及細高物體的】
   ↔ *short* 矮的

59. ※ { *industrious* 勤勉的
   industrial 工業上的

60. { imaginary 虛構的
   imaginative 富於想像力的
   imaginable 可想像的

61. ※ { *infectious* 傳染性的【指間接傳染的】
   contagious 傳染性的【指直接傳染的】

62. ※ { *invaluable* = *priceless* 無價的
   valueless = *worthless* 無價值的

63. { ill 生病的【不可做限定用法形容詞；當做限定用法形容詞時意思是「壞的」】
   sick 生病的
   sickly 多病的（樣子）

64. { intelligent 聰明的
   intelligible 可以理解的
   clever 聰明的（伶俐的；機靈的）
   wise 聰明的（賢明的；明智的）

65. { judicial　司法的
　　 { judicious　深思遠慮的；明智的

66. { loyal　忠誠的
　　 { royal　皇家的

67. { latest　最新的
　　 { last　最後的

68. { less　較少的；較小的【數量】
　　 { lesser　較少的；較小的【價值或重要性】

69. { lifelong　終生的
　　 { livelong　漫長的

70. { lovable　可愛的；惹人愛的 = loveable
　　 { lovely　（指外表上）美麗的
　　 { loving　親愛的

71. { luxurious　奢侈的
　　 { luxuriant　繁茂的；叢生的

72. { like　像的【做限定用法】
　　 { alike　像的【做敘述用法】
　　 { likely　可能的

73. { lazy　懶惰的【指厭惡工作或不勤勉的】
　　 { idle　懶惰的；閒散的【指不做事的】

74. { live　活的（指動物）【可以做限定用法，不可
　　　　做敘述用法】
　　 { living　活的【可做限定用法，亦可做敘述用法】
　　 { alive　活著的【只可做敘述用法或放在名詞
　　　　之後】
　　 { lively　活潑的

75. { magic　魔術的；魔力的
　　 { magical　神奇的；不可思議的

76. { memorial　以資紀念的　n. 紀念物
　　 { memorable　值得紀念的

77. { married　已婚的
　　 { marriageable　適合結婚的；在結婚年齡的

78. { nearest　最接近的【距離；關係】
　　 { next　下；再【指次序】

79. { *noted = reputed*　著名的
※ { *notorious*　聲名狼藉的

80. { negligent　怠慢的；疏忽的
　　 { negligible　可以忽略的；不關重要的

81. { no use　沒用的【前面要有 of 才能當形容詞用】
　　 { useless　沒用的

82. { native　本地的；生來的【著重於與生俱來的】
　　 { natural　自然的；天然的

83. { official　官方的；正式的
　　 { officious　多管閒事的；非官方的

84. { proud　驕傲的；自豪的
　　 { haughty　傲慢的

85. { poisoned　中毒的
　　 { poisonous　有毒的

86. { practical　實際的
　　 { practicable　可實行的

87. { preventive　預防的
　　 { preventable　可防止的

88. { painful　（令人）痛苦的
　　 { in pain（= pained）　在痛苦中的

89. { populous　人口稠密的
　　 { popular　流行的；受歡迎的

90. { pretty　美麗的【細緻；調和柔美】
　　 { beautiful　美麗的【藝術美；女子的美】
　　 { handsome　英俊的【指男子的美貌】；
　　　　相當大的；大方的

91. { pleasant　令人愉快的（使人心滿意足的）
　　 { pleased　滿意的
　　 { agreeable　合意的；令人喜歡的
　　　　【較 pleasant 或 pleasing 為弱】
　　 { pleasing　愉快的；令人喜愛的
　　　　【比 pleasant 弱些】

92. { *respectful*　恭敬的
※ { *respectable*　可尊敬的
　　 { *respective*　個別的

93. { regrettable　令人遺憾的
　　 { regretful　後悔的；惋惜的

94. { righteous　正義的【是公平的並和正義相適
　　　　合的意味】
　　 { rightful　正當的【指依據法律或習慣而有正
　　　　當的要求權的】

95. { social　社會上的
　　 { sociable　愛交際的

96.
※
- *successful* 成功的
- *successive* 連續的

97.
- sensible 明智的
- sensitive 敏感的

98.
- skilled 熟練的；需要技能的
- skillful 巧妙的

99.
- satisfied 滿意的
- satisfactory 令人滿意的

100.
- seasonal 季節性的
- seasonable 應時的；合時宜的

101.
- tasteful 品味高雅的
- tasty 好吃的

102.
- tired 累的；疲倦的
- tiresome 令人疲倦的；令人厭煩的

103.
- whole 完整的
- wholesome 有益健康的

104.
- troubled 煩惱的
- troublesome 令人煩惱的

105.
- triumphant 獲勝的；得意洋洋的
- triumphal 凱旋的；勝利的

106.
- three 三
- threefold 三倍的【凡數字加上 fold 即有表示倍數的意思】

107.
- unhuman 非人類的；非人間的
- inhuman 殘忍的；無人性的

108.
- unorganized 未加以組織的
- disorganized 無組織的；雜亂無章的

109.
- unsatisfied 不滿意的【指不滿足】
- dissatisfied 不滿意的【含有抱怨的意味】

110.
- unqualified 無資格的；不適任的
- disqualified 撤消資格的

111.
- uncomfortable 不舒服的
- discomfortable 痛苦的

112.
- unbearable 無法忍受的
- unborn 尚未誕生的

113.
- unmoral 超出道德的衡量標準的
- immoral 不道德的
- amoral 非道德的（與道德無關的）

114.
- understanding 聰明的；富於理解力的
- understandable 可（被人）了解的

115.
- unable 不能的【指缺乏做事的能力】
- incapable 不能的【指天生能力的缺乏】

116.
- valuable 有價值的；貴重的
- valued 被尊重的；受重視的

117.
- worrying = worried 擔心的
- worrisome 令人擔心的

118.
- wonderful 很棒的
- full of wonder （人對事物）感到好奇

119.
- worth 有價值的【worth 後加動名詞或價格，不可做限定用法】
- worthy 有價值的【可做限定用法或敘述用法】
- worthwhile 值得做的

請立刻做　練習七～九

第六章　冠　詞（Articles）

I.**定義**：a, an 和 the 本來都是屬於指示形容詞（Demonstrative Adjective），但它們卻獨成一格，又常被置於名詞之前，故稱它們為冠詞。

又因 a 和 an 泛指一般普通名詞，就稱之為「不定冠詞」（Indefinite Article）；the 則指一特定名詞，就稱之為「定冠詞」（Definite Article）。

II.**不定冠詞**：

1. **不定冠詞 a 和 an 的區別**：

⑴ a 用在子音前面；an 用在母音前面。

a boy 　　　　　　　　　**an** apple

a dog 　　　　　　　　　**an** egg

⑵ 以子音字母開始，**但讀音卻以母音開始的字要用 an**。

an hour（一小時） 　　　　**an** honest man（一個誠實的人）

an honor（一項榮譽） 　　　**an** honorable duty（一個光榮的職務）

an heir（一個繼承人） 　　　**an** honorary degree（一個榮譽學位）

※ 以上的字第一個字母 h 都不發音。

⑶ 以母音字母開始，**但讀音卻以子音開始的字要用 a**。

a useful thing（一件有用的東西） 　　　**a** used car（一輛舊車）

a union（一個工會） 　　　　　　　　　**a** unit（一個單位）

a university（一所大學） 　　　　　　　**a** universal law（一個普遍的法則）

a European（一個歐洲人） 　　　　　　　**a** ewe（一隻母羊）

【注意】一個名詞之前用冠詞 a 或 an，不在於該名詞第一個字母的拼法為母音或子音，而在於其讀音為母音起首或子音起首，見下面的例子就會明瞭：

- **a** European〔͵jurə'piən〕j 為子音
- **an** Englishman〔'ɪŋglɪʃmən〕ɪ 為母音
- **a** house〔haʊs〕h 為子音
- **an** hour〔aʊr〕h 不發音，aʊ 為雙母音
- **a** one-eyed man〔wʌn〕w 為子音
- **an** old man〔old〕o 為母音
- **a** university〔͵junə'vɝsətɪ〕j 為子音
- **an** umbrella〔ʌm'brɛlə〕ʌ 為母音

※ h 開頭第一個音節沒有重音時，前面用 a 或 an 均可。

- **a** hotel〔ho'tɛl〕旅館
- **an** hotel〔ho'tɛl〕【以前 h 不發音，現在少用，在「文馨英漢辭典」p.685 有用到 an hotel】

⑷ **開始讀母音的字母或數字之前用 an**（字母除 a, e, i, o, u 外，其他以母音開始發音的字母有 **f, h, l, m, n, r, s, x** 等八個。）如：f 讀作〔ɛf〕是母音 /ɛ/ 開始發音。

開始讀子音的字母或數字之前用 a。

The word "study" begins with **an** "s". （"study" 這個字是以 "s" 開始。）

That word ends with **an** "m". （那個字是以 "m" 結尾。）m 讀作〔ɛm〕

Is he **an** M.P.? （他是一位國會議員嗎？）

I remember his telephone number begins with **a** "2" and ends with **an** "8".

（我記得他的電話號碼是以 "2" 開頭，以 "8" 結尾。）

2. **不定冠詞的用法**

⑴ **a 或 an 若置於單數普通名詞之前指該類名詞的全體（總稱），此時的 a 帶有 any 的意味**。

（參照 p.49）

A fox is **a** cunning animal.（狐狸是狡猾的動物。）

（ = *Foxes are cunning animals.* ）

（ = *The fox is a cunning animal.* ）

I like **an** honest man better than **a** rich man.（我喜歡誠實的人勝過喜歡有錢的人。）

（ = *I like honest men better than rich men.* ）

【注意】 a, an 只可加在單數可數名詞之前；不可數名詞不可加 a(n)，但可加 some。

　　　　　 Give me **some** milk.（給我一些牛奶。）

(2) **a(n)** 等於 **one**。

I shall finish it in **a** day or two.（我將在一、二日之內完成它。）

A bird in (the) hand is worth two in the bush.（一鳥在手勝過二鳥在林。）

Do not attend to two things at **a** time.〔一（同）時不可做二事。〕

In **a** word, he tried to be rich without working.（總而言之，他想不勞而致富。）

其他例子：

a dozen（一打）　　　　　　　half-**a**-dozen（半打）

an hour（一小時）　　　　　　half **an** hour（半小時）

【註1】 a (an) 雖然可以用作 any 或 one 的意味，但三者各有其重點：

　　　　 Give me **any** pen.【重點在 any（任何一枝），不論是鋼筆還是鉛筆，也不管是好的還是不好的。】

　　　　 Give me **one** pen.【重點在 one（一枝），不要兩枝或三枝。】

　　　　 Give me **a** pen.【重點在 pen（筆），不要刀、棍等。】

【註2】 a(n) 雖有「一」的意思，但並不和 two（二）、three（三）等成對比；one 才有這種對比的意思。下面兩句都該用 one，而不用 a。

　　　　 I have **one** pen, but my sister has three pens.（我有一枝鋼筆，而我妹妹有三枝。）

　　　　 I have **one** pen, but three pencils.（我有一枝鋼筆，卻有三枝鉛筆。）

　　　　 但：I have **a** pen and three pencils.（我有一枝鋼筆和三枝鉛筆。）

　　　　 最後一句沒有對比的意思，所以用 "a"。

　　　　 再者有些慣用語裡的 a 或 one 不能相互換用，就像中文成語「三三兩兩」不能說「三三二二」一樣的道理。雖然「兩」等於「二」。

　　　　 要説：**one** day（有一天）　　　　　 不說：*a* day

　　　　　　　 once upon **a** time（從前）　　　 once upon *one* time

　　　　　　　 an hour or two（一兩個小時）　 *one* hour or two

　　　　　　　 one or two hours（一兩個小時）　 *a* or two hours

【註3】 有些語詞裡用 **a(n)** 和用 **one** 的意思完全不同

　　　　　 ⎧ more than **a** year（比一年多些 —— 即一年多）
　　　　　 ⎩ more than **one** year（超過一個年頭 —— 即兩年或三年）

　　　　　 ⎧ at **a** time（每次；同時）：Do not attend to two things **at a time**.
　　　　　 ⎩ at **one** time（曾經；一度）：**At one time** I lived in London.

　　　　 但：in **a** word 和 in **one** word 的意思相同，都作「總而言之」解。

(3) **a(n)** 相當於 **the same**。

They were nearly of **an** age.（他們差不多是同年齡。）

No two men are of **a** mind.（沒有兩個人的想法是相同的。）

Birds of **a** feather flock together.（物以類聚。）

Two of **a** trade seldom agree.（同行相忌。）

⑷ **a(n) = each**, **every**, *or* **per**

He earns five thousand dollars **a** month. （他每個月賺五千元。）

The train was running at the rate of 70 miles **an** hour.

（火車以每小時七十哩的速度行駛。）

⑸ **人名及頭銜前用 a(n) = a certain 表示說話者對此人並不認識。**（參照 p.60）

A Mr. Smith left a message this morning. （有位史密斯先生今天早上留下口信。）

He introduced me to **a** Mr. Wang, a lawyer. （他把我介紹給一個姓王的律師。）

【**註1**】 同家族的人也用 a。

His father was **a** Lee, and his mother **a** Chen. （他父親姓李，母親姓陳。）

【**註2**】 與某名人相仿的人　a = one…like （像…的人）

He wishes to become **an** Edison. 〔他希望變成像愛迪生那樣的人（偉大的發明家）。〕

He is not **a** Newton, **but** a Shakespeare.

（他不是牛頓，而是莎士比亞。）　意思是說：他不是科學家，而是文學家。

※ 既然**專有名詞做了普通名詞**所以**也可有複數形態。**

There are three **Wangs** in our class. （我們班上有三個姓王的。）

There are many future **Newtons** in this school.

（這所學校有許多未來的牛頓 —— 這所學校有許多未來的科學家。）

⑹ **a(n) 可以放在專有名詞的地名之前，指某一時期或某種樣子的某地。**（參照 p.61）

She is now **a** different Japan from what she was ten years ago.

（現在的日本和十年前的日本不同了。）

Did you dream of such **a** Taipei? （你夢想過這樣的台北嗎？）

⑺ **物質名詞或抽象名詞之前有 a(n) 時，即變成普通名詞，表個別化、製成品或種類：**

I picked up **a** stone and threw it at the dog. （我撿起一塊石頭打這隻狗。）

This is **a** good cloth for summer. （這是夏天穿的好布料。）

She was once **a** beauty. （她從前是個美女。）

He has done me **a** kindness. 〔他曾幫過我（一個）忙。〕

Honesty is **a** virtue. （誠實是一種美德。）

⑻ **have** (*or* **take**) + **a** + **抽象名詞　與該抽象名詞的動詞同義。**

I **have had a long talk** with him on the subject. （對於這個主題我已和他做了一次長談。）

= I **have long talked** with him on the subject.

Let us **take a swim**. = Let us **swim**. （我們去游泳吧。）

其他如：

have a walk （ *n.* ） = walk （ *v.* ）

have a rest （ *n.* ） = rest （ *v.* ）

have a dance （ *n.* ） = dance （ *v.* ）

have a look （ *n.* ） = look （ *v.* ）

have a bath （ *n.* ） = bathe （ *v.* ）

have a quarrel （ *n.* ） = quarrel （ *v.* ）

⑼ **不定冠詞通常置於別的形容詞前面。**

an interesting book

a pretty girl

【例外 1】

① $\begin{cases} \text{many} \\ \text{such} \\ \text{what} \end{cases}$ + a (an)

② so, as, too, how, however, no more, no less + 形容詞 + **a (an)** + 名詞

many a boy（很多男孩）	How nice a day it is!
such a program	so good a book as that
What a fine day!	as good a book as that
	too easy a sentence

【例外 2】 **quite, rather** + **a(n), the** + **名詞**　但是當名詞之前有形容詞修飾時，a(n) 放在 quite 和 rather 前後均可。

He is *quite a* fellow.（他是一個相當了不起的人。）

It is $\begin{cases} \textit{quite a} \\ \textit{a quite} \end{cases}$ good book.（那是一本相當不錯的書。）

She is *rather a* dear.（她是個相當可愛的人。）

She is $\begin{cases} \textit{rather an} \\ \textit{a rather} \end{cases}$ old woman.（她是個相當老的女人。）

【例外 3】 遇有 half 時，**a(n)** 可放在 **half** 前後

half a mile = a half mile（半哩）

half an hour = a half hour（半小時）

但在 **and** 後用 **a half**

two miles *and a half* = two *and a half* miles（二哩半）

one month *and a half* = one *and a half* months（一個半月）

⑩ 一些有 "**a**" 的慣用語

As a rule, he arrives at the office about eight-thirty in the morning.

（<u>照例地</u>，他每天早上八點半到達辦公室。）

As a whole, the relocation seems to have been beneficial.

（<u>整個看來</u>，這次的搬移似乎是有好處的。）

All of a sudden, the ship struck a rock.（<u>突然間</u>，這艘船撞到了岩石。）

He sold his house **at a loss**.（他<u>虧本地</u>賣了他的房子。）

I **am** quite **at a loss** what to do.（我<u>茫然不知</u>所措。）

I leaped over the fence **at a** (*or* **one**) **bound**.（我<u>一躍</u>而過籬笆。）

Why are you **in such a hurry**?（你為何<u>這般的匆忙</u>？）

They were **in a hurry** to leave.（他們<u>匆忙地</u>離開。）

Oil paintings appear to advantage **at a distance**.（油畫<u>隔遠一些</u>看為妙。）

III. 定冠詞（**the**）：

  1. 定冠詞在讀音上的分別：

    ⑴ **在母音之前讀**〔ði；ðɪ〕：重讀為〔ði〕；輕讀為〔ðɪ〕，如 the ink 中的 the。

    ⑵ **在子音之前讀**〔ðə〕：如 the pen 中的 the。

2. **定冠詞的用法：**(參照 p.60)

⑴ 在單數的普通名詞前加 the 即**表該名詞之全體總稱**。

The cow is a useful animal. (牛是有用的動物。)

(= A cow is a useful animal.)

(= Cows are useful animals.)

This book will prove of great value to **the** Chinese student.

(= This book will prove of great value to a Chinese student.)

(這本書對中國學生確實是很有價值的。)

【例外】*man*, *woman* 代表全體時不加冠詞。

　　　　Man for the field; **woman** for the hearth. (男主外，女主內。)

⑵ 前面已提過的名詞，**再度提到時前面加 the**。

I want a boy and a maid. **The** boy must be able to speak English.

(我需要一個男孩和一個女孩。該男孩必須會說英文。)

There was once a man. **The** man had a hen. **The** hen gave him a gold egg every day.

(從前有個人。這個人有隻母雞。這隻母雞每天為他生個金蛋。)

⑶ 由於上下文的關係，**某名詞所指的東西已非常明顯或已有了一定的範圍時，該名詞前應加 the**。

Please hand me **the** key on the desk. (請把書桌上的鑰匙拿給我。)

I don't want to talk to **the** man who insulted me in public. (我不想和公開侮辱我的人講話。)

⑷ **the 用在單數普通名詞、複數普通名詞、物質名詞、抽象名詞之前有限制的（特定的）作用。**

She is **the** teacher *whom I told you of yesterday*. (她就是我昨天和你提起的那位老師。)

Most of **the** books *on the shelf* are novels. (書架上大部分的書是小說。)

The water *in the well* is not good to drink. (那井裡的水不能喝。)

The honesty *of my servant* is beyond doubt. (我傭人的誠實不容置疑。)

【註】 物質名詞若不加限制時則**不用加 the**。

比較 { Tea is better than coffee. (茶比咖啡好。)

The tea *produced in Taiwan* is well-known all over the world.

(台灣產的茶全世界有名。)

⑸ **the 用在某些單數普通名詞之前以表示抽象觀念。**(參照 p.49)

The pen is mightier than **the** sword. (筆誅勝過劍伐；文勝於武。)

Pan Chao gave up **the** pen for **the** sword. (班超投筆從戎。)

What is learned in **the** cradle is carried to **the** grave. (幼年所學終生不忘。)

⑹ **用在專有名詞之前有下面幾種情況：**(專有名詞前本來不加冠詞)(參照 p.61)

① 用在人名或地名之前指**和那人或該地相似的人或地或指某時的某人或某地**。

He is **the** Edison of today. 〔他是當代的愛迪生（發明家）。〕

Taipei is **the** New York of Taiwan. 〔台北是台灣的紐約（第一大城）。〕

When he came back, he was not **the** Tom we had known ten years before.

(當他回來時，他不再是我們十年前所認識的那個湯姆了。)

He found Shanghai was not **the** Shanghai he had then known.

(他發現上海不再是他當時所知道的那樣的上海了。)

② 用在姓氏的複數前指**其全家人**。

The Chens will move to the country. (陳家人要搬到鄉下去。)

My father forbade me to play with **the Wangs**. （我父親禁止我和王家人玩。）
【the Wangs 指王姓這一家人】

③ **用於全體國民前**：the Chinese（中國人），the Americans（美國人）
The Chinese are a peace-loving people.（中國人是愛好和平的民族。）

④ **其他雜項**：

　1. 用在海洋、河流、港灣名詞前
　　　the Pacific (Ocean)（太平洋）　　　　　**the** Red Sea（紅海）
　　　the Gulf of Mexico（墨西哥灣）

　2. 山脈、群島、半島
　　　the Scandinavian Peninsula（斯堪地那維亞半島）
　　　the Himalayas（喜馬拉雅山脈）
　　　the Philippines（菲律賓群島）
　　　※ 孤島與獨山不是複數形的專有名詞，前面就不用冠詞。
　　　　Mt. Ali（阿里山）　　　　　　　　Taiwan (Island)（台灣島）

　3. 經典、書籍、報章、雜誌等
　　　the Central Daily News（中央日報）　　**the** Koran（可蘭經）
　　　※ 以人名爲書名時，不加冠詞。如：Robinson Crusoe（魯濱遜漂流記）

　4. 朝代及說明政治體制的國家名稱
　　　the Chin dynasty（秦朝）
　　　the United States of America（美國）

　5. 公共建築、機關、劇院、公路、鐵路、航線等名稱
　　　the Ministry of Education（教育部）
　　　the Empire State Building（帝國大廈）
　　　the Grand Hotel（圓山大飯店）
　　　the Central Highway（中央公路）
　　　the National Theater（國家劇院）

(7) **用在宇宙間「獨一無二」的天體名詞之前。**
　the sky（天空）　　　　**the** North Pole（北極）　　**the** equator（赤道）
　the moon（月亮）　　　 **the** sun（太陽）　　　　 **the** universe（宇宙）
　the earth（地球）　　　 **the** world（世界）

(8) **用在方向、方位等名詞之前。**
　the east（東方）　　　　**the** past（過去）　　　　**the** north（北方）
　the south（南方）　　　 **the** future（將來）　　　**the** left（左邊）
　the right（右邊）　　　 **the** west（西方）　　　　**the** present（現在）

The sun rises in **the** east and sets in **the** west.（太陽從東邊升起，西邊落下。）
Take the first turn to **the** right and the second turn to **the** left.
（在第一個轉彎向右轉，第二個轉彎向左轉。）
We cannot change **the** past.（我們無法改變過去。）
We should think of **the** future.（我們應該想想未來。）
The past helps us to judge of **the** present.（過去有助於我們判斷現在。）

⑼ **表示單位的名詞前要加 the。**

Sugar is sold by **the** pound.（糖是以磅計價賣的。）

Gasoline is sold by **the** gallon.（汽油是論加侖賣。）

I have hired the car by **the** hour.（我已按小時租車。）

There are about six or seven eggs to **the** pound.（每磅約有六七個蛋。）

其他的例子：

by **the** dozen（按打）　　　　by **the** yard (foot)〔按碼（呎）〕

by **the** day (week, month, year)〔按日（星期、月、年）〕

by **the** thousand（= by thousands）（成千地）

※ **但交通工具就不加 the：**

Shall we go by train or by bus?（我們是坐火車去還是坐公車去？）

Going by plane is more expensive than going by train.（搭飛機去比坐火車去更貴。）

其他的例子：

by air（搭飛機）	by sea（由水路）	by land（由陸路）
by taxi（搭計程車）	by boat (ship)（坐船）	by water（由水路）
by mail（用郵寄）	by telephone（用電話）	by walk（= on foot）（走路）
by car（坐汽車）	by bicycle（騎腳踏車）	

⑽ **樂器的名稱前要加 the。**

She plays **the** piano (**the** violin, **the** flute…).

〔她彈鋼琴（拉小提琴，吹笛子…）。〕

※ **樂器當成課程時就不加 the。**

He makes his living by teaching piano.（他以教鋼琴謀生。）

⑾ **語言名詞之後有 language 時，要有 the。** 如：English = the English language。

Your knowledge of **the** English language is insufficient.（你的英文知識不夠。）

⑿ **the + 形容詞 =** $\begin{cases} 人的集合名詞 \\ 人的單數名詞 \\ 抽象名詞 \end{cases}$

Only **the brave** deserves **the fair**.（唯有勇者才配得到美人。）

The learned are apt to despise **the ignorant**.（有學問的人往往會輕視無知的人。）

The beautiful lives forever.（美是不朽的。）

【註】 the 在 the…, the… 中的用法是副詞而非冠詞。（詳見 p.245, 504）

The more you tell him, **the less** notice he takes.（你越告訴他，他越不注意。）

The more I see him, **the better** I like him.（我越看到他，我就越喜歡他。）

The closer air is to the earth, **the greater** is its density.

（空氣離地球越近，其密度就越大。）

⒀ **在最高級的形容詞或序數（the first, the second）前面要加 the，或其他限制語。**

This is **the** most delicious cake I have ever eaten.（這是我所吃過的最好吃的蛋糕。）

Taiwan is **the** best place to live in.（台灣是最好的居住地。）

This may be **my** best work.（這可能是我最佳的作品。）

【注意】相當於最高級形容詞的字，如 **first**, **last**, **same**, **very**, **only**, **unique**, **main**, **chief** 等字之前也要加 **the**。

Who was **the first** man to land on the moon?（誰是登陸月球的第一人？）

This may be **the last** chance.（這可能是最後的機會。）

He is **the only** man for the job.（他是這個工作的最佳人選。）

We were born on **the same** day and in **the same** town.

（我們在同一天出生於同一個城鎮。）

That's **the very** thing I've been looking for.（那正是我一直在尋找的東西。）

⑭ **the** 用以加強語氣

① all the + 比較級，none the + 比較級

I love him **all the** more because he is honest.（因為他很誠實，使我更加愛他。）

② the + 單數名詞 + 不定詞 = such a + 單數名詞 + as will + 動詞原形

I am not **the** person to tell a lie.（我不是那種會說謊的人。）

= I am not *such a* person *as will* tell a lie.

③ have the + 抽象名詞 + 不定詞 = be so + 形容詞 + as + 不定詞

She **had the beauty to attract** my attention.（她的美吸引我的注意。）

= She **was so beautiful as to attract** my attention.

⑮ 有關 **the** 的慣用語：

① 一日中之時間：

in **the** {
morning（早上）
afternoon（下午）
evening（晚上）
night（≠ on the night）（晚上；夜裡）
}

【on the night 後面須接 of，如 on the night of the 21st; on the night of the big storm】

※ 但 at dawn, at dusk, at noon, at night, at midnight 則不用 the。

② 場所：

in **the** {
light（在亮處）
dark（在暗處）
sun（在陽光下）
shade（在蔭涼處）
rain (wet)（在雨中）
ocean（在海裡）
distance（在遠處）
}

③ 時間：

in **the** {
meantime（同時）
long run（終於）
month of March（在三月）
}

另外還有： at **the** same time（同時），in **the** year 2010（2010 年），for **the** present =
for **the** time being（目前；暫時），all **the** year round（一整年），
the other day（前幾天），at **the** present time（現在）

④ **in the** + 形容詞：

in **the** $\begin{cases} \text{wrong（錯誤的；不對的）} \\ \text{right（對的；有理的）} \\ \text{negative（否定地；拒絕地）} \\ \text{affirmative（肯定地）} \end{cases}$

⑤ **the** 用以代替代名詞的所有格：

He took her $\begin{cases} \text{by **the** hand.（他牽著她的手。）} \\ \text{by **the** throat.（他扼住她的咽喉。）} \end{cases}$

He $\begin{cases} \text{struck} \\ \text{hit} \end{cases}$ me on **the** head.（他打我的頭。）

【注意】動詞 + 人 + 介詞 + **the** + 人身的一部分，不可用 his, her,…代替 the。

⑥ 其他：

to **the** point（切中要點）　　on **the** other hand（另一方面）

on **the** contrary（相反地）　　on **the** whole（大體上）　　**(The)** odds are…（可能…）

IV. 冠詞的省略：(參照 p.60)

1. **稱呼用語之前不加冠詞。**

Waiter, bring my bill, please.（服務生，請拿帳單來。）

Come, **boys**. Let us play football.（來呀！孩子們，我們來打橄欖球。）

2. **家庭稱謂如父母兄弟等之前不加冠詞，甚至傭人也都不須加冠詞。**

Father has gone to Taipei on business.（父親已經去台北出差。）

Nurse has taken **Baby** out to the park.（褓姆已經帶嬰兒到公園去了。）

Uncle promised to take me to the zoo.（叔叔答應要帶我去動物園。）

Where is **Brother** now?（哥哥現在在哪裡？）

※ 以上是家族內的用法，具有專有名詞的性質。對外人提起自己的父母兄弟姊妹時，前面須加 my。

My mother went to see my father.（我母親去看我父親了。）

My brother is a doctor.（我的哥哥是醫生。）

3. **表示官職、身份、頭銜的名詞不加冠詞。**

⑴ 在人名前當稱號用時：

Queen Elizabeth（伊莉莎白女王）　　**King** George（喬治國王）

President Eisenhower（艾森豪總統）　　**Admiral** Chen（陳將軍）

Uncle Tom（湯姆叔叔）　　**Professor** Wang（王教授）

⑵ 當專有名詞的同位語時，通常不加冠詞：

Henry IV, **King of** England（英王亨利四世）

Winston Churchill, **Prime Minister** of Great Britain（英國首相邱吉爾）

⑶ 當不完全動詞的補語時：

He was elected **chairman**.（他被選為主席。）

He was appointed **principal** of this school.（他被任命為這所學校的校長。）

He was once **mayor** of this city.（他以前是這個城市的市長。）

※ 如果用人名做船名時，要加冠詞 the。

the Queen Mary（瑪麗皇后號）　　**the** Victoria（維多利亞號）

4. **兩個相對的名詞並用時不加冠詞。**

> **Husband and wife** rejoiced at the news.（夫妻聽到這個消息時很高興。）
> They were walking **arm in arm** along the river.（他們挽著臂沿著河散步。）
> The captain looked at the boy **from head to toe**.（船長從頭到腳打量著那個男孩。）
> 其他例子：
>
> | | |
> |---|---|
> | father and son（父子） | mother and child（母子） |
> | master and servant（主僕） | rich and poor（貧富） |
> | day and night（日夜） | old and young（老少） |
> | hand in hand（手牽手） | side by side（肩並肩） |
> | face to face（面對面） | step by step（一步一步地） |
> | one by one（一個接一個） | day by (*or* after) day（一天一天地） |
> | from door to door（挨家挨戶） | from place to place（到處） |
> | from morning till night（從早到晚） | from beginning to end（自始至終） |
> | from south to north（從南到北） | |

5. **運動、遊戲、顏色、感官的名詞前不加 the。**

He likes **basketball**.（他喜歡籃球。）
Do you play **bridge**?（你玩橋牌嗎？）
White is a beautiful color.（白色是美麗的顏色。）
Sight is one of the five senses.（視覺是五種感官之一。）

6. **除 (the) measles（麻疹），(the) flu（流行性感冒）可加 the 或不加之外，其他疾病的名詞，如：dysentery（痢疾），chronic bronchitis（慢性支氣管炎），cholera（霍亂），malaria（瘧疾），scarlet fever（猩紅熱）前，多不加 the。**

Smoke pollutes the air we breathe, and is a contributory cause of **chronic bronchitis**.
（煙污染了我們呼吸的空氣，是造成慢性支氣管炎的原因。）

※ 上述病名之前不加冠詞，但症狀之前則要加冠詞，如 fever, headache, pain, cut, wound, cough, sore arm。而 cold 這個字取決於它的動詞，如它的動詞用 catch，則 catch (a) cold；動詞用 have，則 have a cold。

7. **除 The Hague（海牙），the Ginza（銀座）之外，都市多不加冠詞。**

8. **school, college, church, hospital, market, prison, bed, table 等字指原有的用途時為抽象名詞，不用冠詞；若指建築物本身或場所時為普通名詞，就要加冠詞。但 hospital 和 table 在美語中常加冠詞。比較下列各句：**

> The children go to **school** every morning.（孩子們每天早上去上學。）
> He lives near **the school**.（他住在學校附近。）

> The Chens go to **church** every Sunday.（陳家每週日都上教堂做禮拜。）
> Do you pass **the church** on your way to school?（在你上學途中會經過教堂嗎？）

> They were sent to **prison** for stealing.（他們因為偷竊而入獄。）
> I once visited **a prison**.（我曾經參觀過一所監獄。）

9. **breakfast, lunch, dinner, supper 等前不加冠詞。**

How about coming for **dinner**?（來吃晚餐如何？）

We are going to the movies after **supper**.（晚餐後我們要去看電影。）

Breakfast (**lunch**, **supper**, **dinner**) is ready.〔早餐（午餐、晚餐）準備好了。〕

※ 但若指特定的一餐飯時要用 **the**。

　　The dinner (breakfast, lunch, supper) *I had at his house yesterday* was a little too heavy.
　　〔我昨天在他家吃的飯（早餐、午餐、晚餐）有點難消化。〕

10. 學科的名稱前不加冠詞。

He teaches **English** in a middle school.（他在中學裡教英文。）

He majored in **chemistry** in college.（他在大學主修化學。）

※ 上述學科如作修飾語用則其前要加冠詞：

　　The *English* language is easy to learn.（學習英語並不難。）

　　He is **a** *geography* teacher.（他是個地理老師。）

　　What is *the Chinese* word for *the English* word "book"?
　　（英文的 "book" 是中文的什麼？）

11. **a kind of**, **a sort of**, **a type of**, **a species of** 後面的單數普通名詞不加冠詞。

What kind of **book** do you like best?（你最喜歡哪種書？）

She leads a special type of **life**.（她過一種特別的生活。）

This is a curious species of **bamboo**.（這是一種奇異的竹子。）

【例外】 what kind of man = what kind of a man

12. **most** 作「大多數」解時不加冠詞，如 most people（大多數人）。（詳見 p.205）

13. 以 as 代 though 之句中，冠詞省略。（詳見 p.529）

Hero as he is（= Though he is a hero），he is sometimes afraid.
（雖然他是個英雄，他有時候也會害怕。）

14. 代名形容詞 my, your, his, her, its 等及 one, some, any, no, each, every, either, neither 是 a 和 an 之相當語，亦是說**一個名詞前若有上列的字就不能有 a 和 an 出現。**

【注意】 certain 和 such：前者須以 a certain，後者須以 such a 出現，始可加可數單數名詞。
　　　　又 whose, which, this, that 是 the 的相當語，若有這些字出現，則 the 不能出現。
　　　　※ what 在問句中絕不可與 a 共用，但在感嘆句中例外。（詳見 p.148）
　　　　　　What a lovely girl she is!（她是個多麼可愛的女孩！）

15. 副詞的最高級不加冠詞。

He knew **best**.（他知道得最清楚。）

16. 省略冠詞的其他慣用語：

at	best（充其量只不過是）	at	most（最多）
	church（在做禮拜）		present（目前）
	desk（在寫字；在辦公）		play（在玩）
	fault（迷惑；不知所措）		school（在上課）
	first（起初）		sea（在航海途中）
	hand（在手邊）		stake（在危險中）
	home（在家中）		table（在吃飯）
	last（最後）		worst（在情況最壞時）
	least（至少）		war（在交戰）
	leisure（閒暇時）		

by
- accident（偶然地）
- air (airplane)（搭飛機）
- car（坐車）
- chance（偶然地）
- land（用陸路）
- mistake（因為錯誤）
- name（名叫…）
- telegram（用電報）

for
- example（例如）
- instance（例如）

in
- bed（在睡覺）
- brief（簡言之）
- debt（在負債）
- danger（在危險中）
- fact（事實上）
- order（整齊地）
- private（私下地）
- prison（坐牢）
- public（公開地）
- question（議論中的）
- school（在求學）
- secret（秘密地）
- short（簡言之）
- time（及時）
- trouble（在困難中；有了麻煩）
- use（在使用中）

on
- demand（來取即付）
- earth（在世界上；究竟）
- foot（步行）
- fire（在燃燒）
- horseback（在騎馬）
- purpose（故意地）
- time（準時）

- give ear (to)（傾聽）
- give birth (to)（生）

- make faces (at)（對…做鬼臉）
- make fun (of)（取笑）
- make friends (with)（和…交朋友）
- make haste（趕快）
- make room for（讓位給）
- make way for（為…開路）

- take place（發生）
- take part in（參加）

- be at home (in)（精通）
- cast anchor（拋錨；停留）
- leave word（留言）
- lose heart（失去勇氣；灰心）
- send word（通知）
- shake hands（握手）

V. 有關冠詞應注意事項：

1. **一些英文慣用語中有的一定要加冠詞，有的不加冠詞**，下面有一些例句，**有無冠詞能造成意義上很大的差別。**

   (1)
   - in the distance（在遠處）
   - at a distance（在稍遠的地方）

   The picture looks better **at a distance**.（這幅畫遠一點看就會更好。）
   I see a cottage **in the distance**.（我看見遠處有間農舍。）

   (2)
   - with child（懷孕）
   - with a child（帶著孩子）

   Three months after her marriage, she was **with child**（= pregnant）.
   （她婚後三個月就懷孕了。）
   She came to see me **with a child**.（她帶著孩子來看我。）

   (3)
   - as a whole = altogether（全部地；整體）
   - on (*or* upon) the whole = in general（大體上；一般而言）

   We must look at the matter **as a whole**.（我們必須看這件事的整體。）
   My opinion is **on the whole** the same as yours.（我的意見大體上和你的一樣。）

(4) {
  take place（發生）
  take the place of（代替）

His wedding ceremony will **take place** next Sunday.（他的婚禮將在下週日舉行。）

Mr. Smith being absent, Mr. Jones **took his place**.（史密斯先生不在，瓊斯先生代替他。）

(5) {
  out of（= beyond, past, without）question（毫無疑問）
  out of the question（不可能）

He may be a little careless in his behavior, but his loyalty to his friend is **out of question**.（他的行為可能有些粗心大意，但他對朋友的忠誠是不容置疑的。）

The boys had no money, so it was **out of the question** for them to go to the movies.
（男孩們沒有錢，所以他們想去看電影是不可能的。）

(6) {
  in possession of（擁有）——主詞為人
  in the possession of（為…所擁有）——主詞為物

That old widow is **in possession of** a large fortune.
（那個老寡婦擁有一大筆財產。）【主動意義】

A large fortune is **in the possession of** that old widow.
（一大筆財產掌握在那個老寡婦的手裡。）【被動意義】

(7) {
  go to sea = follow the sea（當水手）
  go to the sea（去海邊）
  put (out) to sea（出海）

He **went to sea** at 12 years old.（他十二歲時去航海。）

My uncle **followed the sea** for ten years.（我叔叔當了十年船員。）

I will **go to the sea** with my brother.（我將和哥哥一起去海邊。）

The ship **put (out) to sea** at dawn.（那艘船天亮時出海。）

2. 原則上兩個或兩個以上的名詞並列時，若指不同的人或物，每個名詞之前都要有冠詞；**若指同一人或物，則只有第一個名詞需要冠詞。**

They are **a** poet and **a** novelist.（他們是一位詩人和一位小說家。——兩個人）

He was **a** poet and novelist.（他是詩人兼小說家。——同一個人）

【註】 **為了加強語氣，兩個名詞並列而指同一人或物時，第二個名詞前也可加冠詞。**

He was **a** poet and **a** novelist.（他是個詩人，也是小說家。——同一個人）

He became **a** husband and **a** father before he was out of his teens.
（在他未滿二十歲以前，他就做了丈夫和爸爸了。）

The editor and publisher of this magazine is a very able man.
（這雜誌的編輯兼發行人是一位很能幹的人。——同一個人）

The editor and **the** publisher of this magazine are very able men.
（這雜誌的編輯與發行人都是很能幹的人。——兩個人）

【註1】 兩個名詞並列而不可能指同一人或物時，第二個名詞之前的冠詞就可以省略。

I met a lady and (**a**) gentleman.（我遇見一位女士和一位男士。）

The lady and (**the**) gentleman were walking arm in arm.
（那女士和那男士挽著臂散步。）

【註2】 在一件東西附屬於其他東西上而成為一件東西時，冠詞只用一個。

a watch and chain（附有鍊子的錶）

a needle and thread（穿著線的針）

a cup and saucer（有碟子的茶杯）

the bread and butter（奶油麵包）

3. **the** 加在複數普通名詞前，就指其全體。

⑴ They are **the teachers** of our school.（他們是我們學校的老師。── 全體老師）

⑵ They are **teachers** of our school.（他們是我們學校的老師。── 老師的一部分）

例句⑴加了 the，意思就是說，那些人是學校裡的全部老師，此外別無老師；假使那些人是學校裡老師的一部分，此外還有老師，就不可以加 the，如例句⑵。

4. 在同一個名詞之前有兩個形容詞並列時，若指兩個人或兩件東西，每個形容詞之前都需要冠詞；**若指同一個人或同一件東西，只有第一個形容詞之前需要冠詞。**

The carriage was drawn by **a** black and white horse.

（這馬車是由一匹黑白相間的馬所拖的。── 只有一匹馬）

The carriage was drawn by **a** black (horse) and **a** white horse.

（這馬車是由一匹黑馬和一匹白馬所拖的。── 兩匹馬）

The black and white horse was an Arabian breed.

（這匹黑白相間的馬是阿拉伯種。── 只有一匹馬）

The black and **the** white horse were both Arabian breeds.

（這黑馬和白馬都是阿拉伯種。── 兩匹馬）

The black **and** white horses were both Arabian breed.

（這兩匹黑白相間的馬都是阿拉伯種。── 兩匹馬）

注意下面幾種不同情形：

a black and white horse	◑（一匹黑白相間的馬）
a black and a white horse	●＋○（一匹黑馬和一匹白馬）
the black and white horse	◑（一匹黑白相間的馬）
the black and the white horse	●＋○（那匹黑馬和那匹白馬）
the black and white horses	◑◑…（那些黑白相間的馬）

【註】名詞之前的兩個形容詞顯然不可能指同一件事物時，**第二個形容詞之前的冠詞常被省略。**

the 19th and (the) 20th centuries（第十九和二十世紀）

the East and (the) West coasts of Africa（非洲的東西兩岸）

the first and (the) second chapter（第一和第二章）

5. 像 pipe in mouth 這類表狀態的副詞片語，是由 with a pipe in his mouth 省略而來。

He was standing, *pipe in mouth*.（他嘴裡刁著煙斗站著。）

= He was standing, *with a* pipe in *his* mouth.

He waited, *hat in hand*.（他手裡拿著帽子在等待著。）

= He waited, *with his* hat in *his* hand.

【類例】

stick in hand（= with a stick in his hand）

cap in hand（= with a cap in his hand）

flute in hand（= with a flute in his hand）

hand in pocket（= with a hand in his pocket）

請立刻做　練習十～十一

第五篇　副 詞（Adverbs）

第一章 序 論（Introduction of Adverbs）

Ⅰ. 定義： 副詞是用來修飾動詞、形容詞或其他副詞，有時候也可以用來修飾一個片語、
子句，甚至整個句子等。

Ⅱ. 分類： 依用法分，副詞有簡單副詞（**Simple Adverbs**）、疑問副詞（**Interrogative
Adverbs**）、關係副詞（**Relative Adverbs**）三類；從意義上區分，則有表時間、
地點、程度、狀態、原因等。

Ⅲ. 功用：

1. 修飾動詞（包括不定詞、動名詞、分詞等動狀詞）

Mary recovered *slowly*.（瑪麗復原得很慢。）

Melrose munched the peaches, *casually* tossing the pits on the floor.
（瑪爾羅絲大嚼桃子，無意中把果核扔在地板上。）

The accused was driving *recklessly* in a school zone.（這名被告在學校區魯莽駕駛。）

He pretended *not* to know me when I met him in the party last week.
（上週在宴會碰面時，他假裝不認識我。）

2. 修飾形容詞

The food is *very* delicious.（這個食物很可口。）

His grades are not good *enough* for a scholarship.（他的成績還未好到可以得獎學金。）

3. 修飾副詞、副詞片語、副詞子句

He speaks English *quite* fluently.（他講英文十分流利。）

Some grains are *not* less nutritious than rice.（有些穀類的營養並不比稻米差。）

He came to Taiwan *soon* after the war.（戰後不久，他就來到了台灣。）

He left there *soon* after I arrived.（我到達之後不久，他就離開那裡。）

4. 修飾全句

Happily, he didn't die.（幸虧他沒死。）

Certainly, I will stand by you forever.（當然，我會永遠支持你。）

【註】修飾全句的副詞，若放句中或句末，必須加逗點，句前則可有可無。
Nothing, *certainly*, is more important than health.（的確，沒有什麼比健康更重要。）
He escaped being killed in the car accident, *fortunately*.
（很幸運地，他沒有在車禍中喪命。）

5. 修飾名詞和代名詞

有些副詞如：also, especially, even, exactly, hardly, just, merely, not, only, particularly, precisely, quite, scarcely, simply, solely, too 等，可用來修飾名詞或代名詞。其中除了 too 須放在（代）名詞之後外，其餘的通常放在前面；但（**代**）**名詞為一個字時，這些副詞也可放在（代）名詞之後。**

William thinks so, *also* John (*or* John *also*).（威廉認為如此，約翰也是。）

Even a worm will turn.（【諺】狗急跳牆。）

What *exactly* (*or* *Exactly* what) paganism was we shall never know.
（邪教究竟是什麼，我們永遠不會懂。）

Hardly anybody noticed it.（幾乎沒有人注意到它。）

I got *just* one.（我只有一個。）

He did it, *not* I.（他做的，不是我。）

All were there. *Only* John (*or* John *only*) was missing.
（所有的人都在那裡。只有約翰不見了。）

All of my arithmetic problems are hard, but *particularly* this one.
（我所有的算術問題都很難，尤其是這一題。）

Quite a crowd had already gathered there.（已有大批的人聚集在那裡。）

Scarcely a drop of rain has fallen since last summer.

（從去年夏天以來，幾乎沒有下過一滴雨。）

She, *too*, loves him.（她也愛他。）

6. 代替名詞或形容詞

(1) **代替名詞做主詞或受詞：**（因少數副詞沒有同意義的名詞）
Now is the time to leave.（現在是該走的時候了。）
I haven't seen him since *then*.（從那時起我就沒再見過他了。）
The museum is very far from *here*.（博物館離這裡很遠。）

(2) **代替形容詞：**（因少數副詞沒有同意義的形容詞）
Is anybody *home*?（有人在家嗎？）
She is *out*.（她出去了。）
Read the sentences *above*.（讀上面的句子。）
the *above* sentences（上面的句子）
in *after* years（後來的歲月）
the *up* (*down*) train〔上（下）行火車〕
the *then* Prime Minister（當時的首相）

IV. 副詞的形成與應注意的事項：

1. 形容詞 + ly

(1) 一般形容詞字尾加 **ly**

clear（清楚的）
diligent（勤勉的）
$\Big\}$ + **ly** = $\Big\{$ clearly
diligently

(2) 形容詞字尾若爲 **y**，則將 **y** 改成 **i**，再加 **ly**

easy（容易的）
happy（快樂的）
$\Big\}$ – **y** + **ily** = $\Big\{$ easily
happily

(3) 字尾爲 **le** 者，直接改爲 **ly**

single（單獨的）
humble（謙卑的）
$\Big\}$ – **e** + **y** = $\Big\{$ singly
humbly

【例外】　sole（唯一的）→ *solely*　　　whole（全部的）→ *wholly*

(4) 字尾爲 **ue**，把 **e** 去掉再加 **ly**

due（適當的）
true（眞實的）
$\Big\}$ – **e** + **ly** = $\Big\{$ duly
truly

(5) 字尾爲 **ll** 只加 **y**

dull（枯燥的）
full（充實的）
$\Big\}$ + **y** = $\Big\{$ dully
fully

(6) 字尾爲 **ic** 時要加 **ally**

automatic（自動的）
democratic（民主的）
energetic（充滿活力的）
fanatic（= fanatical）（狂熱的）
fantastic（很棒的）
phonetic（語音的）
$\Big\}$ + **ally** = $\Big\{$
automatically
democratically
energetically
fanatically
fantastically
phonetically

【例外】　politic（精明的）→ *politicly*　（political 政治的 → *politically*）
　　　　　public（公共的）→ *publicly*

(7) 字尾爲 **ly** 時，將 **y** 改爲 **i** 後加 **ly**

friendly（友善的）
manly（有男子氣槪的）
lively（活潑的）
$\Big\}$ – **y** + **ily** = $\Big\{$
friendlily
manlily
livelily

【註】　爲避免字尾〔lılı〕發音的重複，所以實用上常以其他同義副詞代替此類副詞。
　　　如用 *amicably* 代 friendlily，用 *manfully* 代 manlily，用 *vivaciously* 代
　　　livelily。

⑻ | **現在分詞或過去分詞當形容詞用時，在字尾加 ly** |

exceeding（非常的）
surprising（驚人的）
supposed（想像的）
confused（困惑的）   ⎱ + **ly** = ⎰
smiling（微笑的）
contented（滿足的）
unexpected（意料之外的）

exceedingly
surprisingly
supposedly
confusedly
smilingly
contentedly
unexpectedly

【註】 名詞 + **ly** = 形容詞，大部分是「像⋯的」的意思：
我們應當記住唯有形容詞 + **ly** 才是副詞，千萬不要以爲加 **ly** 的全是副詞。
例如：**lively**（活潑的）即爲形容詞而非副詞。
其他如：名詞 + **ly** = 形容詞，意思是「像⋯的」

father（父親）	fatherly（像父親的 —— 慈愛的）
man（男人）	manly（像男人的 —— 有男子氣概的）
soldier（士兵）	soldierly（像軍人的 —— 英勇的）
coward（懦夫）	cowardly（像懦夫的 —— 膽怯的）
friend（朋友）	friendly（像朋友的 —— 友善的）
love（愛）	lovely（可愛的；美麗的）

【例外】 如果是表時間觀念的名詞，加 **ly** 後就有副詞及形容詞的雙重身份。
hourly, daily, weekly, fortnightly（= biweekly）, monthly, quarterly, yearly

比較：
This is a *fortnightly* magazine.（這是一本雙週的雜誌。）
　　　　　　　形容詞
This magazine is published *fortnightly*.
（這本雜誌每兩週發行一次。）　副詞

2. 名詞 + ⎰ **wise**
　　　　　　 wards
　　　　　　 ways

He sat with his legs *crosswise*.（他兩腿交叉地坐著。）
He went *backwards*（forwards; homewards）.〔他向後走（向前走；回家）。〕
The crab runs *sideways*.（螃蟹橫著走。）

【註】 有時名詞字首加 **a** 也可做副詞：

ashore（上岸）	asleep（睡著了）	alive（活著）
aloft（在高處）	afoot（走路）	ahead（在前面）
aboard（在船上）	away（離開）	abed（在床上）

3. **由其他詞類轉用而來：**
She is *ten years* old.（她十歲。）【名詞（詳見 p.100）】
He came *late*.（他來遲了。）【形容詞】

The more he gets, *the* more he wants.【冠詞（詳見 p.244）】

（他所獲得的愈多，想要的就愈多。）

We went *up*.（我們走上去。）【介系詞（詳見 p.543）】

I see him *Sundays*（= *of a Sunday*）.【名詞的所有格（of + 名詞）】

（我常在星期日見到他。）

4. **有些字可當形容詞又可當副詞：**

下列每組句子裡相同的字在**第一句為形容詞**，在**第二句則為副詞**：

- That is a very *fast* train.（那是很快的火車。）
- The train goes very *fast*.（火車跑得很快。）

- Draw a *straight* line.（畫一條直線。）
- He went *straight* to the station.（他直接去車站。）

- He has gone to the *Far* East.（他到遠東去了。）
- We didn't walk very *far*.（我們沒有走得很遠。）

- He spoke in a *low* voice.（他說話的聲音很低。）
- He spoke *low* but clearly.（他說話聲音低，但很清楚。）

- He is an *early* riser.（他是個早起的人。）
- He always gets up *early*.（他總是起得很早。）

- Have you *enough* time to do the work?（你有足夠的時間去做那工作？）
- He didn't try hard *enough*.（他還不夠努力。）

- He went on a *long* journey to India.（他長途旅行到印度去。）
- I have *long* been intending to call on you.（我很久以來就想拜訪你。）

- I feel *well* today.（我今天覺得很好。）
- He speaks English *well*.（他英文講得很好。）

- *Ill* news runs apace.（壞事傳千里。）
- Don't speak *ill* of others behind their backs.（不要在背後說人家的壞話。）

- I am sorry to give you so *much* trouble.（給你添這麼多麻煩真是抱歉。）
- I was *much* surprised at what he said.（我聽到他說的話感到很驚訝。）

- There is *little* money left.（剩下的錢不多。）
- I *little* dreamed that it was so.（我做夢也沒想到事情是這樣的。）

- Let's have *more* work and *less* talk.（我們多工作少說話吧。）
- You should work *more* and talk *less*.（你應該多工作少說話。）

- It is never too *late* to mend.（改過永不嫌遲 —— 過則勿憚改。）
- He sits up very *late*.（他熬夜到很晚。）

Practice is the *only* way to learn a language. (練習是學習語言的唯一方法。)
He can *only* do his best. (他只能盡力而為。)

The building is forty feet *high*. (這棟建築物有四十呎高。)
Popular feeling ran *high*. (群情激昂。)

It is *hard* work. (這是個困難的工作。)
He works *hard*. (他努力地工作。)

We waited *half* the afternoon. (我們等了半個下午。)
This is not *half* good enough. (這個不夠一半好。)

He spoke in a *loud* voice. (他以很大的聲音說話。)
Don't talk so *loud*. (不要那麼大聲講話。)

5. 有些形容詞變為副詞，可在字尾加 **ly**，也可以不加；不過在字義上和用法上有些不同：

形容詞：They moved on in a *direct* line. (他們成一直線地繼續前進。)
副　詞：
The goods will be sent *direct* to you. (商品將直接送去給你。)
I will return *directly*（= at once）. (我立刻回來。)

形容詞：That is a very *high* mountain. (那是一座很高的山。)
副　詞：
The birds are flying *high*. (鳥兒飛得很高。)
He was *highly* praised for his work. (他的工作頗受讚賞。)

形容詞：John was *late* for school. (約翰上學遲到了。)
副　詞：
He came *late*. (他來遲了。)
I haven't heard from him *lately*. (最近我一直沒有他的消息。)

形容詞：He is not a very *near* relation of me. (他不是我的近親。)
副　詞：
The time for the examination is drawing *near*. (考期漸漸接近了。)
I *nearly* missed my train. (我幾乎沒趕上火車。)

形容詞：She is a very *pretty* girl. (她是個漂亮的女孩。)
副　詞：
That is a *pretty*（= fairly）good picture. (那是一張相當好的畫。)
The little girl danced *prettily*. (小女孩跳舞跳得很美。)

形容詞：Are we on the *right* road? (我們是不是走對了路？)
副　詞：
Turn *right* at the next corner. (在下個街角右轉。)
He was *rightly* blamed for the accident. (這件意外，他該受責備。)

形容詞：He is a *hard* worker. (他是個勤勉的工作者。)
副　詞：
He works *hard* in order to accomplish his purpose.
（為達到目的，他辛苦地工作。）
I *hardly* understand what you said. (我幾乎不了解你所說的話。)

形容詞：I want a *sharp* knife.（我需要一把<u>利</u>刀。）

副　詞：
> It is ten o'clock *sharp*.（十點<u>正</u>。）
> = It is *just* ten o'clock.
> 【注意】 **just** 也可當「正」或「恰好」解，不過要放在時間之前，**sharp** 要放在時間之後。
> He *sharply* objected to my plan.（他<u>嚴厲地</u>反對我的計劃。）

形容詞：This is a *wide* road.（這是一條很<u>寬的</u>路。）

副　詞：
> The window was *wide* open.（窗戶<u>大</u>開著。）
> He has travelled *widely*.（他<u>遍</u>遊各地。）

形容詞：The room is in *deep* darkness.（房間<u>很暗</u>。）

副　詞：
> The corpse was buried *deep* in the ground.
> （屍體<u>深深地</u>埋在地下。）
> I am *deeply* moved by the story.（我被該故事<u>深深地</u>感動。）

形容詞：The oranges are *cheap*.（柳橙很<u>便宜</u>。）

副　詞：
> If you want to make money, you must buy *cheap* and sell dear.
> （假如你想賺錢，就必須<u>賤買貴賣</u>。）
> They fought a very long time, but the victory was *cheaply* bought, because no men were killed.
> （他們打了很久，<u>但沒付出很大的代價</u>就獲得了勝利，因為沒有人陣亡。）

形容詞：Writing is *easy* to me.（寫作對我來說很<u>容易</u>。）

副　詞：
> *Easy* come, *easy* go.（來得<u>容易</u>，去得<u>快</u>。）
> The question was *easily* answered.（這個問題很<u>容易地</u>被回答了。）

形容詞：This house is *clean*.（這間房子很<u>乾淨</u>。）

副　詞：
> I *clean* forgot to ask him about it.（我<u>完全</u>忘了問他這件事。）
> He was *cleanly* dressed.（他衣著<u>整潔</u>。）

形容詞：That dog is *dead*.（那隻狗<u>死</u>了。）

副　詞：
> He is *dead* tired.（他疲倦<u>極了</u>。）
> This book is *deadly* dull.（這本書<u>極為</u>枯燥乏味。）

形容詞：It was a *fair* fight.（那是一場<u>公平的</u>比賽。）

副　詞：
> You must play *fair*（= fairly）.（你必須<u>公平地</u>比賽。）
> He did *fairly*（= rather）well in his examination.
> （他的考試成績<u>相當</u>不錯。）

形容詞： There is a *short* way home through the woods.
（從樹林中走回家，有條<u>近</u>路。）

副　詞：
　The car stopped *short* (= suddenly) only a few feet from where the child stood.
　（車子<u>突然</u>剎車，離小孩站的地方只有幾呎。）
　He will come *shortly* (= in a short time) . （他<u>馬上</u>就會來。）

形容詞： I didn't want to waken him; he was in a *sound* sleep.
（我不想叫醒他；他睡得<u>很熟</u>。）

副　詞：
　He was sleeping *sound* (= soundly) . （他睡得<u>很熟</u>。）
　In the baseball match, Taipei was *soundly* (= thoroughly) beaten by Tainan.
　（在那場棒球比賽中，台北隊<u>徹底地</u>輸給了台南隊。）

形容詞：He is a *just* man. （他是個<u>正直的</u>人。）

副　詞：
　This is *just* what I wanted. （這<u>正</u>是我想要的。）
　You should treat him *justly*. （你應該<u>公正地</u>對待他。）

形容詞：It is a *close* (= airless) afternoon. （今天下午<u>真悶熱</u>。）

副　詞：
　Keep *close* to me. （<u>靠近</u>我。）
　She takes after her mother *closely*. （她<u>極像</u>她的母親。）

形容詞：He is a *firm* friend of the family. （他是這家人的<u>忠實</u>朋友。）

副　詞：
　If you stand *firm*, I *firmly* believe that we shall succeed.
　（如果你們站得<u>穩</u>，我<u>堅</u>信我們一定能成功。）

形容詞：He is a *slow* driver. （他開車開得很慢。）

副　詞：
　Go *slow* through the village. （經過鄉村要開<u>慢</u>一點。）
　The hours pass *slowly* while I have nothing to do.
　（當我無事可做時，時間過得很<u>慢</u>。）

形容詞：He was wearing very *tight* shoes. （他穿的鞋子很緊。）

副　詞：
　Hold *tight*, the car is going. （抓<u>牢</u>，車子要開了。）
　The passengers were *tightly* packed in the bus.
　（乘客<u>緊緊地</u>擠在公車裡。）

形容詞：I think we are on the *wrong* road. （我想我們走<u>錯</u>路了。）

副　詞：
　We went *wrong*. （我們走<u>錯</u>了。）
　He was *wrongly* accused of the crime. （他被<u>誣</u>告。）

第二章　副詞的種類與用法

I. **副詞的種類**：按**用法**分可分為**簡單副詞**（Simple Adverbs）、**疑問副詞**（Interrogative Adverbs），以及**關係副詞**（Relative Adverbs）。就副詞的**意義**而言，**可用來表示時間、場所（地點）、程度、狀態、方法、理由、肯定否定、次數**…等。

意義＼用法	簡　單　副　詞	疑　問　副　詞	關　係　副　詞
時　　間	now, then, ago, before, afterwards, soon, early, late, lately, today, formerly…	when? how long? how often?	when(ever)
地　　點	here, there; in, out; above, below; far, near; off; away, aside…	where? whence? whither? how far?	where(ever)
程　　度	very, much, quite, rather, enough, only, scarcely, hardly…	how?	how(ever)
狀態方態　態法度	thus, so, well, badly, quickly, slowly, easily, kindly…	how?	how(ever)
原因理由	therefore, accordingly…	why?	why
肯定否定	yes, no, yea, nay, not, surely…		
次　　數	once, twice, again, often, first(ly)…	how often?	

II. **簡單副詞**（**Simple Adverbs**）：簡單副詞乃是**純粹用來修飾其他字或詞句的**，依意義來區分，又可分為時間副詞、地方副詞、程度副詞、方法或狀態副詞、肯定或否定的副詞，現分述如下：

1. **時間副詞（包括片語）**：用來表示當什麼時候完成一個動作或一件事情的副詞，稱爲時間副詞。又可分爲：

   ⑴ **Time（時候）：可用作 when（什麼時候）的答語**，如：

   > now（現在），lately（最近），soon（不久之後），today（今天），early（早），
   > at once（立刻），long ago（很久以前），next year（明年），…

   Call me **early**; I want to see the sunrise. （早點叫醒我；我想看日出。）
   I'll be with you **soon**. （我不久就可以來陪你。）
   I haven't seen him **lately**. （我最近都沒見到他。）

   ⑵ **Duration（期間）：用來作 how long（多久）的答語**，如：

   > long（很久），forever（永遠），all day（整天），for ten years（十年之久），…

   He went away **forever**. （他永遠離開了。）
   She has been teaching **for ten years**. （她已經敎了十年的書。）

   ⑶ **Repetition（反覆）：用來作 how often（幾次）的答語**，也可稱爲頻率副詞，如：

   > once（一次），daily（每天），often（常常），seldom（很少），at times（有時候），
   > always（總是），usually（通常），frequently（經常），continually（持續地），
   > regularly（定期地），occasionally（偶爾），sometimes（有時候），rarely（很少），
   > scarcely（不常），once in a while（偶爾），hardly ever（幾乎不曾），
   > never（絕不），…

   She goes to the movies **once** a week. （她每週看一次電影。）
   He **always** does his work well. （他總是把工作做得很好。）

   ⑷ **Order（順序）：**

   > first（最先），next（其次），last（最後），…

   The king arrived **first**, and **next** came his retinue. （國王先到，其次是他的侍從。）
   It is a long time since I saw him **last**. （自從我上次見到他以來，已經很久了。）
   "When did you see him **last**?" （「你最後一次見到他是什麼時候？」）
   "It is a year since." （「在一年前。」）

2. **場所（地方）副詞：表示 where?（在哪裡？）的副詞**，也包括「動態方向」的副詞。如：

   > here（這裡），there（那裡），home（在家），far（遠），near（近），back（向後），
   > out（在外面），to and fro（來來回回），above（在上面），inside（在裡面），
   > away（離開），forward(s)（向前），outside（在外面），across（越過），off（離開），
   > over（在…之上），backward(s)（向後），everywhere（到處），under（在…之下），
   > hither（到這裡），thither（到那裡），thence（從那裡），upstairs（在樓上），
   > downstairs（在樓下），somewhere（某處），nowhere（無處），…

   Come **nearer**. （靠近一點。）
   The sailors went **ashore**. （水手們上了岸。）

He paced **to and fro** in the room. （他在房間裡走來走去。）

I went to market, and **thence** to the office. （我先上市場,再從那裡去辦公室。）

The child was **nowhere** to be found. （到處都找不到那個小孩。）

【註】 表示地方的副詞（here, there, home 等）和部分時間副詞（today, tomorrow, yesterday, next week, next Monday, next month, next year, last night, last week, last month, last year, this morning, this week 等）前面不加介系詞。

He came **here last night**. （他昨晚來過這裡。）

We are going **there next Sunday**. （下星期日我們要去那裡。）

Let's go **home**. （我們回家吧。）

3. **程度副詞**：

> very（很）, rather（相當）, quite（十分地）, much（非常）, greatly（非常）,
> nearly（幾乎；近乎）, almost（幾乎）, completely（完全地）, entirely（全部地）,
> perfectly（完美地）, absolutely（絕對地）, thoroughly（徹底地）, extremely（極端地）,
> exactly（確切地；恰好地）, partly（部分地）, slightly（稍微地）, so（那麼）,
> too（太）, awfully, terribly, frightfully（相當；很,都等於 very）, just（正是）,
> scarcely（hardly 幾乎不）, utterly（全然地）, enormously（非常地）, …

I am so tired, I can **hardly** walk. （我很累,幾乎走不動了。）

I am **terribly**（= very）sorry. （我很抱歉。）

The patient is **slightly** better today. （病人今天稍微好一點了。）

It is **absolutely** impossible. （那是絕對不可能的。）

The town has changed **enormously** during recent years.

（最近幾年這個城鎮已經有很大的改變。）

They are **equally** clever. （他們同樣聰明。）

4. **方法或狀態的副詞**：

> actively（活躍地）, willingly（願意地）, gladly（高興地）, wisely（聰明地）,
> wrongly（錯誤地）, carefully（小心地）, fast（快地）, quickly（快地）,
> promptly（立即地）, how（如何）, anyhow（無論如何）, calmly（平靜地）,
> quietly（安靜地）, distinctly（清楚地）, easily（容易地）, simply（只）, …

The little boy behaved **badly**. （那個小男孩行為惡劣。）

The birds sang **sweetly**. （這些鳥唱歌真美。）

Better **late** than **never**. （遲做總比不做好。）

Every soldier fought **bravely** and **well**. （每個士兵都英勇作戰。）

Anyhow you can try, even if there is not much chance of success.

〔縱然沒有多大成功的機會,至少（無論如何）你要試一試。〕

5. **肯定或否定的副詞：**

> yes（是的），certainly（的確），surely（確實），of course（當然），evidently（顯然地），
> indeed（的確），naturally（自然地），obviously（明顯地），precisely（正是），
> entirely（完全地），no（不），not（不），never（絕不），…

下面是一些例句：

> Do you know Mr. Smith?（你認識史密斯先生嗎？）
> **Yes**.（= *Yes, I know him.*）（是的。）

> Is John here?（約翰在嗎？）
> **No**.（= *No, he isn't here.*）（不在。）

> Will you help me?（你願意幫我嗎？）
> **Certainly**.（= *Yes, I will help you.*）（當然。）

> Do you agree?（你同意嗎？）
> Oh, **absolutely**.（= *Oh yes, I agree completely.*）（噢，我完全同意。）

> Will you do what he wants?（你會照他希望的去做嗎？）
> **Never**!（= *I shall never do what he wants!*）（絕不！）

III. 疑問副詞（Interrogative Adverbs）：疑問副詞只有 **when**, **where**, **how**, **why** 四個字，
按照意義上之用途分為：

1. **表時間的疑問副詞：**

  ⑴ **when**（= **at what time**）…?（何時？）
  ⑵ **how long** ………………?（多久？）
  ⑶ **how often** ………………?（多久一次？）

  When will you come back?（你什麼時候回來？）
  Next month.（下個月。）

  (**At**) **What time** do you go to bed?（你何時就寢？）
  At ten o'clock.（十點。）

  Until **when** will you stay here?（你打算在此停留多久？）
  = **How long** will you stay here?
  I will stay here until next week.（我打算待到下個星期。）

  How long have you been in Taipei?（你在台北有多久了？）
  Three years.（三年。）

  How often do you write home?（你多久給家裡寫封信？）
  Twice a month.（一個月兩次。）

> 【註】 **用 when 詢問過去的動作時間，其動作該用過去式**，不可用現在完成式，
> **但暗含否定意味的修辭疑問句例外**。（參照 p.663）
> <u>比較下列句子：</u>
> **When** did you bring it here?（你是什麼時候把它帶到這裡來的？）
> **When** have I told a lie?
> = *I haven't told a lie.*（我幾時說過謊的？——我從來沒有說過謊。）

2. **表地方的疑問副詞：**

where（= **to** *or* **in what place**）…?
whence ……………………………?　　　問地方？
whither ……………………………?

how far ……………………………? 問多遠？
how long ……………………………? 問多長？

Where does he live?（他住在什麼地方？）
Where are you from?（你是哪裡人？）【問籍貫】
Where are you going to?（你要到哪裡去？）
How far is it from here to the airport?（從這裡到機場有多遠？）
How long is the Tamsui River?（淡水河有多長？）

【注意】　在文言上以 **whence** 代 **from where**，以 **whither** 代 **where to**。
　　　　We know neither **whence** we came nor **whither** we are going.
　　　　（我們不知自己從何處來，也不知要往何處去。）

【註】① "**where**" 除詢問地方外，可用於抽象場合，非指實際的場所。
　　　　Where am I wrong?〔我什麼地方（哪一點）錯了呢？〕

　　　② 在 **where**…**there** 中，**where** = **if** 是引導表「條件」的副詞子句。（詳見 p.523）
　　　　Where（= **If**）there is no fire, **there** is no smoke.（無風不起浪。）

3. **表方法或狀態的疑問副詞：**

How ……………?

How（= In what manner）has he done it?（他做得如何？── 是好是壞）
How（= By what means）did he do it?（他是如何做的？── 指方法）
How（= In what state of health）is your mother?（你母親好嗎？── 指狀態）

【註】① **how** 問及行為方式，用「**by** + 動名詞」回答。
　　　　How did you learn English so well?
　　　　（你是怎麼把英文學得這麼好？）
　　　　(I learned English) **By speaking** it every day.
　　　　（我是靠每天說。）

　　　② **how** 問工具或裝備，用「**with** + 工具或裝備」回答。
　　　　How did you open the door?
　　　　（你是怎麼把門打開的？）
　　　　(I opened it) **With a key**.
　　　　（用鑰匙。）

　　　③ **how** 問交通工具或連絡方法，用「**by** + 單數名詞」回答。
　　　　How can we get to Taichung?
　　　　（我們怎樣可以到台中去？）

$$
(\text{You can get there})
\begin{cases}
\textbf{By plane}. \,(\text{搭飛機。}) \\
\textbf{By train}. \,(\text{搭火車。}) \\
\textbf{By bus}. \,(\text{搭巴士車。}) \\
\quad \vdots
\end{cases}
$$

【例外】on foot（步行），on a bicycle（騎腳踏車），on horseback（騎馬）。

4. **表程度或數量的疑問副詞：**

How ················? (= **To what extent**···?)

How many ·······? (加可數名詞)

How much ·······? (加不可數名詞)

How do you like your new job? (你喜歡你的新工作嗎？)

How do you like it? (你覺得它怎麼樣？)

$$
\text{回答：}
\begin{cases}
\text{It's not bad.}\,(\text{不錯。}) \\
\text{It's O.K.}\,(\text{還可以。}) \\
\text{I like it very much.}\,(\text{我很喜歡它。}) \\
\text{I don't like it very much.}\,(\text{我不太喜歡它。})
\end{cases}
$$

How many times a week do you go to the movies? (你一週看幾次電影？)

(= *How often do you go to the movies in a week?*)

How much time did you spend there? (你在那裡待多久？)

(= *How long did you stay there?*)

5. **表原因的疑問副詞：**

Why ················? (= **For what reason**···?)

Why did you not attend the meeting? (你為何不參加會議？)

Why is it so difficult to learn English? (學英文為何這麼難？)

Why not let her do as she likes? (為什麼不讓她隨心所欲地去做？)

【注意】① 有時 **why** 可用 **what**···**for**? 來代替。

　　　　　Why did he propose such a thing? (他為何提議這樣的事？)

　　　　　= **What** did he propose such a thing **for**?

　　　　② 「**why not** + 原形動詞」在口語中用來向對方提出勸告，回答時用 yes 之類的詞語。

　　　　　Why not go to church? (為什麼不上教堂做禮拜？)

$$
\begin{cases}
\text{O.K.} \\
\text{Yes.}
\end{cases}
(\text{好，我去。})
$$

【註 1】 疑問副詞的加強語氣：

　　　　① 通常我們說 Why are you always so late? (你為何老是遲到？)

　　　　　如果要**強調上句話**可以寫成 **How is it that** you are always so late?

　　　　　(你究竟為什麼老是遲到？)

② 一般我們說 When were you last in Hong Kong?

〔你最後一次（上一次）在香港是什麼時候？〕

如果要強調「**什麼時候**」就應寫成：

When was it that you were last in Hong Kong?

③ 如果**強調地點**就把 Where had you been last night? 寫成：

Where was it that you had been last night?（你昨晚去了哪裡？）

④ 回答此類加強疑問詞的疑問句用 "**It is (was)**…" 的句型。

When was it that you were last in Hong Kong?

（你最後一次在香港是什麼時候？）

It was five years ago.（五年前。）

【註 2】 關於 **How** 的幾個特別用法：

① **How come** you called me a fool?（你為什麼叫我傻瓜呢？）

= *Why did you call me a fool?*

② I didn't pass the examination.（我考試不及格。）

How come?（怎麼會呢？）

③ **How about** going for a walk?（去散散步如何？）（參照 p.148, 441）

= *How do you feel about going for a walk?*

④ **How's that?** 有三種意思：

ⓐ What did you say? Will you please repeat that?

（你說什麼？請你再說一次好嗎？）

ⓑ What is the explanation of that?（怎麼回事？）

ⓒ What's your opinion of that?（你的看法如何？）

【註 3】 **How** 與形容詞或副詞並用，可以作成許多疑問句。

How long（問多長或多久）	How far（問多遠）
How soon（問還要多久）	How well（問健康）
How fast（問速度）	How wide（問多寬）
How often（問頻率）	How deep（問深度）
How old（問年齡）	How tall（問身高）
How high（問高度）	How much（問數量）
How heavy（問多重）	How many（問數目）

【註 4】 疑問副詞與不定詞：（參照 p.418）

疑問副詞 + 不定詞 = 名詞片語，可以做主詞、主詞補語或受詞。

He was not sure of **where to go**.（他不確定要去哪裡。）

I shall tell you **how to write a composition**.（我要告訴你如何寫一篇作文。）

【註 5】 疑問副詞與名詞子句：

將疑問副詞所引導的句子變為名詞子句可做主詞、受詞，或補語，**要注意其主詞與動詞位置的排列**：

Where did he come from?（他來自何處？）

Where he came from is still unknown.（他來自何處，仍然沒人知道。）【做主詞】

Why was he late?（他爲什麼遲到？）

I don't know **why he was late**.（我不知道他爲何遲到。）【做受詞】

When could we get there?（我們什麼時候能夠到達那裡呢？）

The question is **when we could get there**.【做補語】

（問題是我們什麼時候能夠到達那裡。）

IV. 關係副詞（**Relative Adverbs**）：**關係副詞是兼有連接詞作用的副詞**，通常用於表示時間、地點、方法、理由等名詞之後，**引導形容詞子句**，這些名詞則稱爲關係副詞的**先行詞（或前述詞）**，有時候可以省略。

The time ***when this took place*** was five o'clock.（這件事發生的時間是五點鐘。）── 表時間

The village ***where I was born*** is very small.（我出生的那個村莊很小。）── 表地方

That is (the reason) ***why I cannot consent***.（那就是我不能同意的理由。）── 表理由

This is (the way) ***how it happened***.（那就是這樣發生的。）── 表方法

【註】 關係副詞 **where** 也可用來引導副詞子句表條件：（詳見 p.523）

Where there is a will, there is a way.（有志者，事竟成。）【Where = If】
　　副　詞　子　句

Where there is no rain, farming is difficult.（沒雨水的地方很難耕種。）
　　副　詞　子　句

1. **關係副詞與疑問副詞的區別**：這兩種副詞很容易混淆，其實要分辨它們並不困難，只要記住下面的原則：

> 關係副詞所引導的是形容詞子句。
>
> 疑問副詞所引導的是名詞子句。

The year ***when I was born*** is 1978.（我出生的那一年是 1978。）
　　　　　關係副詞

He asked me ***when I was born***.（他問我何時出生。）
　　　　　　　　　疑問副詞

The town ***where he lives*** is far from here.（他所居住的城鎮離這裡很遠。）
　　　　　關係副詞

Do you know ***where he lives***?（你知道他住在哪裡嗎？）
　　　　　　　疑問副詞

I know the reason **why** *he did so*. （我知道他為何這樣做的理由。）
關係副詞

I know **why** *he did so*. （我知道他為何這樣做。）
疑問副詞

【注意】連接詞 when 與關係副詞 when 的比較：

> 連接詞 when 引導副詞子句，修飾主要子句裡的動詞。
> 關係副詞 when 引導形容詞子句，修飾其先行詞。

The fog will clear away **when** *daylight comes*. （陽光出來時，霧就會消失。）
連接詞

He doesn't know the exact time **when** *daylight comes*. （他不知道天亮的確切時間。）
關係副詞

2. **關係副詞與關係代名詞的比較**：關係副詞與關係代名詞的主要功能都是引導形容詞子句；不過**關係副詞充當副詞用，而關係代名詞充當代名詞用**。

This is the village **which** I visited last year. 【正】（這是我去年到過的村莊。）
This is the village *where* I visited last year. 【誤】
【where 沒有代名詞作用，在形容詞子句裡不能做 visit 的受詞】

This is the village **where** I was born. 【正】（這是我出生的村莊。）
This is the village *which* I was born. 【誤】【關代 which 在形容詞子句中沒有位子】

【注意】事實上有時候在關係代名詞之前加一介詞，其作用即等於關係副詞。

The summer vacation is the only part of the year **when** I am free.
= The summer vacation is the only part of the year **during which** I am free.
（暑假是我一年當中唯一有空的時候。）

Tell me the exact time **when** he is expected to arrive in Taipei.
= Tell me the exact time **at which** he is expected to arrive in Taipei.
（告訴我他預計抵達台北的確切時間。）

【註】① 在口語中亦可用 **that** 代替關係副詞 **when, why, how** 等字，或省略。

Joe was born on the very day **that** (= when) his grandmother died.
（喬就是在他祖母去世的那天誕生的。）

I am rather satisfied with the way **that** (= how) he has done it.
（我非常滿意他做這件事的方法。）

The reason **that** (= why) he was dismissed is not difficult to explain.
（他被解雇的理由不難解釋。）

以上三個例句中的 that 均可省略。

② 只有在 "**the place**" 之後的 **where** 才可用 **that** 代替，或省略。

This is the place (*where*) we used to live. (這是我們以前住的地方。)

= This is the place **that** we used to live.

= This is the place **at which** we used to live.

> 【比較】
>
> This is the house **where** I live. (這是我住的房子。)【 不可用 that 代替 where 】
>
> = This is the house **in which** I live.
>
> = This is the house **which** I live **in**.

3. **關係副詞的限定用法與補述用法：**(參照 p.161)

(1) **限定用法：**關係副詞所引導的形容詞子句，若旨在修飾其先行詞時，則用限定用法。

Mary arrived at the very hour *when the child had the accident.*

(瑪麗就在那孩子發生意外的時候到達了。)

This is the house *where the murder took place.*

(這就是發生謀殺案的那棟房子。)

I never found out the reason *why she was dismissed.*

(我老是查不出她被解雇的理由。)

That is the way *he always treats me.* (那就是他平常對待我的樣子。)

= That is *how* he always treats me. 【 the way how…是古老的用法，現已不用 】

(2) **補述用法（非限定用法）：**在此用法中，關係副詞所引導的子句不是形容詞子句，而是一個對等子句，**主要作用在於補述前面子句之不足或意有未盡者**，所以補述用法中，關係副詞前面要用**逗點**(,)。

He went to Taipei, **where** (= and there) he stayed for three weeks.

(他去了台北，在那裡住了三個星期。)

He stayed there till Saturday, **when** (= and then) he started for Keelung.

(他在那裡住到星期六，然後動身前往基隆。)

【注意】補述用法的關係副詞僅限於 **when** 與 **where** 兩字。

4. 為簡潔起見，口語中常將關係副詞的先行詞省略，如此，**原來修飾先行詞的形容詞子句，由於先行詞省略而變成名詞子句或副詞子句。**

Tell me the reason *why you dislike him.* (告訴我你為什麼不喜歡他的理由。)
　　　　　　　　　形　容　詞　子　句

Tell me *why you dislike him.* (告訴我你為什麼不喜歡他。)
　　名　詞　子　句

Put it at the place ***where*** *you found it.*（把它放在你找到它的地方。）
　　　　　　　　　　　　形　容　詞　子　句

Put it ***where*** *you found it.*（把它放在你找到它的地方。）
　　　　副　詞　子　句

5. 關係副詞 **the**（參照 p.504）

公式：the ＋ 比較級 ＋ 主詞 ＋ 動詞…, the ＋ 比較級 ＋ 主詞 ＋ 動詞…

在此公式中，the 不是冠詞而是副詞，**第一個 the 是關係副詞，意即 by how much**；**第二個 the 則為指示副詞，意即 by so much**。

The *sooner you do it*, ***the*** better it will be.
　　　副　詞　子　句
＝ ***By how much*** *sooner you do it*, ***by so much*** better it will be.
＝ ***In what degree*** *sooner you do it*, ***in that degree*** better it will be.
（你越早去做這件事，這件事的成效就越好。）

The *higher up you go*, ***the*** colder it becomes.（你爬得越高，就越寒冷。）
　　　副　詞　子　句

The *harder you work*, ***the*** sooner you will improve.（你越用功，進步得就越快。）
　　　副　詞　子　句

The *more money a man has*, ***the*** more greedy he will be.（一個人錢越多，就會越貪心。）
　　　副　詞　子　句

V. 複合關係副詞（**Compound Relative Adverbs**）：when, where 和 how 三個關係副詞字尾各加 ever 成為複合關係副詞。

複合關係副詞 whenever, wherever, however 可加強語氣或表示讓步。（參照 p.527）

whenever ① { ＝ **at any time when**（在任何時候…）
　　　　　　　　 ＝ **every time when**（在每個時候…）
　　　　　　② 　＝ **no matter when**（無論什麼時候…）

wherever ① { ＝ **in (at) any place where**（在任何地方…）
　　　　　　　　 ＝ **to everywhere**（每個地方…）
　　　　　　② 　＝ **no matter where**（無論什麼地方…）

however ＝ **no matter how**（無論如何…）

1. 表加強語氣：

Please come ***whenever***（＝ at any time when）*it is convenient for you.*
＝ Please come ***whenever*** *it is to your convenience.*
＝ Please come at your convenience.
（只要對你方便，請隨時來。）
Sit ***wherever*** *you like.*（想坐哪裡就坐哪裡。）
＝ Sit at any place ***where*** *you like.*

2. 表示讓步：

Whenever（= No matter when）*you may go*, you will find him at his books.
（無論你什麼時候去，都會發現他在讀書。）

Whenever（= No matter when）*you may come*, you will find me at home.
（無論你什麼時候來，你都會發現我在家。）

Wherever（= No matter where）*one may go*, one will never find a place like home.
（無論一個人到哪裡，都找不到像家那樣溫暖的地方。）

Wherever（= No matter where）*you may go*, you cannot succeed without
    perseverance.
（無論你到什麼地方去，沒有毅力就無法成功。）

However（= No matter how）*hard you may try*, you cannot master a language in a
    month or two.
（無論你多麼努力，都無法在一兩個月內精通一種語言。）

However（= No matter how）*hard I try*, I can never catch up with him.
（無論我多麼努力，我永遠趕不上他。）

【注意】 **表示讓步也可有不同的結構**，見下例：（詳見 p.532）

　　　　However（= No matter how）*hard he tries*, he will never succeed.
　　　　= *Hard **as** he may try*, he will never succeed.
　　　　= ***Though** he tries hard*, he will never succeed.
　　　　（無論他如何努力嘗試，他絕不會成功。）

【註】 **however** 還可當對等連接詞，作「但是；然而」解，與 **still**, **yet**, **nevertheless**
　　　可通用。（詳見 p.472）

　　　Later, **however**, she made up her mind to study hard.
　　　（可是，後來她終於下定決心努力用功。）

　　　It may be possible or not; **however**, we shall see.
　　　（那也許可能也許不可能，然而，我們將來就知道。）

第三章　幾個特殊副詞的用法

I. 時間副詞：

1. ago, before, since

(1) 句中伴有表示時間長短的副詞（如 a long time, a few days 等）時：

ago 和過去簡單式連用。

before 常和過去完成式連用。

since 可代替 ago，也可代替 before，但很少用。

He died three years **ago** (*or* **since**).（他三年前去世了。）

He said his father had died three years **before** (*or* **since**).

（他說他父親已經死了三年了。）

【註】before 也可以用於以未來為基準的情形，等於 earlier。

If you are to take the 10 p.m. train, you should reach the station at least
ten minutes **before** (= earlier) .

（如果你要搭晚上十點的火車，你必須至少早十分鐘以前到達火車站。）

(2) 句中沒有表示時間長短的副詞時：(ago 不可單獨用)

① **before** 單獨使用，表示 **before now**（現在以前）或 **before then**（當時以前），可以
和現在完成式、過去簡單式，或過去完成式連用。

I have met him **before**.（我以前曾遇到過他。）

I met him once **before**.（我以前遇到過他一次。）

She said she had met him **before**.（她說她以前遇到過他。）

② **since** 單獨使用時，表示 **since then**（從那時以後），而且有繼續到現在的意思，因此
動詞用現在完成式。

I met him last month and have not seen him **since**.

（我自上個月遇到他以後，就再也沒見過他了。）

【註】為加強語氣，可在 **before** 和 **since** 之前加 ever。

He was then happier than **ever before** or **since**.

（他當時比當時以前或當時以後都幸福。）

【注意】since 和 before 除了做副詞外，還可做連接詞（p.492）和介系詞（p.557）。

2. ever, once

(1) **ever** 的用法

① **用在疑問句、條件句、否定句時，作「曾經」或「一旦有機會的時候」解，（此時**
ever = at any time)。

Have you **ever** seen an alligator?（你曾經看過鱷魚嗎？）

If you **ever** go to Taipei, be sure to visit the Palace Museum.

（如果你一旦去台北，一定要參觀故宮博物院。）

He scarcely **ever** (= *almost never*) comes to see me now.（他現在很少來看我。）

② **用於比較級或最高級**（此時 ever 不可換用 never）。

This is the best book that I have **ever** read.（這是我所讀過最好的書。）

Shakespeare was the greatest playwright that **ever** lived.
（莎士比亞是有史以來最偉大的劇作家。）

It is raining harder than **ever**. （雨下得比以前大。）

③ **用來加強語氣**

He is **ever so** rich a man. （他是非常有錢的人。）

= He is **ever such** a rich man.

= *He is a very rich man.*

Thank you **ever so** (= very) much. （非常謝謝你。）

Home is home, be it **ever so** humble. （家雖簡陋，沒有一個地方比家更溫暖。）

= *Home is home, however humble it may be.*

I have known him **ever since** he was a boy. （從他還是小孩的時候起，我就認識他了。）

I am happier now than **ever before**. （我現在比以前任何時候都快樂。）

④ **ever 用於疑問詞後**，其意為「到底；究竟」，此時

ever = in the name of God   = the devil

     = in nature   = the deuce

     = in the world   = on earth

What **ever** do you mean? （你究竟是什麼意思？）

When (Where, How) **ever** did you lose it? 〔你到底何時（何地，怎樣）將它遺失的？〕

※此時疑問詞不能和 ever 相連，即不可寫成 Whenever, However 等。

⑤ **ever 的慣用語**

She seldom, **if ever**, goes to the cinema. （她很少去看電影。）

※ **seldom if ever**
   = seldom or never   （很少；難得；簡直不）
   = very seldom

He is a hero, **if ever** there was one. （倘若有過英雄，他便是一個。）

As if he would **ever** do such a thing! （就好像他一直做這種事似的！）

= *He would certainly not do it.* （ = 事實上，他絕不會做這種事。）

⑵ **once 的用法**

① **用於肯定句時**，作「曾經」、「從前」、「一度」解。

I **once** saw him. （我曾經見過他。）

The novel was **once** very popular but nobody reads it today.
（這本小說一度很流行，但現在沒人讀它了。）

Once upon a time there was a princess… （從前有一個公主…）

There **once** lived a King who… （從前有一個國王…）

② **置於句末作「一次」解。**

I saw him **once**. （我見過他一次。）   I have been there **once**. （我到過那裡一次。）

This clock needs winding **once** a week. （這個時鐘每週須上發條一次。）

③ **用於條件句作「一旦」解。**

*If you **once** understand this rule*, you will have no further difficulty.

= ***Once** you understand this rule*, you will have no further difficulty.

（你一旦了解這個規則，就不會再有困難。）【Once 放在條件子句句首時是連接詞（詳見 p.523）】

3. **now**, **just**, **just now**

　now：與現在簡單式、現在進行式、現在完成式連用，作「現在」解。

　just：與現在完成式和過去完成式連用，作「剛剛」解。

　just now：與**過去簡單式**連用時＝a moment ago；與**現在簡單式**或**現在進行式**連用時
　　　　　　　＝just at the moment，都是加強 now 的語氣。

Where do you live **now**?（你現在住在哪裡？）

I am studying **now**.（我現在正在唸書。）

We have **now** left the station.（我們現在已經離開了車站。）

I have **just** finished my homework.（我剛剛做完我的作業。）

I had **just** finished my homework when you came in.（當你進來時，我剛做完作業。）

It's **just** four o'clock.（正好四點鐘。）

= *It's four o'clock sharp.*

I (*only*) **just** caught the train.（我剛好趕上火車。）=（我差點兒沒趕上火車。）

The train started **just now** (= a moment ago).（火車剛開走。）

My father is staying in London **just now** (= just at the moment).
（我父親此刻正在倫敦。）

He is rather busy **just now** (= just at the moment).（他現在相當忙。）

4. **already**, **yet**, **still**

(1) **already**：用於肯定句，作「已經」解。

　yet：用於否定句，作「還」解；用於疑問句，作「已經」解。

　Have you read it **yet**?（你已經讀過它嗎？）

　Yes, I have read it **already**.（是的，我已經讀過它了。）

　No, I have not read it **yet**.（不，我還沒讀過它。）

　※ **already**：用在疑問句和否定句中表驚訝。

　　【比較】{ Have you done it **already**?（你已經做完了？）【表驚訝】
　　　　　　{ Have you done **yet**?（你已經做好了嗎？）【單純問句】
　　　　　　　You're not going **already**, are you?（你不會是要走了吧？）【表驚訝】

(2) **yet**：① 有時用在肯定句中，表否定的意味。

　　　　　　　He is **yet** alive.（他還活著。）

　　　　　　　= He is not yet dead.（＝他還沒死。）

　　　　　② **yet** 與比較級連用，作「更；愈」解。

　　　　　　　I have **yet** more important things to do.（我還有更重要的事要做。）

(3) ① **still** 置於動詞前後，表動作與狀態的持續，作「仍然」解。

　　　He is **still** at school.（他還在上學。）

　　② **still** 與比較級連用，作「更；愈」解。

　　　Mary is young but Edith is **still** younger.（瑪麗很年輕，但伊蒂絲更年輕。）

　　③ **still** 作連接詞用表讓步，作「可是」解。（詳見 p.471）

　　　I am tired; **still** I will walk farther.（我雖然疲倦，可是我還要向更遠的地方走。）

II. 場所的副詞：

1. **here, there**

(1) **there**（那裡），**here**（這裡）

We shall soon be **there**.（不久我們就會到那裡。）

I live **here**.（我住在這裡。）

(2) **there + is (are)**…（有…） 此種用法 there 不可譯成「那裡」，**be 動詞後的名詞才是主詞。**

There is a book.（有一本書。）

There are many students *there*.（有許多學生在那裡。）【句尾的 there 才可譯成「那裡」】

【比較】 **There is** a chair *in the room*.（有一把椅子在房間裡。）

【註1】 可用於此種句型的不及物動詞還有 sit（坐），lie（躺），stand（站著），live（住），come, arrive, go, enter（進入），appear（出現），happen（發生）…等表示「**存在、生死、來去、事件**」的動詞。

Once **there lived** an old man.（以前住著一位老人。）

There came a monkey and a dog.（來了一隻猴子和一隻狗。）

【註2】 here 也可用於此種句型，但 **here 有表示「在這裡」的意思。**

There is a book.（有一本書。）

Here is a book.（這裡有一本書。）

【註3】 當主詞成為代名詞時，要改為 **There (Here) + 主詞（代名詞）+ 動詞**的形式。（參照 p.5, 643）

比較下面兩句：

There comes **the bus**!（公共汽車來了！）

There **it** comes!（它來了！）

(3) **There is no + 動名詞 = It is impossible + 不定詞 = No one can + 原形動詞**（參照 p.439）

There is no undoing the past.

= *It is impossible to undo the past.*

= *No one can undo the past.*

（要使過去的事恢復原狀是不可能的。—— 覆水難收。）

(4) **there is to be**（預定有）

There is to be a very good TV program tomorrow.（明天將有一個很好的電視節目。）

(5) **there being**（因為）（獨立分詞構句，參照 p.458, 462）

There being no buses or taxis, we had to go home on foot.

= *As there were no buses or taxis, we had to go home on foot.*

（因為沒有公車或計程車，我們只好步行回家。）

(6) **there, here 的一些慣用語：**

Here they are!（他們終於到了！）

Here we are.（到了，我們到了我們的目的地。）

Here you are!（你要的東西在這裡。）

= *Here is what you asked for.*

Are you **there**?（喂！是你嗎？）【電話用語 = Hello!】

2. **far**

(1) **表距離：**

My house is not **far** from the station.（我家離車站不遠。）

How **far** is it from here to the airport?（從這裡到機場有多遠？）

(2) **表程度或範圍：**

Your work is **far from** (being) satisfactory.（你的工作離讓人滿意還差得遠呢！）

= Your work is **not** satisfactory **at all**.（你的工作一點也不令人滿意。）

The newspaper accounts are **far from** being true.（報紙上的報導絕非事實。）

(3) **far 形容比較級、最高級均可；by far 用於最高級前，不可用於比較級前，但比較級前有 the 時，也可用 by far。**（參照 p.207）

He is **by far** the best boy in the class.（他是班上最好的小孩。）

It is **far** hotter today than yesterday.（今天比昨天還要熱得多。）

This is **by far** the best of all.（這是所有當中最好的。）

This is **by far** the better of the two.（這是兩者中較好的。）

III. 程度、量的副詞：

1. **very, much**

(1) **very 修飾形容詞、副詞；much（或 very much）修飾動詞。**

This picture is **very** beautiful.（這幅畫很美。）

He walks **very** fast.（他走得很快。）

I like it **very much**.（我非常喜歡它。）

Mary doesn't sing **much**（= often）.（瑪麗不常唱歌。）

(2) **very 修飾原級形容詞及副詞；much (very much) 修飾比較級、最高級的形容詞及副詞。**

He is **very** tall.（他很高。）

He is **much** taller than you.（他比你高多了。）

He walks **very** fast.（他走得很快。）

He walks **much** faster than you.（他走得比你快多了。）

This is **much**（= by far）the best.（這是最好的。）

John is **much** the best player in the town.（約翰是這鎮上最好的選手。）

【註 1】 **若 very 之前有定冠詞，則可修飾最高級形容詞或副詞，即**

> the very + 最高級 = much the + 最高級

This is **the very** best of all.（這是所有當中最好的。）

= This is **much the** best of all.

This CD is **the very** best for learning English pronunciation.

= This CD is **much the** best for learning English pronunciation.

（這片 CD 是學習英語發音最好的 CD。）

I will do **the very** best I can. (我將盡我的全力。)

= I will do my utmost.

He drank it to **the very** last drop. (他喝完了最後的一滴。)

【註2】 **very** 作形容詞用，置於 **the, this, that** 或所有格形容詞與名詞之間，此時 **very** 作加強語氣用，譯為「正是」或「同一的」。

This is the **very** book I want. (這正是我要的書。)

At that time I was standing on this **very** spot. (當時我就站在這個地方。)

⑶ **very** 修飾現在分詞；**much** (**very much**) 修飾過去分詞。

I heard a **very** surprising item of news. (我聽到一個非常令人驚訝的消息。)

I was **much** surprised at the news. (對於這個消息我覺得非常驚訝。)

This novel is **very** interesting. (這本小說很有趣。)

He is too **much** exhausted after the long journey. (長途旅行後，他非常疲憊。)

【註1】 **tired** (疲倦的)，**learned** (有學問的)，為純粹形容詞，用 **very** 修飾，不用 **much**。

The teacher must be **very** tired. (老師一定很累了。)

He is **very** tired of having the same kind of fruit every day.

(他對於每天吃同一種水果覺得很厭倦。)

【註2】 限定用法 (即置於名詞之前) 的過去分詞常用 **very** 來修飾。

He is a **very** experienced English teacher. (他是個很有經驗的英文老師。)

He wore a **very** surprised expression at seeing me.

(他看到我時，顯露非常驚訝的表情。)

【註3】 有些常見**作形容詞用的過去分詞**，按規則應該用 much 或 very much 修飾，但口語中卻**常用 very 修飾**。

George is **very** (**much, very much**) delighted to see his aunt.

(喬治很高興看到他的阿姨。)

I am **very** (**much, very much**) pleased at your coming. (你來了我很高興。)

【注意】 此類可用 **very** 或 **much, very much** 同時修飾的作形容詞用的過去分詞有：

frightened (害怕的)，delighted (高興的)，excited (興奮的)，
disappointed (失望的)，pleased (高興的)，annoyed (困擾的)，
satisfied (滿意的)，contented (滿足的)，ashamed (感到可恥的)，
limited (有限的)，celebrated (有名的)，interested (有興趣的)，
surprised (驚訝的)，disgusted (覺得噁心的)，dejected (沮喪的) …

⑷ 只能做敘述用法的形容詞，多以 **a-** 字起頭者，不能用 very 來修飾，只能用 **much** (**very much**)，如 alone, alike, alive, aware 等，但 afraid 例外，也可用 very 修飾。(參照 p.191)

The twins look **much** alike. (這對雙胞胎看起來很像。)

【比較】 He is **much** afraid of it. 【正，文言】

He is **very** afraid of it. 【正，口語】

He is **very much** afraid of it. 【正，常用】

2. so, too

⑴ **so, too** 作「非常」（ **very** ）解，so 用於口語，**too** 則強調語氣。

I'm **so** (= *very*) glad to see you. (我很高興見到你。)

It was **so** kind of you! (你人眞好！)

We have had **too** much rain lately. (最近這裡下太多雨了。)

It is **too** hot for work. (天氣熱得無法工作。)

⑵ **so** 的幾個句型
{
① **not so +**（ 形或副 ）**+ as**
② **so + 形 + as to +** 原形動詞
③ **so + 形或副 + that**
④ **so + 形 + a + 名詞…**
}
(參照 p.507, 516)

① It is **not so** big **as** an elephant. (牠不像大象那麼大。)

He was **not so** <u>much</u> angry **as** disappointed. (他的失望超過憤怒。)
　　　　　　　　 (副)

② He is not **so** stupid **as to** do that. (他不會笨到去做那事。)

Would you be **so** kind **as to** help me? (你能好心幫我的忙嗎？)

③ He was **so** ill **that** we had to send for a doctor.

(他病得很嚴重，我們必須去請醫生來。)

He spoke **so** fast **that** we couldn't understand what he said.

(他說得那麼快，所以我們無法了解他所說的話。)

④ He is not **so** clever **a** boy (= *such a clever boy*) as his brother.

(他沒有他兄弟那麼聰明。)

She is **so** lovely **a** girl (= *such a lovely girl*) that everybody likes her.

(她是那麼可愛，每個人都喜歡她。)

⑶ **too…to~** (太…以致於不能~)(參照 p.415)

That is **too** good **to** be true. (那太好了，不可能是眞的。)

This tea is **too** hot **to** drink. (這杯茶太燙不能喝。)

He was **too** frightened **to** speak. (他驚訝得說不出話來。)

= *He was so frightened that he could not speak.*

⑷ **含 too 之片語：**(參照 p.416)

I am **but too** glad to be of help to you. (我很高興能幫助你。)

= *I am **only too** glad to be of help to you.* 【 but too = only too = very, very 】

The holidays ended **all too** soon. (假期結束得太快。)【 all too 總是太；過於 】

We were **none too** early for the train. (我們剛好趕上火車，一點也不早。)

【 在 too 前 none = not at all 】

It is **never too** hard for you to study. (你儘量用功好了。)

= *You **cannot** study **too** hard.*

You **cannot** be **too** careful. (你再怎麼小心也不爲過。)

※ **cannot…too~** 作「無論怎樣…也不爲過」解。(參照 p.314)

One cannot be too faithful to one's duties.

(一個人不論對他的職務多忠實都不爲過。＝一個人對他的職務越忠心越好。)

(5) **too 置於句尾作「也」解,要用於肯定句。**

I like music, too. (我也喜歡音樂。)

如果怕有模稜兩可的情形時,too 則緊置於所修飾字的後面。比較下列兩句:

I, **too**, have been to Paris.

(= *I, as well as he, you, have been to Paris.*) (你們去過巴黎,我也去過。)

I've been to Paris, **too**.

(= *I've been to Paris as well as to Rome, Milan, etc.*)

(我去過羅馬、米蘭等地,還去過巴黎。)

【註】① **also 亦作「也」解,也用於肯定句**,但通常置於 be 動詞或助動詞之後,其他動詞之前。

The fruit crops are **also** good this year. (今年水果的收成也很好。)

Grown-ups **also** like to play with toys. (成年人也喜歡玩玩具。)

I've **also** had pains in my back. (我的背也在痛。)

② **否定句及疑問句中的「也」用 "either"。**

I don't want the yellow one and I don't want the white one, **either**.

(我不要那個黃的,也不要那個白的。)

Haven't you smelt it, **either**? (你也沒有聞到它嗎?)

3. **hardly, scarcely, rarely, seldom, barely**

這五個字作「幾乎不;不常」解,**都含有否定的意味**,不可與否定詞並用。通常置於 be 動詞之後,其他動詞之前。(參照 p.662)

(1) **hardly 與 scarcely** (= **almost not**) **可以互換。**

We had **hardly** (*or* **scarcely**) left the house, when (*or* before) it began to rain.

(我們剛離開家,就下雨了。)

She is **hardly** (*or* **scarcely**) twenty. (她還不到二十歲。)

【註】嚴格地說,scarcely 偏重在頻繁的觀念,是指數量,而 hardly 表困難的程度。

He is **hardly** strong enough to take such a long journey.

(他的精力不足以做這樣的一個長途旅行。)

He **scarcely ever** (= almost never) goes to church. 【scarcely ever 是加強語氣】

(他幾乎不去做禮拜。)

(2) **seldom 與 rarely** 作「不常;很少」解,是 often 的相反詞。

He is **seldom** (*or* **rarely**) ill. (他很少生病。)

She **seldom** (*or* **rarely**) reads newspapers. (她不常看報紙。)

IV. **狀態副詞:**

1. **well, ill, badly** (參照 p.198)

(1) **well 的單純反義字是 badly。**

She speaks French **well**. (她法文說得很好。)

She speaks French **badly**. (她法文說得很差。)

(2) **成語中 well 的反義字為 ill。**

They speak **well** (*or* **ill**) of him. 〔他們說他的好話(壞話)。〕

(3) **badly** 表程度時，作「劇烈地；嚴重地」解。

We were **badly** beaten in the baseball match. (在棒球比賽中，我們輸得很慘。)

2. **so**

(1) 作「如此；這樣」解。(詳見 p.502)

As you treat me, *so* I shall treat you. (你怎樣對待我，我也怎樣對待你。)

As the father is, *so* is the son. (有其父必有其子。)

As you sow, *so* will you reap. (種瓜得瓜，種豆得豆 —— 惡有惡報，善有善報。)

As the lion is king of beasts, *so* is the eagle king of birds. (鷹為鳥王，猶如獅為獸王。)

As you make your bed, *so* you must lie on it. (自作自受。)

(2) **so that** 作「為了」(= **in order that**) 或「以致於」解。(參照 p.513)

Work *so that* you may earn your bread. (你要工作以謀生。)

Speak clearly, *so that* they may understand you. (說清楚一點，以便他們能聽懂你的意思。)

【註】 **so as to** 也作「以便於；以致於」解，接原形動詞 (= **in order to**)。(參照 p.413)

She is **so** young **as to** look quite like a child.

= She is so young that she looks quite like a child.

(她是如此的年輕，以致於看起來像個孩子。)

(3) **so** + 助動詞 (或 **be** 動詞) + 代名詞 (或名詞)，作「也」解，用於肯定句中。(參照 p.643)

You are young and **so am I**. (你年輕，我也年輕。)

Tom speaks French and **so does his brother**. (湯姆會說法文，他弟弟也會。)

(4) **so** + 代名詞 + 助動詞或 **be** 動詞，表贊同。(參照 p.643)

Tomorrow will be your birthday. (明天將是你的生日。)
You are right, **so** it will. (你說對了，明天是我的生日。)

It was cold yesterday. (昨天天氣很冷。)
Yes, **so** it was. (是的，是很冷。)

It is hot today. (今天天氣很熱。)
Yes, **so** it is. (是的，是很熱。)

(5) 一些片語：

or so = *about* 　　 It costs a dollar **or so**. (它值一塊錢左右。)

and so on = *and so forth* (等等)

so-so (馬馬虎虎)

so far as I am concerned = *as far as I am concerned* = *as for me* (就我而言)

so long as = *as long as* (只要)

so far as I know = *within my knowledge* (就我所知)

so to speak = *so to say* (可以說是)

so much as = *even* (甚至)

so (thus, this) far (到此程度)

so far from (不但不…反而)

even so = *very* (很)

V. 肯定與否定的副詞：

1. **yes**, **no**

(1) **在回答問句時，yes 表示肯定，no 表示否定。**

a. Are you a student?（你是學生嗎？）
- Yes, I am.〔是的，我是（學生）。〕
- No, I am not.〔不，我不是（學生）。〕

b. Aren't you a student?（你不是學生嗎？）
- Yes, I am.（不，我是學生。）
- No, I am not.（是的，我不是學生。）

c. Do you speak English?（你會說英文嗎？）
- Yes, I do.（是的，我會說英文。）
- No, I don't.（不，我不會說英文。）

d. Don't you speak English?（你不會說英文嗎？）
- Yes, I do.（不，我會說英文。）
- No, I don't.（是的，我不會說英文。）

【注意】 Yes 與 No 許多人在回答時常常混淆，尤其是在**對否定式的問句更甚**，如上例 d. 句中，「你不會說英文嗎？」按中文的習慣，必定回答：「是的，我不會說英文。」但在英文中卻不能用 Yes 而要用 No 來回答，因為後面的句子是否定的形式。我們只要牢記無論問句是肯定還是否定的，**在回答時 Yes 後要接肯定的內容，No 後要接否定的內容。**

(2) **yes 也可回答對方的呼喚：**

"Waiter!"（「服務生！」）

"Yes, sir."（= *What do you want, sir?*）（「是的，先生。」）=（「要點兒什麼，先生？」）

(3) **在祈使句中有下列一些標準回答：**

Open the door.（開門。）
- Yes, sir.（是的，先生。）
- I'm sorry, but my hands are full.（抱歉，我手上拿滿了東西。）

Don't open the door.（不要開門。）
- Yes, sir. (*or* Okay, I won't.)（是的，先生；好，我不開。）
- I'm sorry, but I have to go out.（抱歉，我非出去不可。）

Please sit down.（請坐。）
- Thank you.（謝謝。）
- I prefer to stand, thank you.（我寧願站著，謝謝。）

Hand in your paper, please.（請把作業交來。）
- I haven't finished yet.（我還沒做完。）
- Yes, Mr. Wilson.（是，威爾遜先生。）

Close the door, please.（請關上門。）
- Yes, certainly.（好的。）
- Sorry, I'm busy.（抱歉，我在忙。）

Let's go now!（我們現在走吧！）
- All right.（好的。）
- That's fine with me.（我沒意見。）

Please don't smoke in here.（請不要在這裡吸煙。）
【here 在此是名詞，in here「在這裡」，near here「在這裡附近」】
- Why not?（為什麼不行？）
- Sorry, I didn't see the sign.（抱歉，我沒看到那禁止吸煙的告示牌。）

Don't hurry.（不要急。）
- All right, I won't.（好的，我不會急。）
- Don't worry, I'll take my time.（別擔心，我會慢慢來。）

Do you mind opening the door?（你介意把門打開嗎？）
- Not at all.（一點也不。）
- Certainly not.（當然不會。）　這三句回答都是願意把門打開。
- Of course not.（當然不會。）

Would you mind sitting here?（你介意坐在這裡嗎？）
- No, I wouldn't mind.（不，我不介意。）　這兩句都是願意坐在那裡。
- Thank you.（謝謝。）

Do you mind if I turn on the radio?（你介意我打開收音機嗎？）
- No, go right ahead.（不介意，你儘管開吧。）　這兩句都贊成他開收音機。
- Of course not.（當然不介意。）
- I'm sorry, I'd rather you didn't.（很抱歉，你最好不要開。）

May I have some coffee?（我可以喝一點咖啡嗎？）
- Certainly.〔當然（可以喝）。〕
- Help yourself.（自己動手。）
- Yes, I'll bring it right away.（好的，我立刻端來。）

Would you mind if I didn't come?（我不能來你介意嗎？）
- Oh, I wish you would.（噢，我希望你能來。）
- No, that'll be all right.（不介意，沒關係。）
- Well, everyone will miss you.（嗯，我們大家都會想你的。）

⑷ **即使不是問句而對於對方否定事件有同感時用 No，反對時用 Yes；同意對方肯定事件用 Yes，反對時用 No。**
He does not work hard.（他不太努力。）
- **No**, he doesn't.（是的，他不太努力。）
- **Yes**, he does.（不是的，他很努力。）

2. not, no

⑴ **not 置於 be 動詞或助動詞之後，形成否定句。**

He can **not** swim.（他不會游泳。）
She is **not** a good nurse.（她不是個好護士。）

⑵ **not** 置於分詞、不定詞、動名詞之前表否定。（參照 p.422）

He insisted on **not** going there. （他堅持不去那裡。）

He warned me **not** to be late. （他警告我不要遲到。）

⑶ **not** 用於一些動詞之後，形成否定回答，相當於一個 that 子句。（參照 p.646）

A: Do you think he is ill? （你認爲他生病了嗎？）

B: I hope **not**. （我希望不是。）

= I hope *that he is not ill*.

A: Can you come next week? （下週你能來嗎？）

B: I'm afraid **not**. （我恐怕不能來。）

= I'm afraid *that I cannot come*.

此類動詞有：

think, suppose, believe, expect, fear, fancy（幻想；想像）, trust, hope, seem, appear, be afraid 等。

⑷ **no** 通常當形容詞，但**置於比較級形容詞或副詞之前時爲副詞**。

She is **no** better than before. （她沒有比以前好。）

He is **no** more able to read English than I am. （他和我都不懂英文。）

A: I can't understand this at all. （我完全不懂這個。）

B: **No** more can I. （我也不懂。）【此處 no more = neither，爲一特殊用法】

3. **never…without**; **never…but** （參照 p.440, 661）

I **never** see you **without** thinking of him. （我從來沒有看見你而不想到他。）

= **Whenever** I see you, I think of him. （每當我見到你，我就想到他。）

It **never** rains **but** it pours. （不雨則已，一雨傾盆。）

= **Whenever** it rains, it pours. （每當下雨，必定下傾盆大雨。）

4. **little**

⑴ **little** 和 **know, think, dream, imagine, guess, suspect, expect, realize** 等動詞連用時，等於 **not at all**（完全不；毫不）的意思，屬於準否定。（詳見 p.662）

You **little know** what mischief you have done! （你完全不知道你做了什麼壞事！）

I **little thought** that it was you. （我沒想到那就是你。）

I **little expected** that he would come. （我沒料到他會來。）

They **little suspect** that their plot has been discovered.

（他們絲毫沒想到他們的陰謀已被人發現。）

Little did I **dream** of ever seeing this day! 【是倒裝句，詳見 p.629】

（我作夢也沒想到會看到今日！）

⑵ 伴用 **how, so, as, too** 的 **little** 也可以說是一種否定。

This anecdote shows **how little** he knows the world. （從這軼事可知他多麼不知世故。）

He knows the world **so little** that he trusts everybody.

（他是如此的不知世故，以致於他會相信任何人。）

He knows the world **as little** as a baby. （他不知世故，正如一個嬰兒一樣。）

He knows the world **too little** to be a lawyer. （他太不知世故，以致於不能當律師。）

【註 1 】 little, a little 也可做表程度的副詞，其區別與做形容詞時是一樣的。

He is **little** better than he was yesterday. 【little = almost not 】

（他沒有比昨天好多少。）

He is **a little** better this morning. 【a little = somewhat 】

（他今天早上好一些了。）

【註 2 】 **not a little = very much**（不少）; not in the least = not at all（一點也不）。

He was **not a little** surprised when he heard the news.

（他聽到這個消息時很驚訝。）

I am **not in the least** interested.（我一點也不感興趣。）

VI. 其他幾個容易錯用的副詞：

1. sometimes, some times, sometime, some time 的用法

sometimes（有時候；偶爾）(= occasionally)

He **sometimes** smokes.（他偶爾抽煙。）

some times（好幾次）(= several times)

I have been in Hong Kong **some times**.（我到過香港好幾次。）

sometime（某一個時候）(現在或未來均可)

Come over and see me **sometime**.（找個時間來看看我。）

some time（一些時間）

He had been waiting for us for **some time** when we arrived at the station.

（當我們抵達車站時，他已等候我們一些時候了。）

2. almost, nearly 的用法：二字均作「幾乎」解。但 nearly 之後不可接否定字，almost 則可。

Almost【正】
Nearly【誤】 } no one believed her.（幾乎沒有人相信她。）

= Hardly anyone believed her.

3. all together, altogether 的用法

all together (*adv.*)：在一起地

They came { **all together**.【正】
altogether.【誤】 }（他們一起來。）

altogether (*adv.*)：總共；完全地

His debt amounted { **altogether**【正】
all together【誤】 } to one million dollars.

（他的債務總計達一百萬元。）

4. rather, fairly 的用法：rather（相當地）可與 too 或比較級連用，但 fairly（相當地；適度地）則不可。

The examination is { **rather**【正】
fairly【誤】 } too difficult for a high school student.

（這考試對高中生來說相當難。）

My sister is { **rather**【正】
fairly【誤】 } better today.（我妹妹今天好多了。）

He is a **fairly** good actor.（他是個相當好的演員。）

第四章 副詞的比較

I. **比較變化**：表程度、分量等的副詞，也和形容詞一樣，有比較的變化。

1. **規則變化**

(1) 單音節與少數二音節的副詞字尾**加 er 成比較級**，加 **est 成最高級**。

原級（Positive）	比較級（Comparative）	最高級（Superlative）
close（接近地）	closer	closest
fast（快地）	faster	fastest
hard（努力地）	harder	hardest
high（高地）	higher	highest
long（長久地）	longer	longest
loud（大聲地）	louder	loudest
often（常常）	{ oftener { more often	{ oftenest { most often
quick（快地；敏捷地）	quicker	quickest
soon（很快地）	sooner	soonest
straight（直接地）	straighter	straightest

(2) 大多數二音節以上的副詞及字尾為 ly 的副詞，通常**加 more 成比較級**，**加 most 成最高級**。

原　　　級	比　較　級	最　高　級
bravely（勇敢地）	more bravely	most bravely
cleverly（聰明地）	more cleverly	most cleverly
gladly（高興地）	more gladly	most gladly
hopefully（充滿希望地）	more hopefully	most hopefully
kindly（親切地）	more kindly	most kindly
seldom（不常）	more seldom	most seldom

【例外】

early（早地）	earlier	earliest

【注意】completely, universally, immortally, uniquely, weekly, totally 等不可比較。

2. **不規則變化**

原級（**Positive**）	比較級（**Comparative**）	最高級（**Superlative**）
poorly badly（壞地；拙劣地） ill	worse	worst
far（遠地）	farther further	farthest（距離） furthest（程度）
late（遲地）	later	latest（時間） last（順序）
little（少地）	less	least
much（多地）	more	most
well（好）	better	best

(1) 原則上 **farther** 指距離，**further** 指程度，但兩者常互用。

We can't go any **farther** without a rest.（我們若不休息便走不動了。）

It's not safe to go any **further**（= **farther**）.（再走遠一些就不安全了。）

We will not discuss the subject any **further**.（我們不再討論這個主題。）

【注意】further 又作 moreover, besides 解（亦可寫成 furthermore，參照 p.469）。

He said that he could not find it and, **further**, that nobody would ever find it.

（他說他找不到它，並且沒有人會找到它。）

(2) **ill** 為「惡劣地；不完美地；不利地」等意思。

Don't speak **ill** of your neighbors.（不要說鄰居的壞話。）

They were **ill**（= insufficiently）provided with ammunition.

（他們的軍火供應不足。）

(3) **badly**：in a bad manner（拙劣地；壞地）；very much（非常地）。

He is very **badly** off.（他很窮。）【badly off 是 well off 之反義詞】

I need money **badly**.（我非常需要錢。）

The soldier was **badly** wounded.（那士兵傷得很重。）

(4) **latest**（最遲）指時間，**last**（最後）指次序。（參照 p.198）

Who got up **latest** this morning?（今天早上誰起來得最遲？）

When did you **last** get a letter from her?

（你上次什麼時候接到她的信？）

It is a long time since I saw him **last**.

〔從上次（最後一次）我見到他已是很久的時間了。〕

Who came in **last**?（誰最後進來？）

(5) like, love 的原級副詞通常用 very much 修飾，**比較級和最高級時，like 和 better, best 連用，而 love 常和 more 和 most 連用。**

I **like** apples **very much**.（我非常喜歡蘋果。）

I **love** her **very much**.（我非常愛她。）

I **like** apples **better** than oranges.（我喜歡蘋果甚於柳橙。）

= *I prefer apples to oranges.*（參照 p.204）

I **like** apples **best** of all.（我最喜歡蘋果。）

I **love** her **more than** him.（我愛她甚於喜歡他。）

I **love** her **most**.（我最愛她。）

II.比較之句型：

1. 兩者比較時

(1) 表「**A 和 B 一樣**」：A + 動詞 + as + 原級副詞 + as + B

She drives **as fast as** he (*does*).（她開車和他一樣快。）

He works **as hard as** she (*does*).（他和她一樣努力。）

(2) 表「**A 不如 B 那樣**」：A + 助動詞 + not + 原形動詞 + so (as) + 原級副詞 + as + B

He does **not** study **so** diligently **as** she (*does*).（他不像她那麼勤勉地讀書。）

(3) 表「**A 較 B⋯**」：A + 動詞 + 比較級副詞 + than + B

My brother studies **harder than** I (*do*).（我弟弟比我更用功。）

He walked **faster than** I (*did*).（他走得比我快。）

2. 三者或三者以上比較時

A + 動詞 + (the) + 最高級副詞 + (of the three⋯, of all⋯)

She works (**the**) **hardest of** the three.（三者之中她工作最努力。）

I like spring **best**.（我最喜歡春天。）

I like spring (**the**) **best of** all the seasons of the year.（一年的季節中，我最愛春天。）

He studies (**the**) **most diligently of** all the students.（在這些學生當中，他最用功。）

3. 絕對最高級，不可加 the。所謂絕對最高級即是沒有明確地和其他的人、物相比，此時 most = very。

He played **most poorly**.（他演奏得非常糟。）

Birds sang **most sweetly** everywhere in the forest.

（鳥在林中到處唱歌，唱得非常美妙。）

4. 副詞和形容詞一樣，也可用比較級或原級來表示最高級。

(1) **用比較級表示最高級**

① A + 動詞 + 副詞比較級 + than + { any other + 單數名詞 / all the other + 複數名詞 }

He works (the) **hardest** of all the employees.（他是所有員工中最努力的。）
= He works **harder than** any other employee.
= He works **harder than** all the other employees.

② { No other + 單數名詞（人或事物）/ No one（人）或 nothing（事物）} + 動詞 + 比較級 + than + A（參照 p.507）

No other employee works **harder than** he.（沒有其他的員工像他那樣努力。）

(2) **用原級表示最高級**

{ No other + 單數名詞（人或事物）/ No one（人）或 nothing（事物）} + 動詞 + so + 原級 + as + A（參照 p.507）

No other employee works **so hard as** he.（沒有其他員工像他那樣地努力。）

Ⅲ. 含比較字詞的慣用語句：

I couldn't care *less*.（我不在乎。）

= I don't care.

第五章 副詞的位置

原則上，副詞必須儘量靠近被修飾的字，因此，**如果副詞在句子中的位置變動，句意或語氣也會隨著改變**。比較下列句子：

Only I saw the unidentified flying object a month ago.【副詞修飾代名詞】
（一個月前只有我看到那不明飛行物體。）

I *only saw* the UFO a month ago.【副詞修飾動詞】
（一個月前我只是看到那不明飛行物體。）

I saw *only the UFO* a month ago.【副詞修飾名詞】
（一個月前我看到的只是不明飛行物體。）

I saw the UFO *only a month ago*.【副詞修飾副詞】
（我看到那不明飛行物體只是一個月前的事。）

I.
副詞 + 形容詞
副詞 + 副詞（片語或子句）

副詞修飾形容詞、副詞（片語或子句）時，通常放在其前面。

It is ***very hot*** today.（今天天氣很熱。）

Yesterday was an ***unusually warm*** day for winter.（就冬天而言，昨天是異常暖和的日子。）

He can run ***very fast***.（他能夠跑得非常快。）

He came ***long before the appointed time***.（他早就在約定時間之前來了。）

The police arrived ***immediately after it happened***.（警察在那事發生之後立刻到達了。）

但是 enough 作為副詞時，位置在被修飾字詞的後面；而作為形容詞修飾名詞時，前後皆可放置。

The dictionary was *small **enough*** for me to put in my pocket.
（這字典很小，所以我能放入口袋裡。）

Is he *old **enough*** to go to school?（他已達到上學的年齡嗎？）

She sings *well **enough***.（她唱歌唱得夠好了。）

She has { ***enough money*** / ***money enough*** } for the journey.（她有足夠的錢去旅行。）【enough 是形容詞】

II.
副詞 +（代）名詞
（代）名詞 + 副詞

副詞修飾名詞、代名詞時，副詞的位置在被修飾字詞的前面或後面。（詳見 p.228）

Even Homer sometimes nods.（智者千慮，必有一失。）

*I, **too***, have caught cold.（我也感冒了。）

He is ***only a child***.（他只是個小孩。）

Ⅲ. 修飾動詞的副詞，位置比較複雜，<u>分述如下：</u>

1.
> 不及物動詞 + {
> 副詞
> 補語 + 副詞
> }　修飾不及物動詞時，在動詞之後，有補語時在補語之後。

He *lived* **well** and *died* **happily**.（他活得很舒適，死得很幸福。）

The rumour *spread* **quickly**.（謠言很快地傳開了。）

As it *snowed* **heavily**, their arrival was delayed.
（雪下得很大，所以他們到達的時間被延誤了。）

My boy *got* ill **suddenly**.（我兒子突然生病了。）

2.
> 及物動詞 + {
> 受詞 + 副詞
> 副詞 + 長受詞（子句）
> }

修飾及物動詞時，在受詞之後；但是，如果受詞是名詞子句或帶有長的修飾語時，副詞可插在動詞與受詞之間。（詳見 p.639）

He *admitted* his error **frankly**.（他坦白地承認了自己的錯誤。）

He *closed* the door **quietly** behind him.（他悄悄地關上了他後面的門。）

He *finished* his homework **patiently**.（他有耐心地做完了他的家庭作業。）

I *answered* his question **carefully**.（我小心地回答他的問題。）

We should have the courage to *speak* **openly** just what we mean.
（我們應該有勇氣率直地說出我們的意思。）

Please *describe* **faithfully** what you saw.（請誠實地敘述你所看到的。）

She *heard* **distinctly** a voice like that of her husband.（她清楚地聽到了像她丈夫的聲音。）

He *rewarded* **liberally** all those who had served him well.
（他慷慨地獎賞那些曾為他盡力的人。）

【註】修飾及物動詞時，如果副詞本身語氣弱時，可以置於動詞之前。

He *frankly* **admitted** his error.（他坦白地承認了自己的錯誤。）

He *quietly* **closed** the door behind him.（他悄悄地關上了他後面的門。）

He *kindly* **showed** me the way.（他親切地指引我路線。）

I *utterly* **forgot** it.（我完全忘了那件事。）

He *idly* **turned** the pages.（他無所事事地翻著書。）

He *briefly* **explained** his intention.（他簡潔地說明了自己的意圖。）

She *gently* **closed** the door.（她輕輕地關上了門。）

= She *closed* the door **gently**.

3. be + { 副詞 + p.p. / p.p. + 副詞 }　副詞修飾被動語態的動詞時，一般位置在過去分詞之前或之後均可。

I was { *badly injured* / *injured badly* } in both legs. (我兩隻腳都受了重傷。)

That cannot be *easily* done. (那是無法輕易做到的。)

He has been *well* spoken of. (他受到好評。)

His name is *well* known to boys and girls. (他的名字男孩和女孩都很熟悉。)

4. 像 put down, ring up 之類由「**動詞 + 介副詞**」所組成的動詞片語，受詞是代名詞時，副詞在代名詞之後；受詞是名詞時，位置在名詞之前後皆可；受詞是片語、子句時，副詞的位置在其前。

分述如下：

① | 動詞 + { **介副詞** + 受詞（名詞）/ 受詞（名詞）+ **介副詞** } |

Put down your textbook. 【正】(放下你的教科書。)
Put your textbook *down*. 【正】

② | 動詞 + 受詞（代名詞）+ **介副詞** |

Put it *down*. 【正】(放下它。)
Put down it. 【誤】

但是，代名詞是 each other, one another, something, somebody 時，副詞位置在其前。
They *rang up* each other. (他們彼此互通電話。)

③ | 動詞 + **介副詞** + 受詞（片語或子句）|

Put *down* whatever you don't use. (你不用的東西都放下。)
Speak *up* what you have in your mind. (心中有什麼事都說出來。)

5. **表示確定時間的副詞（片語）**，通常放置在句首或句末，放在句首時的語氣較強。

On Saturdays shops are *allowed* to be open till ten. (星期六商店准許開到十點。)

Some friends *dropped* in on us *last night*. (昨晚一些朋友順道來拜訪我們。)

He *worked* hard for many hours *yesterday*. (昨天他努力工作了好幾小時。)

Yesterday he *worked* hard for many hours.

6. often, seldom, occasionally, always, usually 等**頻率副詞的位置**：
① **在一般動詞之前。**

He *often* stays at home all day. (他經常整天待在家裡。)

He *seldom*, if ever, *speaks* ill of others. (他很少說別人的壞話。)

We *occasionally see* George at the beach. (我們偶爾會在海邊看到喬治。)

② 句中有 **be** 動詞時，放在 **be** 動詞之後。

He *is always* in and out of the hospital. (他時常進出醫院。)

He *is seldom* at home on Sundays. (星期天他很少在家。)

Bears *are rarely seen* in these mountains. (在這些山中很少看到熊。)

③ 句中有助動詞時，在助動詞與動詞之間。

We *have always lived* in this house. (我們一直都住在這間房子裡。)

This job *will never be* finished. (這工作將永遠不會完成。)

I *have seldom seen* him scold his children. (我很少看到他責罵孩子。)

【註 1】 為了加重語氣而加強助動詞或 be 動詞的發音時，頻率副詞的位置可在其前。
　　　　You *never can* tell. 〔(將來的事) 誰也不知道。〕
　　　　He *always will* do so. (他一定會這麼做。)
　　　　I *never am* happy. (我從未快樂過。)

【註 2】 頻率副詞在「**主詞 + 助（be）動詞**」的省略形式的對話中，**必須放在助（be）動詞之前。**
　　　　{ "He is late." (「他遲到了。」)
　　　　　"He *always* is." (「他一向如此。」)
　　　　{ "Don't trust politicians." (「不要信任政客。」)
　　　　　"I *never* have, and I *never* will." (「我不曾，也絕不會。」)

【註 3】 already, seldom, nearly 等副詞，除適用於上述情形外，**還可置於句末。**
　　　　She attends our meeting very *seldom*. (她很少參加我們的會議。)
　　　　I have seen that film *already*. (我已經看過那部影片了。)

7. soon, sometimes, afterwards, lately 等**非確定時間的副詞**，修飾動詞或全句時，**可任意放置在句首、動詞之前或句末**，並且對意思的強弱沒有影響。
　{ *Sometimes* he tells us stories. (他有時候說故事給我們聽。)
　　He *sometimes* tells us stories.
　　He tells us stories *sometimes*.

8. **before, ago** 一般置於句末。

It never *happened before*. (那件事以前從未發生過。)

He had *known* it *before*. (他以前就知道那件事了。)

I had *met* her two years *before*. （我兩年以前就遇見過她。）

I *met* her two years *ago*. （我在兩年前遇見她。）

9. once 作「**曾經；以前**」解時，置於句首或動詞之前（但置於 be 動詞之後）；
   作「**一次**」解時，置於動詞之後。（參照 p.248）

   > *Once* there was a great king. （<u>從前</u>有一個偉大的國王。）
   > = There was *once* a great king.

   I *once* have seen him. （我<u>曾經</u>看過他。）

   I have been there *once*. （我去過那裡<u>一次</u>。）

   We die but *once*. （我們都只死<u>一次</u>。）

10. 否定副詞 never, seldom, rarely, hardly, scarcely, little, few 放在句首表示加強語氣，
    此時要將**助動詞放在主詞之前**。（有關副詞的倒裝，詳見 p.629）

    > I have *never* seen such a thing in my college days.
    > *Never* have I seen such a thing in my college days.
    > （我大學時代從未看見過那樣的東西。）

    > I had *scarcely* reached the station when the train left.
    > *Scarcely* had I reached the station when the train left.
    > （我剛剛到車站，火車就開走了。）

IV. 修飾全句時副詞的位置：

修飾全句的副詞位置如下所示，但是，有許多情形無法明確區分副詞是修飾全句或
只修飾動詞。

1. 一般情形，副詞置於動詞之前，或 be 動詞之後。

   He *slowly* began to realize the fact. （他慢慢地開始明白事實了。）

   He *suddenly* burst out laughing.
   （他突然大聲笑了起來。）

   He *wisely* did it himself. （他很聰明，自己做那件事。）
   = *It was wise of him that he did it himself.*

   He *foolishly* killed his goose for golden eggs.
   = *It was foolish of him to kill his goose for golden eggs.*
   （他愚笨得為了金蛋殺死他的鵝。）

   This place is *rightly* called an earthly paradise.
   = *It is right that this place should be called an earthly paradise.*
   （這地方理當被稱為人間樂園。）

2. 為加強副詞的意思時，將其置於句首修飾全句，此時副詞之後可加逗點或不加。

Slowly(,) he began to realize the fact. （慢慢地他開始明白事實了。）

【比較】
{
Happily(,) he did not die. （幸好他沒死。）

= He did not die, *happily*.

He did not *die happily*. （他含恨而終。）【happily 只修飾 die】
}

這種加強語氣的副詞有時候也被置於句末，但必須在副詞與本句之間加上逗點。

Unfortunately, the message failed to arrive in time.

The message failed to arrive in time, *unfortunately*.

（不幸的是，這個訊息未能及時送達。）

He knew the fact already, *undoubtedly*! （他確實已知道了那個事實！）

V. 同類兩個以上的副詞須依「單位較小者＋單位較大者」的順序排列。

He lives *in Taichung*, *in Taiwan*, *Republic of China*.
    小   中   大

（他住在中華民國台灣的台中。）

My sister usually gets up *at six o'clock* *in the morning* *in the summer*.
       小   中   大

（我妹妹在夏天通常早上六點起床。）

【註 1】 如果重點在大的單位，而小單位只是後來才想到而附帶提起時，大的單位可在前，**但須用逗點與小的單位分開。**

He was born *in London*, *in a small house facing the Thames*.

（他出生於倫敦，是在面對泰晤士河的一個小房子中。）

It happened *in 1902*, *early in spring when it was still snowing*.

（那件事發生於一九〇二年，是在還下著雪的早春。）

I arrived *early this morning*, *about five o'clock*.

（我今天早上一早就到了，大約在五點時。）

【註 2】 二個表示地方的副詞並列時，**地方確定的副詞在後面，地方不確定的副詞在前面。**

He is *out in the garden*. （他在外面的花園裡。）
  ↑   ↑
 地方不確定 地方確定

The path led *down to the river*. （那條小路向河的方向延伸。）

She slipped *out on to the veranda*. （她偷偷地溜到外面的走廊上。）

Ⅵ.當有兩個以上的修飾語時，其正常的順序爲**地點，狀態（或方法），次數，時間**。

　見下表：

	地　　方	狀　　態	次　　數	時　　間
He is going	*to Japan*	*by ship.*		
The postman comes			*twice a day*	*during December.*
I saw them	*at the game*			*last Saturday.*
John went	*to the library*		*every night*	*last week.*
The King left	*here*	*secretly*		*on Sunday.*

We come *here early every day*. （我們每天都很早來這裡。）

I brought it *home for my son a few days ago*. （我幾天前把它帶回家給我兒子。）

She arrived *there safely the other day*. （她前幾天安全到達那裡。）

但是當該動詞有二個以上的修飾語，或其受詞帶有形容詞時，指狀態、次數或時間的單字副詞要置於主動詞之前。

He	*secretly*	burned the letters *in the fireplace last night.*
The Smiths	*often*	go *to Florida in the winter.*
John	*recently*	took a trip *around the world.*
Mr. Dall	*quickly*	opened the telegram *on his desk.*

【註 1】 時間副詞也有爲了**強調**、**對照**等而位置在前面的情形。

　　　　Before supper he walked *around the lake*.

　　　　（晚飯前他在湖的周圍散步。）

【註 2】 副詞的長短相差顯著時，爲了調整句子的語調，也有將上述位置變更的情形。

　　　　We saw him *yesterday at school when he was making a speech*.

　　　　（我們昨天在學校當他演說時看見了他。）

　　　　He rushed *quickly to that building with his ax in his hand*.

　　　　（他手持斧頭很快地衝向那棟建築物。）

　　　　The officer lived *by himself in this hut of his own making for thirty years or so*

　　　　　after the end of World War Ⅱ.

　　　　（那士官在第二次大戰結束後，將近三十年都一個人住在他自己建的小屋中。）

第六章 副詞的相等詞

相當於副詞作用的詞語共有下列幾種：
- ① 副詞性的受詞（Adverbial Objective）
- ② 介系詞片語（Prepositional Phrase）
- ③ 不定詞（Infinitive）
- ④ 分詞（Participle）
- ⑤ 副詞子句（Adverbial Clause）

I. 副詞性的受詞：即具有副詞作用的名詞，表時間、距離、重量、價格、程度、狀態等。
（詳見 p.100）

1. 表時間：

I have slept (*for*) **hours**.（我睡了幾個小時。）

【for hours 是副詞片語，hours 做省略介詞的受詞，但有副詞性，故稱副詞性的受詞】

He is at work **all day long**.（他整天在工作。）

It rained **last night**.（昨天晚上有下雨。）

2. 表距離：

My house is **a mile** from the town.（我家距鎮上一哩。）

We walked **ten miles**.（我們走了十哩。）

3. 表重量：

He weighs sixty **kilogrammes**.（他重六十公斤。）

4. 表價格：

These apples are **four pence** a pound.（這些蘋果一磅四辨士。）

5. 表程度：

This problem is **ten times** harder than that one.（這個問題比那個難十倍。）

It is nearly **four times** smaller.（它幾乎小四倍。）

6. 表狀態：

The man was bound **hand and foot**.（那個人手腳被綁住了。）

II. 介系詞片語：即由介詞開頭後跟名詞，其作用可當副詞片語，可表地方、時間，或狀態。

1. 表地方：

He hunts <u>in the woods</u>.（他在森林中狩獵。）

I looked <u>through the window</u>.（我從窗子望出去。）

Put the book <u>on the shelf</u>.（把書放在架子上。）

2. 表時間：

I shall go to the movies <u>on Sunday</u>.（在星期天我要去看電影。）

They will launch an attack <u>before daybreak</u>.（在破曉之前，他們會發動攻擊。）

3. 表狀態：

She ran away <u>in despair</u>.（她絕望地跑開。）

He spoke <u>in a low voice</u>.（他低聲說話。）

III. 不定詞：作副詞用，不定詞有下列四種用法：

1. **修飾動詞**：表結果、目的、原因、理由、條件。（詳見 p.413）

   She grew up <u>to be a famous teacher</u>.（她長大後成了有名的老師。）【表結果】

   Men eat <u>to live</u>, but do not live <u>to eat</u>.（人吃飯是為了活命，不是活著為了要吃飯。）【表目的】

   She wept <u>to hear the news</u>.（她因聽到這個消息而流淚。）【表原因】

   He must be a fool <u>to say so</u>.（他說出這種話，一定是個傻瓜。）【表理由】

   It would be wrong <u>to tell him a lie</u>.（你若是跟他說謊，那你就不對了。）【表條件】

   （= It would be wrong *if you were to tell him a lie*.）

2. **修飾形容詞**：（參照 p.415）

   I am anxious <u>to hear</u>.（我急著想聽到。）

   I am happy <u>to see you</u>.（我很高興見到你。）

3. **修飾其他副詞**：表程度等。（參照 p.415）

   The child is old enough <u>to walk alone</u>.（這孩子已夠大，能自己走路了。）

4. **修飾全句**：（參照 p.417）

   <u>To be frank</u>, I love her madly.（坦白說，我瘋狂地愛著她。）

   <u>To tell the truth</u>, he is stupid.（老實說，他真笨。）

IV. 分詞：

1. **分詞當副詞用**：有些現在分詞可作副詞用（過去分詞不行），用以加深形容詞的程度。
   （詳見 p.455）

   It is **burning** hot today.（今天非常熱。）

   He has a **shocking** bad temper.（他有火爆的脾氣。）

2. **分詞構句**：表時間、原因等。（詳見 p.462）

   It being very cold, we made a fire.（因為天氣很冷，所以我們生了火。）

   The agent being absent, the business was suspended.（因為代理人缺席，所以交易延期。）

   Night coming on, we sought shelter in a farmhouse.（夜晚來臨時，我們找一個農家過夜。）

V. 副詞子句：是用作副詞以修飾動詞、形容詞或副詞的從屬子句。（詳見 p.489～532）

修飾動詞的子句通常置於**主要子句之後**，有些也可放在句首。

主　要　子　句	從　屬　子　句	
He put the sign	*where* everyone could see it.	（他把告示牌放在每個人都可看到之處。）
I sing	*when* I am happy.	（我快樂時就唱歌。）
He hurried	*because* he was late.	（他遲到了，所以很匆忙。）

※ 從屬子句也可與主要子句次序顛倒。

Because *it is getting late*, we had better go home.（因為天晚了，所以我們最好回家。）

Since *I didn't know the answer*, I kept quiet.（因為我不知道答案，所以我保持沉默。）

請立刻做　練習十二～十七

練 習 一 【第三篇代名詞 p.105～164】

請改正下列各題句子中的錯誤。（用最少的字數）

1. Knowledge is there for whomever will seek it.

2. Depend upon that he will come here.

3. Whom do you think is the writer of this book?

4. His brother's case is quite different from me.

5. The population of London is two times as large as this city.

6. People find increasingly difficult to make their living.

7. "I must say good-bye now." "So I must."

8. He is taller than any one in his class.

9. I spoke to a man who I thought to be my cousin.

10. Only yesterday the hotel manager assured my husband and I that he would accept our reservation for a room.

11. My friend, whom I thought would pass the examination, has failed.

12. Here are two watches. What is yours?

13. She loves money more than everything else.

14. He offered me a considerable sum, but which I declined.

15. It has often been said that books do for us today that universities did in earlier days.

16. It is him who made so much noise in the hall.

17. "Have you a knife?" "Yes, I have it."

18. Mine is larger than your's.

【解答】

1. whomever → **whoever**，做 will seek 的主詞。　　2. Depend upon that → **Depend upon it that**，that 子句不可做介詞的受詞，須在前面加上 it，that 子句做 it 的同位語。　　3. Whom → **Who**，做 is 的主詞。
4. me → **mine**（= my case），case「情況；事例」。　　5. as this city → **as that of this city**，that 代替 the population。　　6. find → **find it**，it 代替 to make their living。（參照 p.114）　　7. So I must. → **So must I.**，So 在此指 Also。　　8. any one → **anyone else**　　9. who → **whom**（或 to be → **was**），～a man who I thought was～ = ～a man whom I thought to be～。　　10. I → **me**，做 assured 的受詞。

11. whom → **who**，做 would pass 的主詞，I thought 是插入語。　　12. What → **Which**「哪一支」。
13. everything → **anything**，everything else 意義不正確。　　14. but which → **which**，which 本身已有連接詞的作用不可再加 but；如果要用 but，則改為 "…, but I declined it."。　　15. that → **what**，what universities did…做 do 的受詞。　　16. him → **he**，此句是 He made so much noise in the hall. 加強主詞 He 語氣的形式。　　17. it → **one**，one 指與前面所提到的名詞同類；而 it 指同一個。　　18. your's → **yours**。

練 習 二 【第三篇代名詞 p.105～164】

請改正下列各題句子中的錯誤。（用最少的字數）

1. After the court had recessed, the jury came in and took its seats.

2. She was smaller in stature than either of her three sisters.

3. The stone was so heavy that he could not lift.

4. He wears the same coat that I wear.

5. He ran off at my sight.

6. I saw the man whom you said was away.

7. This box is too heavy for me to lift it.

8. To make money is one thing, to spend it is the other.

9. The climate here is like southern California.

10. How do you call this flower in English?

11. I have no bookcase, and so I am going to have it made.

12. She was a friend of me.

13. How will become of us if the bank fails?

14. Father is older than me by thirty years.

15. Nobody except you and she saw the prisoner run away.

16. It should have been us, but it was them who received the honor.

17. You should not rely on such a dishonest man like him.

18. I thought it was mine, but it proved to be her.

19. Abraham never forgot which his good mother said to him one day.

20. We will welcome whomever visits our country.

【解答】 ————————————————————

1. its → *their*，*jury*「陪審團」，表集合體時是單數，表集合體的組成份子時是複數，依句意在此是指組成份子，故用 *their*。　　2. either → *any*，*either* 用於二人，*any* 用於三人以上。　　3. lift → *lift it*，*that* 是連接詞，引導副詞子句，*that* 本身沒有代名作用。　　4. that → *as*（參照 p.160）　　5. at my sight → *at the sight of me*，*at the sight of*…「一看見…」。　　6. whom → *who*，做 *was* 的主詞，*you said* 是插入語。　　7. lift it → *lift*，*this box* 已做不定詞 *to lift* 的意義受詞，故不須再接文法上的受詞。　　8. the other → *another*（參照 p.141）　　9. like → *like that of*　　10. How → *What*　　11. it → *one*　　12. me → *mine*　　13. How → *What*，*What will become of us if*…?「假如…，我們會怎麼樣？」（參照 p.367）　　14. me → *I*（*am*）　　15. she → *her*，做 *except* 的受詞。　　16. us → *we*；them → *they*　　17. like him → *as he*（參照 p.125）　　18. her → *hers*，*it* 指「物」。　　19. which → *what*（= *that which*）是複合關代，前面不需先行詞，*which* 之前須有先行詞。　　20. whomever → *whoever*，做 *visits* 的主詞。

練 習 三 【第三篇代名詞 p.105～164】

請改正下列各題句子中的錯誤。（用最少的字數）

1. As much as fifty employees were fired.

2. This ball-point pen is no good. Please show me the other.

3. I have decided to be a physicist because it is now playing such an important role in the progress of science.

4. I will lend you this book of me.

5. He speaks English better than anyone in his class.

6. He likes baseball very much, and so am I.

7. I have less books than he.

8. Some went on foot and another went by bus.

9. The construction work will be finished in other three weeks.

10. He seemed that he was more than forty years old.

11. The news of his having been appointed came as a great surprise to my mother and I.

12. Mr. Johnson was too angry to say something at all.

13. The pencil is Mary's but the notebook is not her.

14. The doctor says that I shall get well in a more week.

15. No one can please anybody.

16. Our school sent Mr. Smith and I to London.

17. He forced the way through the crowd of people.

18. Did who authorize him to issue such an order?

【解答】

1. much → ***many***，*employees* 是複數名詞。   2. the other → ***another***（ = *a different one*）「另一個」用於三者以上；*the other* 只可用於兩者。   3. it → ***he***，指 *physicist*。   4. me → ***mine***   5. anyone → ***anyone else***，比較要把自己除外。   6. am → ***do***，是 *so do I*（*like baseball*…）的省略。   7. less → ***fewer***，*books* 是可數名詞，不可用 *less* 修飾。   8. another → ***others***，*some*…*others*…(*others*…)「有些…有些…（有些…）」。（詳見 p.141）   9. other → ***another***，*in another three weeks*「再過三個星期」。   10. He → ***It***，*It seemed that*…中 *It* 是形式主詞。本句若要以 *He* 為主詞，則須用單句表示，即 He seemed to be more than forty years old.   11. I → ***me***，當介系詞 *to* 的受詞。   12. something → ***anything***，*too*…*to* 有否定意義，因此要用 *anything*。   13. her → ***hers***   14. a more → ***another***（ = *one more*）   15. anybody → ***everybody***，句中 *no* = *not any*，「沒有任何人能夠討好每一個人」，依句意該用 *everybody*。   16. I → ***me***，做 *sent* 的受詞。   17. the way → ***his way***，*force one's way through*「擠過」。   18. Did who authorize → ***Who authorized***，疑問代名詞做主詞時，前面不可放助動詞。（詳見 p.145）

練 習 四 【第三篇代名詞 p.105～164】

請改正下列各題句子中的錯誤。(用最少的字數)

1. This overcoat of me is already worn out.

2. Let John and I go instead of you.

3. What kind of occupation do you know he has?

4. Do you think who is the mayor of that city?

5. I'll have a cigarette; will you have it, too?

6. I think the climate of this year is much milder than last year.

7. No one knows what one's fate will be.

8. This kind of vegetables grows rapidly.

9. You ought to be ashamed of you for behaving so rudely.

10. I don't allow anybody to take anyone of the magazines in this room.

11. What can we expect from such as them?

12. I think it he.

13. There are cherry trees on both side of the river.

14. The house which we live stands on a hill.

15. This is the same man whom I saw in the train.

16. There was a time which I used to attend school with joy.

17. I will reward whomever can solve this problem.

18. Tell me the best way which to express my thanks.

【解答】

1. me → *mine*　　2. I → *me*，當 Let 的受詞。　　3. → *Do you know what kind of occupation he has?*（詳見 p.146）　　4. → *Who do you think is the mayor of that city?*（詳見 p.146）　　5. it → *one*（詳見 p.112）　　6. than last year → *than that of last year*（詳見 p.122）　　7. one's → *his*（詳見 p.139）
8. vegetables → *vegetable*　　9. you → *yourself*，主詞與受詞同一人時，要用反身代名詞為受詞。
10. anyone → *any one*，anyone 用於指人，any one 可用於指人（= anyone）或指物。
11. them → *they*，such as they (expect)　　12. he → *him*，受詞補語該用受格形，等於 I think it *to be* him.　　13. both → *either*，或 side → *sides*，both 須接複數名詞；either 須接單數名詞。（詳見 p.133）
14. which → *in which*，live 是不及物動詞，因此做其受詞的 which 之前須有介詞 in。
15. whom → *that*，the same…that 指同一件事物。（參照 p.127）
16. which → *when*，關代 which 在形容詞子句中必須有代名作用，關係副詞 when 則只作連接詞用。
17. whomever → *whoever*（= anyone who）做名詞子句中的主詞。
18. way which to express → *way to express* 是 in which to express…簡化而來。（詳見 p.154）

練 習 五【第三篇代名詞 p.105～164】

請改正下列各題句子中的錯誤。（用最少的字數）

1. My father bought a typewriter for my brother and I.

2. Your both hands are dirty.

3. "Do you want a pen?" "Yes, I want it."

4. The pleasure of collecting stamps is greater than dancing.

5. One of my two brothers is in London and another is at home.

6. It was they that was scolded for this mischief.

7. Though the comfort of the passengers is important, its safety is still more important.

8. All I know is that neither of the statements are not true.

9. Though she looks like an angel, her actions are that of a devil.

10. Even such a virtuous man as he cannot please anybody.

11. It was the eleventh of September, 1956, that my mother died of pneumonia.

12. One must never forget his friends.

13. I have not had some breakfast this morning.

14. Being penniless, he cannot buy everything.

15. I am sure of he having tried to do his best.

16. There are plenty of people whom we know quite well are innocent of this crime.

17. He invited her and I.

【解答】

1. I → *me*，做 *for* 的受詞。　　2. Your both hands → *Both your hands*（詳見 p.134）　　3. it → *one* = a pen，指同類中的任一個。（詳見 p.112）　　4. dancing → *that of dancing*，that = the pleasure（詳見 p.112）。　　5. another → *the other*（詳見 p.140）　　6. that was → *that were*，that 的先行詞 they 是複數，故用 were。　　7. its safety → *their safety* = the passengers' safety　　8. are not true → *is true*，neither「兩者中沒有一個」做主詞時，動詞用單數；且 neither 已含有否定意義，故不可再加 not。　　9. that of a devil → *those of a devil*，those 指 her actions。　　10. anybody → *everybody*，根據句意該用部分否定 not…everybody。　　11. It was the eleventh → *It was on the eleventh*（詳見 p.116）　　12. his → *one's*（詳見 p.139）　　13. some → *any*（詳見 p.130）　　14. everything → *anything*，not…every 是部分否定；not…any 才是全部否定，依句意該用 anything。　　15. he → *his*（or *him*），做動名詞 having 的主詞。　　16. → There are plenty of people (*that*) we know quite well *who* are innocent…. 　　17. I → *me*。

練 習 六 【第三篇代名詞 p.105～164】

請根據句意和文法選出一個最正確的答案。

1. I am looking for a notebook _____ I have taken down her telephone number.
   (A) in which　　　(B) in that　　　(C) which　　　(D) that

2. On the ceiling you can see the wild animals _____ prehistoric man lived.
   (A) that　　　(B) in which　　　(C) with which　　　(D) who

3. It's hard to imagine _____ our complex business affairs would be like without the services of a bank.
   (A) which　　　(B) what　　　(C) that　　　(D) any

4. Come _____ may, keep calm.
   (A) what　　　(B) whatever　　　(C) however　　　(D) that

5. They consider _____ their duty to be loyal to their country.
   (A) this　　　(B) as　　　(C) it　　　(D) that

6. The god Apollo was the only one of the gods _____ able to keep the horses from running away.
   (A) who is　　　(B) who are　　　(C) that was　　　(D) who were

7. Tom had a car accident twice this month, and _____ was worse, a fire broke out last night and his house burned down.
   (A) there　　　(B) which　　　(C) that　　　(D) what

8. _____ has courage and faith will never perish in misery.
   (A) Those who　　　(B) Such as　　　(C) He who　　　(D) As if

9. How far is _____ from here to the station?
   (A) it　　　(B) there　　　(C) that　　　(D) the road

10. _____ knows what he can do till he has tried.
    (A) People seldom　　　(B) Few　　　(C) A little　　　(D) Nobody

【解答】

1. (A)，關係代名詞做介詞的受詞，介詞不可省，且 that 不能接於介詞之後。(詳見 p.154)　　2. (C)，the wild animals *with which prehistoric man lived*, live with「與…同住」。　　3. (B)，what 在此是疑問代名詞，引導名詞子句，做 imagine 的受詞，在子句中又做 like 的受詞。　　4. (A)，*Come what may* = *Whatever may come* = *No matter what will* (or *may*) *come*「無論如何」是表讓步之副詞子句。　　5. (C)，it 做形式受詞，代替後面之不定詞。(詳見 p.114)　　6. (C)，*the only one* of the gods *that was*…先行詞是 the only one 時，關代用 that，動詞用單數。　　7. (D)，*(and) what is worse*「更糟的是」，是慣用的插入句，當作表累積性的對等連接詞。(詳見 p.654)　　8. (C)，動詞 has 是單數，得知先行詞也是單數，Such as = Those who (表複數)，He who 或 Anyone who 則泛指一般人。　　9. (A)，it 在此表「距離」，當主詞。(詳見 p.111)　　10. (D)，nobody (or no one) + 單數動詞。(詳見 p.143)

練 習 七 【第四篇形容詞 p.165～212】

請改正下列各題句子中的錯誤。（用最少的字數）

1. He was impossible to find it out.

2. You should be respectable towards your teachers.

3. I am absolutely uncapable to tell a lie.

4. I'll be convenient next Sunday.

5. You must make your parents happily.

6. He looked differently after his return from Europe.

7. The number of girls is very few.

8. This shirt is woolen.

9. Let asleep dogs lie.

10. The engine ran good after it had been repaired.

11. When his father dead, he was left poorly.

12. The children were very pleasant, when they got a present.

13. The game was very excited. You should have seen it.

14. He is a little idleness, while his brother is diligence itself.

【解答】

1. impossible → *unable*（或 → *It was impossible for him to find it out.*），*impossible* 是非人稱形容詞，不能用來修飾人。（詳見 p.194） 2. respectable → *respectful*「恭敬的」；*respectable*「可尊敬的」。
3. uncapable → *unable*（或 uncapable to tell → *incapable of telling*），*capable* 的反義字是 *incapable*，*be unable to* + 原形，*be incapable of* + *V-ing*「沒有能力（做）…」。 4. → *Next Sunday will be convenient for me*，*convenient* 是非人稱形容詞。（詳見 p.194） 5. happily → *happy*，形容詞做受詞補語。 6. differently → *different*，做主詞補語，*look different*「看起來不一樣」。 7. few → *small*，主詞為 The number「數目」，表示數目的大小要用 *large* 和 *small*。 8. is woolen → *is (made) of wool*（或 → *This is a woolen shirt.*），*woolen*「羊毛製的」。*woolen* 是限定用法的形容詞。（詳見 p.187） 9. asleep → *sleeping*，*asleep*「睡著的」是敘述用法的形容詞（詳見 p.191），Let sleeping dogs lie.「【諺】勿惹事生非；勿打草驚蛇」。 10. good → *well*，*well* 是副詞，*good* 是形容詞。 11. dead → *died*；poorly → *poor*，*die* 的過去式是 *died*。 12. very pleasant → *very pleased* (or *much pleased*)，*pleased*「滿意的；高興的」；*pleasant*「令人愉快的」。 13. excited → *exciting*「刺激的；令人興奮的」；*excited*「興奮的」用於人當主詞時。 14. idleness → *idle*「懶惰的」，形容詞做主詞補語；*diligence itself* = *very diligent*。

練　習　八 【第四篇形容詞 p.165～212】

請改正下列各題句子中的錯誤。（用最少的字數）

1. This bridge has been under construction since the later part of last month.

2. At the seashore the air felt coldly, even though the sun was shining brilliantly.

3. Do you think him honestly?

4. I always put little sugar into tea than into coffee.

5. He comes of a respectful family.

6. The governor set the prisoners freely.

7. Her father was looking so illness that her uneasiness increased.

8. Football is preferable than baseball in our school.

9. I was pleasant to hear that.

10. Since biography is simply a special type of history, almost everything that can be said about the later holds true for the former.

11. It is surely possible to construct earthquakeproof buildings that are pleased to the eye.

12. The last few games in the pennant race were excited.

13. My mother is less older than you think she is.

14. She is cleverer than wise.

15. He has less books than I have.

16. Pedro seemed happily when I last saw him.

17. You are necessary to start at once.

【解答】

1. later → *latter*，"*late, later, latest*" 表時間；"*late, latter, last*" 表順序。(參照 p.198)　　2. coldly → *cold*，是形容詞做主詞補語。　　3. honestly → *honest*，是形容詞做受詞補語。　　4. little → *less*，little 的比較級是 *less*，最高級是 *least*。　　5. respectful → *respectable*「可尊敬的」；*respectful*「恭敬的」。　　6. freely → *free*　　7. illness → *ill*，是形容詞做主詞補語。　　8. than → *to*，*be preferable to*「…比～較合人意」和 *prefer…to～* 一樣，後面用介詞 to。　　9. pleasant → *pleased*「滿意的」；*pleasant*「令人愉快的」。　　10. later → *latter*，與 *the former*「前者」相對的是 *the latter*「後者」。　　11. pleased → *pleasant*「令人愉快的」。　　12. excited → *exciting*「令人興奮的」；*excited*「興奮的」。　　13. less older → *less old*，*less* 已表示比較級。　　14. cleverer → *more clever*，同一人或物比較其兩種性質或狀態時一律用 *more～than*。(參照 p.201)　　15. less → *fewer*，*less* 用於不可數名詞；*fewer* 用於可數名詞。　　16. happily → *happy*，是形容詞做主詞的補語。　　17. → *It is necessary for you* to start at once. *necessary, difficult, dangerous, impossible* 是非人稱形容詞，不可做人的補語。(參照 p.194)

練 習 九 【第四篇形容詞 p.165～212】

請改正下列各題句子中的錯誤。（用最少的字數）

1. A person with little friends is a miserable creature.

2. He often asked for a loan from the bank on a long terms basis.

3. He felt awkwardly in the presence of ladies.

4. That was a matter of every day occurrence.

5. There is no royally road to learning.

6. Experiments increase scientifically knowledge.

7. The hot weather is suggestion of going swimming.

8. His sister is intentive on becoming a dancer.

9. Grass Mountain is a scenery spot in the suburbs of Taipei.

10. I am difficult to solve this problem.

11. You must work hard to make up for the losing time.

12. It's so fine weather that we should go to the beach.

13. He is equally to the task.

14. They have to attend the prepare school before they can enter the medical school.

15. She watched me with a concern look.

16. His behavior is worth of praise.

【解答】──────────────────────────────

1. little → *few*，*little* + 不可數名詞，*few* + 可數名詞。　　2. long terms → *long-term*「長期的」，terms「條件；關係」。　　3. awkwardly → *awkward* adj.「笨拙的；侷促不安的」，做主詞補語。4. every day → *everyday* adj.「每日的」；*every day*「每天」是副詞片語。　　5. royally → *royal* adj.「容易的」，修飾 road。　　6. scientifically → *scientific* adj.「科學的」，*scientific knowledge*「科學的知識」。　　7. suggestion → *suggestive*，*be suggestive of*「使人聯想到」。　　8. intentive → *intent*，*be intent (up)on*「熱衷於」，intentive 無此字。　　9. scenery → *scenic*「風景的」，a scenic spot「風景區」；scenery「風景」。　　10. → *It is difficult for me to solve this problem.* difficult 是非人稱形容詞，不可做人的補語。(詳見 p.194)　　11. losing → *lost*「失去的；浪費的」。　　12. so → *such*，weather 是不可數名詞。(詳見 p.517)　　13. equally → *equal*，*be equal to* ①「能勝任」②「與…相等」。　　14. prepare school → *preparatory school*「預備學校」。　　15. concern → *concerned*「掛念的」，*a concerned look* (or *air*)「擔憂的神色（態度）」。　　16. worth → *worthy*，*be worthy of* +（動）名詞；*be worthy to* + 原形。(詳見 p.443)

練　習　十 【第四篇第六章冠詞 p.213～226】

請改正下列各題句子中的錯誤。（用最少的字數）

1. Plato left behind him a view of the universe set forth in his dialogue in an unique combination of logic and drama.

2. I have read a interesting story.

3. What kind of a book do you have?

4. You're in right; it's not your fault.

5. The most of us are flattered when we receive a compliment.

6. Why are you at home in such a fine weather?

7. He was elected the Mayor of New York.

8. Horse is useful animal.

9. Goldsmith is said to have travelled from a place to a place.

10. How glad we were when we saw light in a distance!

11. A hero as he was, he was not loved by others.

12. French are very polite people.

13. She is such honest girl that she cannot tell lies.

14. He is youngest boy in his class.

15. I want you to become Edison, not Shakespeare.

16. He has an eye for beautiful.

【解答】

1. an → *a*，unique〔ju'nik〕。　2. a → *an*　3. a book → *book*，kind of 之後不須加 *a*。

4. right → *the right*，in the right「有理的」；in right「在右邊」。　5. The most → *Most*，most 表示「大多數」的時候，不可加 *the*。（詳見 p.205）　6. in such a fine weather → *in such fine weather*（或 *on such a fine day*）。　7. the Mayor → *Mayor*，表官職做主詞補語，不須加冠詞。

8. Horse → *A horse*（或 *The horse*）；useful animal → *a useful animal*。（詳見 p.213, 217）

9. from a place to a place → *from place to place*，兩個相對的名詞並用時不加冠詞。（參照 p.222）

10. light → *a light*；a distance → *the distance*，light 作「光線；燈光」解時是普通名詞，須加冠詞；in the distance「在遠處」。（詳見 p.224）　11. A hero → *Hero*，Hero as he is = Though he is a hero，as 前的名詞須省略其冠詞。　12. French → *The French*；very → *a very*，專有名詞表全體國民須加 the；people 指「民族；國民」時要加冠詞。　13. honest → *an honest*，such + a(n) + 名詞。

14. youngest → *the youngest*，在最高級形容詞之前要加 the 或其他限制語。（詳見 p.219）

15. Edison → *an Edison*；Shakespeare → *a Shakespeare*，此處 a = one⋯like「像⋯的人」。

16. beautiful → *the beautiful*，have an eye for「對⋯有鑑賞力」，「the + 形容詞」等於名詞。（參照 p.219）

練 習 十一 【第四篇第六章冠詞 p.213～226】

請改正下列各題句子中的錯誤。（用最少的字數）

1. Many bright young man fails in life because he does not know value of time.

2. Queen Mary is too large ship to go up Keelung Harbor.

3. Father, let us go for walk into country.

4. He went by the bus and came back by the train.

5. Are you in great hurry?

6. As weather is fine, let us take long walk.

7. Shall you have the school tomorrow?

8. Will you have kindness to tell me a way to station?

9. Man is rational being.

10. World War II was brought to end at last.

11. He is so lucky man that I envy him.

12. All students of our school went on a picnic.

13. Six months is a too short time to learn a language.

14. He possesses a 18th century edition of Shakespeare's works.

15. I prefer life in a city to life in a country.

16. As I had worked more than half hour, I was little tired.

【解答】

1. Many bright → **Many a bright**；value → **the value**，many + 複數名詞，many a + 單數名詞；抽象名詞 value 後有 of time 限制，故要加 the。（詳見 p.217）　　2. Queen Mary → **The Queen Mary**；ship → **a ship**，船艦名要加 the（詳見 p.63）；too + 形容詞 + a(n) + 名詞。（詳見 p.216）　　3. walk → **a walk**；country → **the country**，go for a walk「去散步」，country 作「鄉下」解時，要加 the。

4. by the bus → **by bus**；by the train → **by train**，表示乘坐交通工具，不加冠詞。（參照 p.219）

5. in great → **in a great**，in a hurry「匆忙的」。（參照 p.216）　　6. weather → **the weather**；long walk → **a long walk**（參照 p.215），weather 單獨使用，作「氣候；天氣」解時，通常加 the。　　7. the school → **school**，指用途，表抽象意義，不加 the。（參照 p.222）　　8. have kindness → **have the kindness**；a way → **the way**；to station → **to the station**（詳見 p.217）　　9. rational being → **a rational being**，man 指人類的總稱時不加冠詞；being 是可數名詞，須加 a。　　10. to end → **to an end**，be brought to an end「結束」。　　11. so lucky man → **so lucky a man**（詳見 p.216）　　12. All students → **All the students**，因後有 of our school 限制。（詳見 p.217）　　13. a too short time → **too short a time**（詳見 p.216）　　14. a → **an**，18th（'e'tinθ）。　　15. in a country → **in the country**，life in a city「都市生活」，life in the country「鄉村生活」。　　16. hour → **an hour**（詳見 p.214）；little → **a little**。

練 習 十二 【第五篇副詞 p.227～271】

請改正下列各題句子中的錯誤。（用最少的字數）

1. If you speak too rapid, most of us will not understand what you are saying.

2. Frank couldn't hardly find his friend among the passengers.

3. Ken did his job so good that he is going to get a bonus.

4. I don't know him, still more his brother.

5. It is most ten o'clock.

6. He finished his work very sooner than usual.

7. We dared not move for fear the enemy should not see us.

8. They are to meet at six o'clock sharply.

9. It is hardly necessary to continue this analysis much far along these general lines.

10. We hurried lest we should not miss the train.

11. You had not better waste any more time.

12. I am not very hungry; beside I don't like fish.

13. Is the room enough large for you?

14. Tell me the way how he has failed.

15. "Do you mind posting this letter for me?" "Yes, certainly."

【解答】

1. rapid → ***rapidly***   2. couldn't → ***could***，*hardly* 本身已有否定意味。   3. good → ***well***，*good* 是形容詞；*well* 是副詞。   4. still more → ***still less***，*much more, still more* 用在肯定句之後，*much less, still less* 用在否定句之後，都作「何況；更不用說」解。   5. most → ***almost*** 是「幾乎」，*most* 是「大部分」。   6. very → ***much***，*very* 修飾原級，(*very*) *much* 修飾比較級和最高級。（詳見 p.251）

7. should not see → ***should see***，*for fear* (*that*)；*lest*；*in case* (*that*)「以免；為了不」是否定目的的連接詞，因此不須再用 *not*。   8. sharply → ***sharp***，*sharply*「嚴厲地」，*sharp* 當副詞是「正；恰好」須放在時間之後。   9. far → ***further***，*much* 須接比較級或最高級，此處用比較級 *further* 表程度。（詳見 p.261）   10. should not miss → ***should miss***，理由與第七題相同。   11. had not better → ***had better not***，*had better* 的否定是 *had better not* 或 *hadn't better*（*hadn't* 必須縮寫）。   12. beside → ***besides***「而且」，可做副詞連接詞用於連接子句或句子；*beside* 是介系詞。   13. enough large → ***large enough***，*enough* 當副詞用時通常放在所修飾的形容詞或動詞之後。（參照 p.263）   14. the way how he → ***the way he***，*the way how* ～是古老的用法，現已不用。   15. Yes, certainly. → ***No, certainly not.***，回答問句 *Do you mind* ～？時，表示願意要用 *No*，表示不願意則用 *Yes*。（詳見 p.256）

練 習 十三 【第五篇副詞 p.227～271】

請改正下列各題句子中的錯誤。（用最少的字數）

1. Can't you stay little longer?

2. So I put some bricks on the roof lest it should be blown off, but that was no good too.

3. He arrived lately last night.

4. You can imagine easily how difficult it was.

5. It is raining still, but I think it will before long clear up.

6. I can only see him in the room. （只有我能在那房間和他見面。）

7. He ordered the boys to not go out.

8. Never I have heard of such a thing.

9. Only seldom she took part in the conversation.

10. They will be tomorrow here.

11. He is by two inches taller than I.

12. Where did Molly go to?

13. I know I ever met her. I think it was three months before.

14. The boys are fighting. Please keep them apartly.

15. Most landsmen have a rather dread of water.

【解答】

1. little → *a little*「一些；少許」，*little*「幾乎沒有；很少」，依句意該用 *a little*。　2. too → *either*，表示「也」時，肯定句用 *too*，否定句或疑問句要用 *either*。（詳見 p.254）　3. lately → *late*「遲地；晚地」；*lately*「最近」。　4. can imagine easily → *can easily imagine*，副詞通常置於助動詞與主要動詞之間。（詳見 p.266）　5. is raining still → *is still raining*（理由同第 4. 題）；it will before long clear up → *it will clear up before long*，*before long* 是表時間的副詞片語，通常置於句末。（詳見 p.266）　6. I can only see → *Only I can see*（詳見 p.263）　7. to not go out → *not to go out*（詳見 p.422）　8. Never I have → *Never have I*，形成倒裝句。（詳見 p.267, 629）　9. Only seldom she took → *Only seldom did she take*（詳見 p.631）　10. tomorrow here → *here tomorrow*（詳見 p.269）　11. by two inches → *two inches*，本句可寫成 He is taller than I *by two inches*.（詳見 p.101）　12. go to → *go*，此句中 *where = to what place*，因此句尾不可再加 *to*。（參照 p.239）　13. ever → *once*；before → *ago*（詳見 p.247）　14. apartly → *apart*「分開地；各別地」，本身即是副詞形，不須再加 *ly*，修飾 *keep*。　15. a rather → *rather a*，*rather* 與沒有形容詞修飾的名詞連用時，須放在冠詞之前。（詳見 p.216）

練 習 十四 【第五篇副詞 p.227～271】

請改正下列各題句子中的錯誤。（用最少的字數）

1. Although Franklin was eighty-one at the time, he worked hardly to get the constitution written and ratified.

2. Money is not necessary an avenue to happiness.

3. It was most because the business boom was over and the slump was on.

4. Her room is richly rather than artistic decorated.

5. This is Garry's bike; unmistakable, he is here now.

6. Bacon said that some books are indeed to be read, but not curiosity.

7. Such cases of luck are exceptional rare.

8. The fact that gold is very heavier than tin is without doubt.

9. He is looking suspicious at us.

10. She close resembles her mother.

11. That is the way in which he landed a job.
    = That is why he landed a job.

12. At the whistle, the dog came obedient to his master.

13. The children listened to their teacher attentionally.

14. After graduation, he'll return to his hometown permanent.

【解答】

1. hardly → **hard**，可當副詞用，作「努力地」解，位置在動詞後面，hardly「幾乎不」，ratify「批准（條約等）」。　　2. necessary → **necessarily**，not necessarily「未必；不一定」，avenue「方法；途徑」。　　3. most → **mostly** adv.「主要；大部分」，修飾由 because 所引導的副詞子句，most 當副詞時是 much 的最高級，boom「繁榮」；slump「衰落」。　　4. artistic → **artistically**「精美雅緻地」，與 richly 都是副詞，修飾 decorated，A rather than B「是 A 而不是 B；與其 B，不如 A」，A、B 詞性要相等。　　5. unmistakable → **unmistakably** adv.「明顯地；不會弄錯地」，修飾 he is here now。

6. curiosity → **curiously** adv.「好奇地」，but not (to be read) curiously。　　7. exceptional → **exceptionally** adv.「例外地；非常地」，修飾形容詞 rare。　　8. very → **(very) much**，修飾比較級形容詞用 (very) much。（詳見 p.251）　　9. suspicious → **suspiciously**「疑心地；懷疑地」，修飾 looking。

10. close → **closely**「接近地；嚴密地」，修飾動詞 resembles；close 當副詞時是「靠近地；在…附近」。

11. why → **how**，表「方法」，why 表「原因」。（詳見 p.239）　　12. obedient → **obediently**「順從地；聽話地」，修飾動詞 came。　　13. attentionally → **attentively**「專心地；留意地」，修飾動詞 listened，attention「注意；專心」的形容詞是 attentive，不是 attentional（無此字）。　　14. permanent → **permanently**「永久地；永遠地」= for good = for ever (and ever)，修飾 return。

練 習 十五 【第四篇形容詞第五篇副詞 p.165～271】

請改正下列各題句子中的錯誤。（用最少的字數）

1. There are scarcely no water in the jar.

2. Solomon was the wisest of all the other Jewish kings.

3. She did not go to the park; nor I, too.

4. "Have you ever seen a kangaroo?" "Yes, I have ever seen one."

5. There is yet any water left.

6. He will succeed next time if he studies more hardly.

7. I wish you would stay here few days long.

8. "You returned the book a short time before, didn't you?"
   "Oh no, of course, I did."

9. There are three hundred and sixty five days in a year.

10. In more six months, you will be able to speak fluent English.

11. What do you spell the word?

12. "At what time of the day are you generally in?"
    "I'm generally in the morning."

13. The later half of the program was very interesting.

14. By skillful make-up she managed to look very younger than her thirty-five years.

15. There are times when everyone feels a little sadly.

16. The war broke out in March. About three months ago my brother had been born.

【解答】

1. are → *is*；no → *any*，*water* 是不可數名詞，故動詞用 *is*，*scarcely* 已表示否定代替 *not*，故接 *any*。

2. all the other → *all the*，本題最高級的比較，不可把本身除外，因 *Solomon* 也是猶太王之一。

3. nor I, too → *nor did I*，*nor* 表示否定，*too* 用在肯定句。(詳見 p.254)　　4. Yes, I have ever seen one → *Yes, I have (seen one once)*，*once* 放在句尾作「一次」解。(詳見 p.248)　　5. yet → *still*；any → *some* (詳見 p.249)　　6. more hardly → *harder* (參照 p.231)　　7. few days long → *a few days longer*，根據句意是「再待幾天」，要用比較級 *longer*，如 *no longer*「不再」。　　8. before → *ago* (詳見 p.247)；no → *yes*，肯定的回答用 *yes*。(詳見 p.256)　　9. sixty five → *sixty-five* (詳見 p.174)　　10. In more six months → *In six months more*「再過六個月」，*more = additional*。　　11. What → *How*「如何」是疑問副詞 (詳見 p.239)，*What* 是疑問代名詞，在句中，應有代名作用。　　12. I'm generally in the morning → *I'm generally in in the morning*，第一個 *in* 是副詞，是「在家」的意思；第二個 *in* 是介系詞。　　13. later → *latter* (詳見 p.198)　　14. very → *much*，修飾比較級。(詳見 p.251)　　15. sadly → *sad adj.*「悲傷的」，做主詞補語。　　16. ago → *before* (詳見 p.247)

練 習 十六 【形容詞冠詞副詞綜合 p.165～271】

請根據句意和文法選出一個最正確的答案。

1. We went on a picnic in such _____ fine weather.
   (A) the   (B) a   (C) an   (D) ×

2. They are _____ teachers of our school. (指一部分的教師)
   (A) the   (B) a   (C) an   (D) ×

3. He used to be a liberal but now he has turned _____ conservative.
   (A) the   (B) a   (C) an   (D) ×

4. _____ English language is universally spoken nowadays.
   (A) The   (B) A   (C) An   (D) ×

5. What you say is true in _____ sense.
   (A) the   (B) a   (C) an   (D) ×

6. I hope we meet _____.
   (A) today's week   (B) this day of the week
   (C) this day week   (D) of this on the day

7. He fell ill a month ago and died _____ last week.
   (A) some times   (B) some time   (C) sometime   (D) sometimes

8. Can you always play tennis in the afternoon? Yes, _____.
   (A) I can always   (B) I always can
   (C) I always   (D) always I can

9. It was _____ and dark when we came back last night.
   (A) nice   (B) quite   (C) severe   (D) better

10. Humor _____ his works.
    (A) is combined by   (B) is characteristic of
    (C) becomes truly in   (D) , on every side, is

【解答】

1. (D)，weather 之前有形容詞或所有格修飾時，不加冠詞。　2. (D)，(詳見 p.226)　3. (D)，turn + 無冠詞的名詞（或形容詞）「變成…」，conservative *adj.*「保守的」，*n.*「保守主義者」。　4. (A)，語言名稱之後有 language 時，要有 the，***English = the English language***。(詳見 p.219)　5. (B)，***in a sense***「就某方面來說；在某種意義上」。　6. (C)，meet 後省略 *each other*，***this day week***（= *today week*）「上（下）週今日」。　7. (C)，sometime「某一個時候」。(詳見 p.259)　8. (B)，always（頻率副詞），通常放在助動詞及 be 動詞之後，但表加強語氣及簡答句中，則放在它們之前。例：A: He is late. B: Yes, he always is.（詳見 p.266）　9. (A)，nice and dark（= *very dark*）　10. (B)，***be characteristic of***「是…的特色」。

練 習 十七 【代名詞，形容詞，副詞綜合】

請根據句意和文法選出一個最正確的答案。

1. On my last visit to Taipei I enjoyed _____ very much.
   (A) time   (B) me   (C) there   (D) myself

2. There was no objection on the part of _____ present.
   (A) this   (B) those   (C) who   (D) whom

3. I remember _____ having been extremely cold that winter.
   (A) that   (B) its   (C) it's   (D) it is

4. The issue is one for _____ students to discuss.
   (A) each   (B) every   (C) we   (D) us

5. The judge found him _____ of stealing and sent him to prison.
   (A) innocent   (B) guilty   (C) wicked   (D) weak

6. "What time do we get to Glasgow?" "You're _____ to arrive at 6:25, sir."
   (A) about   (B) impatient   (C) due   (D) owing

7. "What time is it now?" "It's ten o'clock _____."
   (A) just   (B) punctually   (C) sharp   (D) on time

8. He was too tired to go _____ farther.
   (A) any   (B) more   (C) no   (D) very

9. How _____ does the train start?
   (A) fast   (B) quickly   (C) soon   (D) rapidly

10. "Has your father started traveling?" "No, he is _____ at home."
    (A) yet   (B) then   (C) now   (D) still

【解答】

1. (D)，主詞和受詞爲同一人時，該用反身代名詞。(詳見 p.117)　　2. (B)，those 後省略了 who were。
3. (B)，動名詞的意義主詞，該用所有格形式。　　4. (D)，us, students 爲同位語，做介詞 for 的受詞，故用受格。each、every 須接單數名詞。　　5. (B)，*find someone guilty*「判決某人有罪」; *be guilty of stealing*「犯了竊盜罪」。　　6. (C)，*be due* (to + 原形動詞)「預定~」。　　7. (C)，「十點整」如以 just 表示，應爲 It's *just* ten o'clock。punctually「準時地」，如：He always comes to office *punctually*.。Be *on time*.「請準時」。　　8. (A)，*too…to* ~ 含有否定意味，故修飾 farther 的副詞應使用 any。farther 爲 far 的比較級，故不能使用 more；使用 no，則變爲雙重否定；very 修飾原級。
9. (C)，句中四個副詞皆表「很快」的意思，但是，只有 soon 用以指時間，其他皆用以指速度。*How soon* ~ 作「~還要多久？」解。　　10. (D)，表示「還在家」，應使用 still。yet 一般用於否定句、疑問句中；then 表示過去或未來的時間；now「現在」，文法正確，但與前面的問句句意不合。